geog.GCSE

<anna king ><catherine hurst ><john edwards >
<chris stevens ><jack mayhew >

OXFORD
UNIVERSITY PRESS

OXFORD
UNIVERSITY PRESS

Great Clarendon Street, Oxford OX2 6DP

Oxford University Press is a department of the University of Oxford.
It furthers the University's objective of excellence in research,
scholarship, and education by publishing worldwide in

Oxford   New York

Auckland Cape Town Dar es Salaam Hong Kong Karachi
Kuala Lumpur Madrid Melbourne Mexico City Nairobi
New Delhi Shanghai Taipei Toronto

With offices in

Argentina Austria Brazil Chile Czech Republic France Greece
Guatemala Hungary Italy Japan Poland Portugal Singapore
South Korea Switzerland Thailand Turkey Ukraine Vietnam

Oxford is a registered trade mark of Oxford University Press
in the UK and in certain other countries

Authors: Anna King, Catherine Hurst, John Edwards,
Chris Stevens, Jack Mayhew

The moral rights of the author have been asserted

Database right Oxford University Press (maker)

First published 2006

British Library Cataloguing in Publication Data

Data available

ISBN 978-0-19-913466-3

10

Assembled by Q2A, India

Printed in Malaysia by Vivar Printing Sdn Bhd

Paper used in the production of this book is a natural, recyclable product
made from wood grown in sustainable forests. The manufacturing process
conforms to the environmental regulations of the country of origin.

Acknowledgements

P6t AAMR Quresh/AFP/Getty Images; p6b Rafiq Maqbool/AP/Empics; p16 Izhar
Wani/AFP/Getty; p17t7m AAmir Qureshi/AFP/Getty; p17b Sajjad Hussain/AFPGetty; p19
Getty Images; p22l Anguilar Patrice/Alamy; p22r Photodisc/OUP; p23 Thomas J
Casadevall; p24 Les Stone/Corbis; p28 Lightworks Media/Alamy; p34b FLPA/Holt Studios;
p36t Alan Curtis/Leslie Garland Picture Library/Alamy; p37br Geoscience Features Picture
Library; p38t Patrick Ward/Corbis; p38m Mike Kipling Photography/Alamy; p40 John
Peate/Hanson Aggregates; p44t Stefano Lunardi/CuboImages srl/Alamy; p45 Michaelle
Naysmith/Alamy; p46 Bridget Clyde/StockShot/Alamy; p52 John Lamb/Getty Images; p53t
John Lamb/Getty Images; p53b Geophotos; p57 Patrick Ward/Corbis; p58b Nikki
Edmunds/Alamy; p59 Caerwyn Roberts; p63 Photlibrary Wales; p64 Mick Rock/Cephas
Picture Library/Alamy; p66tl Still Pictures, p66rr Mark Edwards/Still Pictures, p66b
www.aerialphotography.com/Air Images Limited; p68 Still Pictures; p71 John
Farmar/Ecoscene; p73t www.aerialphotography.com/Air Images Limited, p73b NASA;
p75t Sipa Press/Rex Features, p75b Ace Stock Limited/Alamy; p76t Aliki Sapountzi/aliki
image library/Alamy, p76b Peter Dean/Agripicture Images/Alamy; p78 Toby
Melville/PA/Empics; p79 Steve Forrest/Guzelian Photographers; p80t Per-Anders
Pettersson/UNEP/Still Pictures, p80b AP/Karel Prinsloo/Empics; p81 Yoav
Lemmer/Reuters/Corbis UK Ltd.; p82t WWI/Still Pictures, p82b Terry O'Brien/LifeFile
Photos Ltd/Alamy; p83 Nils Jorgenson/Rex Features; p84t&b Environment Agency; p85
Still Pictures; p86 Peter Adams Photography/Alamy; p93t geophotos/Alamy; p93b
Geoscience Features Picture Library; p104 Michael Howell/Alamy; p106 Jason
Politte/Alamy; p112 Chinch Gryniewicz/Ecoscene/Corbis UK Ltd.; p113t
nagelestock.com/Alamy, p113b Ace Stock Limited/Alamy; p114 Jeff Morgan/Alamy; p118
Anthony John West/Corbis UK Ltd.; p119t Phil Noble/PA/Empics, p119b Ashley
Cooper/Corbis UK Ltd.; p120 Rex Features; p121 AP/Schalk van Zuydam/Empics; p122
SVS/NASA; p123 JAXA/NASA; p124 Jeff Schmaltz/MODIS Land Rapid Response
Team/NASA; p125 Michael Ainsworth/Dallas Morning News/Corbis UK Ltd.; p126 Tim
Davis/Corbis UK Ltd.; p128 Natalie Fobes/Corbis; p131 David L. Moore/Alamy; p135cl
Louise Murray/Alamy, p135l Sue Cunningham Photographic/Alamy, p135cr Terry
Whittaker/Alamy, p135r Still Pictures; p136 Peter Arnold/Still Pictures; p137 Sue
Cunningham/Worldwide Picture Library/Alamy; p138 Bernard Castelein/Nature Picture
Library/Alamy; p139bl&br Martin Harvey/Still Pictures, p139r D. Davis/www.tropix.co.uk;
p140t Edgar Cleijne/Still Pictures, p140b Still Pictures; p141 Voltchev/UNEP/Still Pictures;

p142 Edward Parker/Alamy; p143l Peter Arnold/Still Pictures, p143c Sindre
Ellingsen/Alamy; p143r Richard Osbourne/Blue Pearl Photographic/Alamy; p144t Birger
Areklett/NN/Samfoto, p144b BÅrd L'ken/NN/Samfoto; p145 Steinar Myhr/NN/Samfoto;
p146 Lori Admaski Peak/Getty; p149l Bill Ross/Corbis UK Ltd., p149r David Keith
Jones/Images of Africa Photobank/Alamy; p156t Konrad Zelazowski/Alamy, p156b PA
Photos/Empics; p160t Scott Nelson/Getty Images, p160b Guillaume Bonn/Corbis UK Ltd.;
p161t Marco Longari/AFP/Getty Images, p161b Scott Nelson/Getty Images; p162 Brian A.
Vikander/Corbis UK Ltd.; p163 Don Mason/Corbis UK Ltd.; p165 Mark Pearson/Alamy;
p166 picturescolourlibrary.com/Alamy; p167 Kapoor Baldev/Sygma/Corbis UK Ltd.; p168
NeilRabinowitz/Corbis; p170tl Michael S. Yamashita/Corbis UK Ltd., p170cl Sergio
Pitamitz/Corbis UK Ltd., p170bl E. Streichan/zefa/Corbis UK Ltd., p170tr Aerofilms/Alamy,
p170cr Sandro Vannini/Corbis UK Ltd., p170br The Travel Library/Rex Features; p171t&b
Mary Evans Picture Library, p171c Historical Picture Archive/Corbis UK Ltd.; p172tc
Richard T. Nowitz/Corbis UK Ltd., p172bc Awad Awad/AFP/Getty Images, p172t Hanan
Isachar/Corbis UK Ltd., p172b David Levenson/Getty Images; p176 Corbis UK Ltd.; p177 G.
Boutin/zefa/Corbis UK Ltd.; p178tl Joe Pepler/Rex Features; p178bl Powered by Light/Alan
Spencer/Alamy, p178bc Alex Segre/Alamy, p178tr&br Martin Bond/Photofusion Picture
Library/Alamy; p179 The Photolibrary Wales/Alamy; p181 Sealand Aerial Photography;
p182 Jonathan Hordle/Rex Features; p183t&b Brindleyplace; p184t Gregg Newton/Corbis
UK Ltd., p184b Tony Morrison/South American Pictures; p185t Fabio Polenghi/Corbis UK
Ltd., p185b Jorge Mario Jáuregui; p186 Howard Davies/Corbis UK Ltd., p187 Ceu Azul de
Copacabana; p188 Roy Garner/Rex Features; p189t Mladen Antonov/AFP/Getty Images,
p189b Zak Waters/Alamy; p190t Skyscan Photolibrary/Alamy; p190b Christa
Stadtler/Photofusion Picture Library/Alamy; p191l&r Martin Bond/Photofusion Picture
Library; p192 John-Francis Bourke/Getty; p194l James Russell Cant/Sygma/Corbis UK
Ltd., p194r Nigel Cattlin/Holt Studios International Ltd/Alamy; p196t Ashley
Cooper/Corbis UK Ltd., p196b Wayne Hutchinson/Holt Studios International Ltd/Alamy;
p197l Holt Studios International, p197tr Peter Dean/Agripicture Images/Alamy, p197br
geogphotos/Alamy; p198 www.face-online.org.uk/Farming And Countryside Education;
p199t Des Topping/Herdship Farm, p199b Nigel Cattlin/Holt Studios International
Ltd/Alamy; p200t Tesco Stores Limited, p200b Holt Studios International; p201l Justin
Kase/Alamy, p201r Nigel Cattlin/Holt Studios International Ltd/Alamy; p202t Herdship
Farm, p202b Holt Studios International; p203 RSPCA Freedom Food; p204t Patrick
Ward/Corbis UK Ltd., p204b Adam Woolfitt/Corbis UK Ltd.; p205t Peter Cairns/Worldwide
Picture Library/Alamy, p205b Tyrrells Potato Chips Ltd; p206 Bernard
Annebicque/Sygma/Corbis UK Ltd.; p207 Danita Delimont Stock Photography; p208t
David R. Frazier Photolibrary, Inc./Alamy, p208b Dung Vo Trung/Corbis UK Ltd.; p209
Lineair Fotoarchief/Still Pictures; p211 Jeremy Hartley/Panos Pictures; p212 Mark
Edwards/Still Pictures; p214tl Marcel Mochet/AFP/Getty Images, p214bl Pictor
International/ImageState/Alamy, p214tr Kin Cheung/Reuters/Corbis UK Ltd., p214br Bill
Varie/Corbis UK Ltd.; p215l Armando Dadi/Rex Features; p215c Yun Suk-
bong/Reuters/Corbis UK Ltd., p215r Toyota (GB) PLC; p216 Toyota (GB) PLC; p218t David
Levenson/Alamy, p218b Jeff.Morgan/Alamy; p219t Roberta Osborne/iStockphoto, p219b
Ted Spiegel/Corbis UK Ltd.; p220 Getty Images; p222 Sipa Press/Rex Features; p223l
Keren Su/Corbis UK Ltd., p223r Kin Cheung/Reuters/Corbis UK Ltd.; p224
Raveendran/AFP/Getty Images; p225 Dibyangshu Sarkar/AFP/Getty Images; p227 Robert
Brook/Photofusion Picture Library/Alamy; p228 The Photolibrary Wales/Alamy; p229
platz.eins - sport incentives; p230t David R. Frazier Photolibrary, Inc./Alamy, p230b
Empics; p231t Colin Garratt/Milepost 92 ?/Corbis UK Ltd., p231b Practical Action; p232
Tom Brakefield/Corbis UK Ltd.; p233 Jose Fuste Raga/Corbis UK Ltd.; p234 Charles
O'Rear/Corbis; p236t Nick Haslam/Alamy, p236b Ron Giling/Still Pictures; p237 Jlp/Jose L.
Pelaez/Corbis UK Ltd.; p238t Hulton-Deutsch Collection/Corbis UK Ltd., p238c Paul
Thompson/Ecoscene/Corbis UK Ltd., p238b Paul Almasy/Corbis UK Ltd.; p239t Bob
Anderson/Rex Features, p239b Humphreys Owen/PA/Empics; p240 Keren Su/Corbis UK
Ltd.; p241 Jean Pierre Amet/Belombra/Corbis UK Ltd.; p246t Anthony
Upton/onEdition/npower renewables, p246b OnEdition/Rex Features; p247 Jason
Hawkes/Corbis UK Ltd.; p248bl Cheapflights Ltd, p248br Mike Powell/Corbis UK Ltd.,
p248t George Shelley/Corbis UK Ltd.; p250tl Martin Siepmann/imagebroker/Alamy,
p250cl Dave G. Houser/Post-Houserstock/Corbis UK Ltd., p250bl Alamy, p250tr Eye
Ubiquitous/Hutchison, p250br Peter Mross/Fan & Mross Travelstock/Alamy; p251
Stephane Cardinale/People Avenue/Corbis UK Ltd.; p252 Andrew Lambert/Leslie Garland
Picture Library/Alamy; p253t&b Peak Pictures; p254l Corbis UK Ltd., p254r Kevin R.
Morris/Corbis UK Ltd.; p255t B. Kohlhas/Zefa/Corbis UK Ltd., p255c Reuters/Corbis UK
Ltd., p255b Sukree Sukplang/Reuters/Corbis UK Ltd.; p257t
Images&Stories/Photographersdirect.com/Chris Barton, p257b Images and Stories; p258
Don Mason/Corbis; p260t Roberta Osborne/iStockphoto, p260r Kamal
Kishore/Reuters/Corbis UK Ltd.; p264 Josef Hinterleitner/UNEP/Still Pictures; p267 Jorgen
Schytte/Still Pictures; p268 Evan Schneider/United Nations/AP/Empics; p270 Charlotte
Thege/Das Fotoarchiv/Still Pictures; p274 Danny Lehman/Corbis UK Ltd.; p275t Pat
Roque/AP/Empics, p275b www.fairtrade.org/The Fairtrade Foundation; p276l Finbarr
O'Reilly/Reuters/Corbis UK Ltd., p276r Maria R. Campbell/UNEP/Still Pictures; p277 Ton
Koene/Still Pictures; p278t Ron Gilling/Still Pictures, p278b Isobel
Perry/www.presentaid.org/Christian Aid Photo Library; p279t Jim Young/Reuters/Corbis
UK Ltd., p279b Radu Sigheti/Reuters/Corbis UK Ltd.

The Ordnance Survey map extracts on pp41,56,68,69,70,71,72,104 and173 are
reproduced with permission of the Controller of Her Majesty's Stationery Office
© Crown Copyright

Illustrations are by:

Martin Aston: p61; Stefan Chabluk: p72; Hardlines: p 21; Oxford Illustrators: p8; Oxford
University Press: pp118,119,148,154,175,260,269; Q2A, India: pp11b,12b,14t&m,17b,18m,
24,26,30,31,32b,34,36t,39,41,42,44,50t,55,58,59,60,66,68,70lt&b,75,77,88b,102,103,104,
105,108,110,112br,114,117,121,122,123,125,126t&b,132,134,138t,140,142,144,150,152,
153,155,158,159,160,164,166,178,179,180,183,186,187,188,190,197,198,199,206,207,208,
209,210,216,217,218,219,221,222,223,226,227,228,230,232,233,237,238,239,241,242,243,
244,245,247,249,250,252,254,263,264,265,266t,270,271272,273,274

p8 Dan White / Alamy; p9 Ric Ergenbright/Corbis; p21 S.Young and G.Frysinger/
travel-images.com;p23 Reuters;

p5c JOHN C. DOORNKAMP / Alamy, p5b Royalty-Free/Corbis; p6bl Roy Rainford / Robert
Harding, p6b Royalty-Free/Corbis; p7t Stephen Bond / Alamy; p8t f1 online / Alamy;
p9tl Richard Knights/rickni.co.in; P11tl Val Vannet/geograph, p11tc Ashley Cooper /
Alamy, p11tr G A Cryer /geoffspage.co.uk, p11bl Annie Griffiths Belt/Corbis, p11bc
Andrew Brown; Ecoscene/CORBIS; p12t Patrick Ward/Corbis, p12b Kim Sayer/Corbis;
p16b nagelestock.com / Alamy; p17t Realimage / Alamy, p17cl Simon Holdcroft /
Alamy,p17cr Paul Glendell / Alamy;

p4t Bill Varie/CORBIS; p6b David Robinson/Snap2000 Images / Alamy; p7t Lee
Frost/Robert Harding / Alamy; p7c The Photolibrary Wales / Alamy; p8b John Lamb/Getty Images;
p9t John Lamb/Getty Images; p10c Patrick Ward / Alamy, p10b Leslie Garland Picture
Library / Alamy; p11cl geoscience.demon.co.uk; p11tr John.Cleare/mountain.camera
picture library; p14c Photolibrary Wales;
p16b Photolibrary Wales; p17cr The Photolibrary Wales / Alamy; p18tr Photolibrary
Wales; p18br John Rawsterne / Alamy

On planet Earth

 nearly 70% of the surface is covered by saltwater

 about 33% is covered by the Pacific Ocean

 roughly 10% of the land is covered by glacial ice

 around 20% is covered by deserts

 and about 25% is mountainous.

It's the third planet from the Sun,
and it's home to over 6.5 billion people.

Contents

The big picture

This chapter is about earthquakes, volcanoes, plates, plate movements and plate margins. These are the big ideas behind the chapter:

- The Earth's crust is broken into pieces called plates.

- Earthquakes and volcanic eruptions are caused by plate movements.

- People continue to live in dangerous areas where earthquakes happen and volcanoes erupt.

- The effects of earthquakes and eruptions are usually worse in LEDCs than in MEDCs.

- The responses to earthquakes and eruptions are different in MEDCs and LEDCs.

- It isn't possible to predict exactly when, or where, an earthquake will happen, but you can predict when a volcano will erupt, and so warn people.

Your goals for this chapter

By the end of this chapter you should be able to answer these questions:

- What do these terms mean?
  oceanic crust, continental crust, plates, constructive margin, destructive margin, conservative margin, collision margin, focus, epicentre, composite and shield volcanoes, crater, magma, lava, pyroclastic flow, ash cloud, mudflow (lahar), plug, hot spot

- What are the Earth's plates made of, and how do they move?

- What happens at the four types of plate margins?

- What causes earthquakes and how are they measured?

- What are the similarities and differences in the effects of earthquakes in an MEDC like the USA, and an LEDC area like Kashmir? What are the differences in their responses to an earthquake?

- What are volcanoes, and why do they erupt? List the hazards they can cause.

- Give an example of an eruption in an LEDC and one in an MEDC. Can you compare the eruptions in terms of processes, effects and responses?

- How do scientists predict volcanic eruptions? And how do they attempt to predict earthquakes?

- Why do people continue to live in dangerous areas where earthquakes happen and volcanoes erupt?

And then . . .

When you finish the chapter, come back here and see if you've met your goals!

Did you know?
The word tectonics comes from the Greek 'to build' – so plate tectonics refers to how the Earth's surface is built of plates.

Did you know?
The theory of plate tectonics was only developed in the 1960s. But it has revolutionised our understanding of our planet.

Did you know?
- Scientists think tectonic plates developed very early in the Earth's history.
- They have been drifting about ever since, like slow-moving bumper cars.

Did you know?
Every year there are about 500 000 earthquakes worldwide. People feel only a small number of those.

Your chapter starter

Look at the photos on page 6.
What do you think happened here?
Could this have been predicted?
What effects has it had?
How long do you think these children will have to live in tents?

We're all on a slow plate to somewhere.

The structure of the Earth

In this unit you will learn how the Earth is made up.

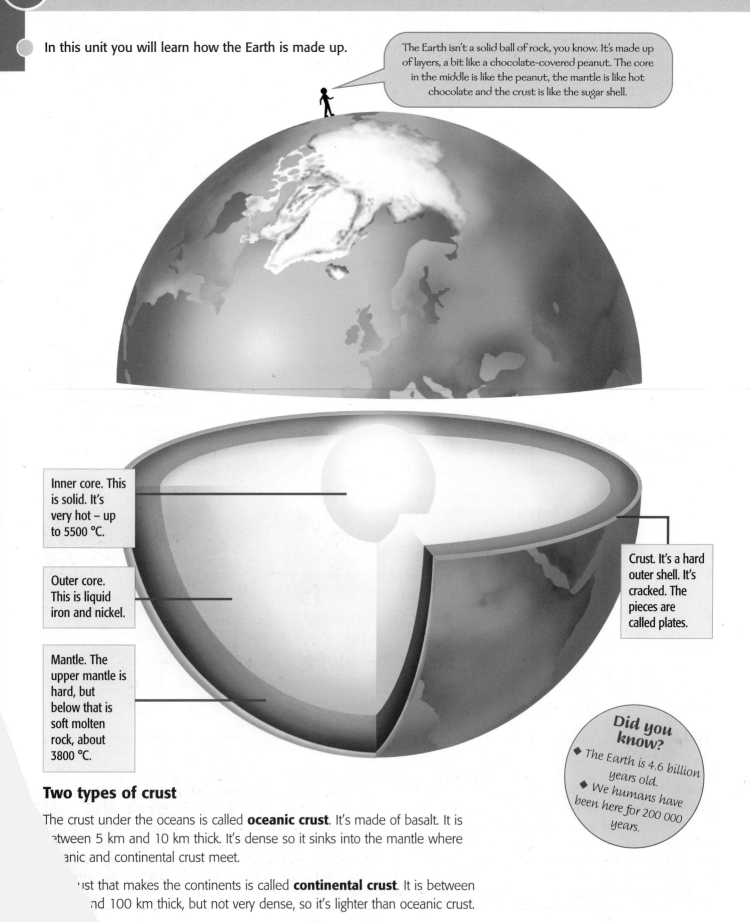

The Earth isn't a solid ball of rock, you know. It's made up of layers, a bit like a chocolate-covered peanut. The core in the middle is like the peanut, the mantle is like hot chocolate and the crust is like the sugar shell.

Inner core. This is solid. It's very hot – up to 5500 °C.

Outer core. This is liquid iron and nickel.

Mantle. The upper mantle is hard, but below that is soft molten rock, about 3800 °C.

Crust. It's a hard outer shell. It's cracked. The pieces are called plates.

Did you know?
- The Earth is 4.6 billion years old.
- We humans have been here for 200 000 years.

Two types of crust

The crust under the oceans is called **oceanic crust**. It's made of basalt. It is between 5 km and 10 km thick. It's dense so it sinks into the mantle where oceanic and continental crust meet.

The crust that makes the continents is called **continental crust**. It is between ... and 100 km thick, but not very dense, so it's lighter than oceanic crust.

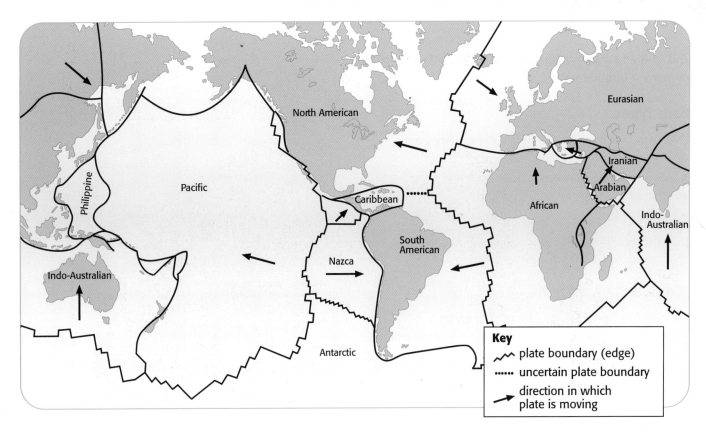

Key

∿∿ plate boundary (edge)

..... uncertain plate boundary

→ direction in which plate is moving

Where the plates are and how they move

The map above shows where the plates which make up the outer crust of the Earth are located.

The broken pieces of crust, or plates, get moved around on convection currents.

The mantle below the crust is liquid. Very thick liquid, but it can still move. It is heated from the core below it. This makes convection currents in the mantle, which allow the plates to move (see the diagram on the right).

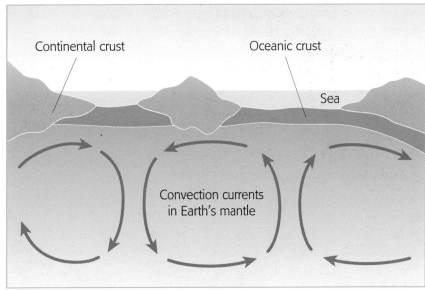

Continental crust

Oceanic crust

Sea

Convection currents in Earth's mantle

Activities

1 Make a simple diagram of the structure of the Earth. Label it with as much information as you can.
2 Why do tectonic plates move?
3 What are the differences between continental and oceanic crust?
4 Look at the map of tectonic plates.
   a What plate is the UK on?
   b What plate is the USA on?

c Why are the UK and USA getting further apart?
d Name two plates that are moving towards each other.
e Name two plates that are sliding past each other.
5 What evidence could you look for to prove that Africa and the Americas were once touching?
6 Plate tectonics is a recent theory. Find out what people thought happened to the continents before plate tectonics.

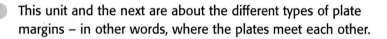

Plate margins

This unit and the next are about the different types of plate margins – in other words, where the plates meet each other.

Four types

There are four main types of plate margin. They are:

- constructive (also called divergent)
- destructive (also called subduction)
- conservative (also called transform)
- collision (see Unit 1.3)

These terms describe what is happening at each type of margin.

Did you know?
Plates are constantly moving – a few centimetres per year.

Constructive margins

At these margins the plates are moving **apart**.
This lets the mantle reach the surface and make – **construct** – new crust. This is happening in the middle of the Atlantic Ocean at the Mid-Atlantic Ridge.

Here you might get **earthquakes**. They are caused by the friction of the plates as they move over the mantle.

You get lots of **eruptions** at these margins – from volcanoes, like the Azores, and from cracks in the ground (or the sea bed) called **fissures**, like in Iceland.

The crust on either side of the margin is often faulted. This means it has big cracks in it. They're caused by the massive pressures that the moving plates cause.

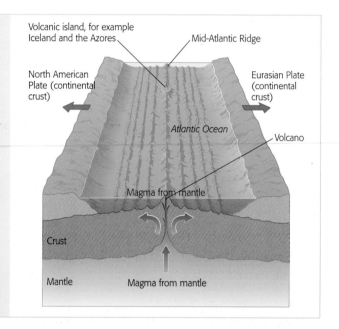

Destructive margins

At these margins an oceanic and a continental plate are moving **together**. The oceanic crust is denser than the continental one, so the oceanic one sinks (**subducts**). The friction between the two plates causes **earthquakes**.

The land on the edge of the continental crust gets squashed up to make **fold mountains**, like the Andes.

The oceanic crust melts as it goes into the mantle. Because it takes some sea water with it, it's less dense than the mantle around it. And this means it rises. It goes up through the crust and explodes at the surface as a **volcano**. The trapped sea water turns into steam and this makes the volcanoes very explosive. There isn't much lava (not like at constructive margins), but there is a lot of ash, steam, and gas.

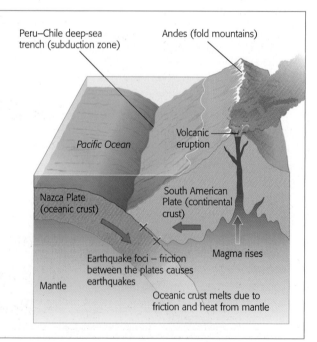

Conservative margins

Here the plates are moving past each other. There aren't any volcanoes here, but the friction between the two plates means there are earthquakes.

A famous example of a conservative margin is the San Andreas Fault in California, between the North American Plate and the Pacific Plate.

Did you know?

Most of the plate margins can't be seen because they're hidden under the oceans.

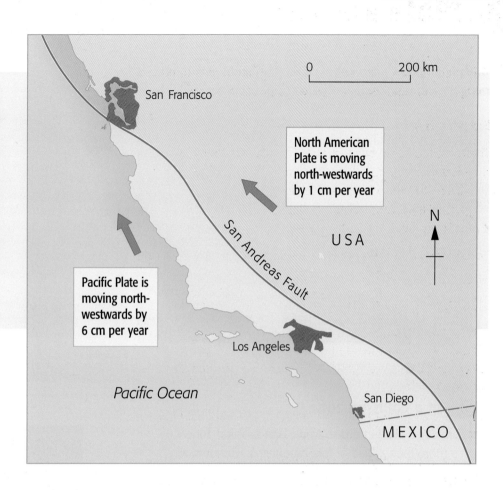

0   200 km

San Francisco

North American Plate is moving north-westwards by 1 cm per year

San Andreas Fault

N

U S A

Pacific Plate is moving north-westwards by 6 cm per year

Los Angeles

Pacific Ocean

San Diego

M E X I C O

Activities

1 What does the term *plate margin* mean?
2 What are the four types of plate margin?
3 Make a copy of the constructive margin on the right.
   Add these labels to it:

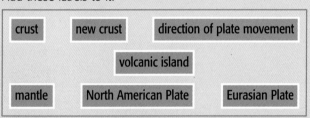

| crust | new crust | direction of plate movement |
| volcanic island |
| mantle | North American Plate | Eurasian Plate |

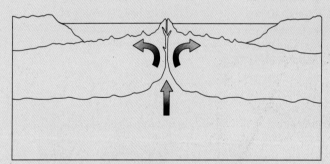

4 Name two landforms you might get at a **constructive** margin. Explain their formation.
   (Remember – earthquakes aren't landforms!)
5 Draw your own diagram for a **destructive** margin.
   Add these labels:

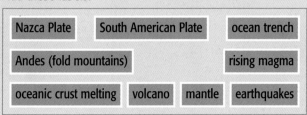

Nazca Plate	South American Plate	ocean trench
Andes (fold mountains)		rising magma
oceanic crust melting	volcano	mantle	earthquakes

6 Name two landforms you might get at a destructive margin. Explain their formation.
7 Draw and label your own diagram for a conservative margin.
8 Why are there earthquakes at constructive, destructive, and conservative margins?

In this unit you'll learn about collision margins – and how people cope with living in one particular collision zone.

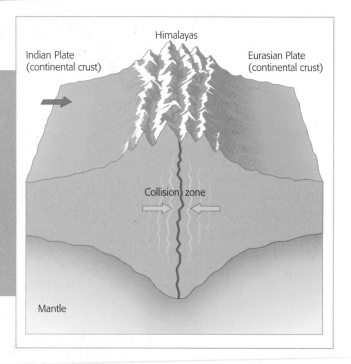

Collision margins

Here two continental plates are pushing into each other. Because they are the same density, neither of them can sink. So they squeeze upwards, making fold mountains.

The Himalayas are a good example of fold mountains made this way.

Because of the massive pressures caused by two plates crashing into each other, there are strong earthquakes at these margins.

Living in a collision zone

The Himalayas is a famous example of a collision zone. But it's more than a load of fold mountains. It's home to people too. So, how do people make a living here?

Farming

2 Farmers in the Himalayas grow some crops and keep animals. The crops are mainly for the animals to eat, but they also grow some rice and vegetables for people.

1 80% of the people in Nepal (a country in the Himalayas) work in farming, and 40% of the country's money comes from selling farm produce.

3 The animals are either cows or buffalo. They give the people meat and milk, and they are also used for carrying and for pulling ploughs. The manure is used as a fertilizer.

4 Most of the crops are grown in the valleys that have been made by rivers. The soil is quite thin. That's because it slides down the steep slopes - a process called mass movement. Also, if it rains or if the farmer puts water on the slopes, it'll flow straight off again! So crops are often grown on terraces. They're like ledges built into the hillside.

Mining

There are some precious rocks and metals like gold, diamonds, and sapphires, and some useful rocks like copper ore and slate, in the Himalayas. They are mined by digging huge pits. This is called open-cast mining. It has good points: it makes money in an area where there isn't much chance of starting big industries. But there are bad points: it causes more erosion, the chemicals used can pollute water, and it ruins the view.

Tourism

This is a really big earner! Almost a million people go to the Himalayas each year. They go for the trekking and climbing, and to see the old Buddhist temples.

Living with danger

Big earthquakes happen pretty regularly in the Himalayas – about once every 25 years. (This is called a *recurrence interval*.)

Local people are trained how to cope with an earthquake. They know how important it is to turn off the gas, to get under a strong table, and to know where the emergency equipment for the village is kept.

Traditional houses here are made of wood and they have thatched straw roofs – so they're not too heavy if they collapse in an earthquake (look at the photo). Richer people might have stone walls, and temple walls are made of stone too, but they still keep the roofs light.

It's not easy to make a good living in the Himalayas, and many people have left to live in the bigger towns and cities like Katmandu. But those who stay can make a living from farming, mining, and tourism. And many feel that it's important for their religion – mainly Hinduism or Buddhism – that they stay in the mountains. They feel the risks of a big earthquake are acceptable compared to what they would lose if they left.

Did you know?
'Himalaya' is a Sanskrit word meaning 'place of snow'.

Activities

1 Draw a diagram to show a collision zone. Add labels to show the fold mountains, the direction of plate movement, the names of the two plates, and the name of the fold mountains.

2 Use this writing frame to make notes about fold mountains.

> Fold mountains are . . .
> They are formed at destructive margins when . . .
> They are also formed at collision margins because . . .

3 For an area of fold mountains you have studied, describe the economic activities that occur. (This is an examination-style question.)

4 Why do some people remain living in the Himalayas?

Earthquakes

In this unit you'll learn about earthquakes – what they are, how they happen, how they're measured, and if they can be predicted.

What?

It's the shaking of the earth, basically!

Why?

The underlying cause of earthquakes is friction. When plates try to move, they are held still by friction. This can be with another plate or with the mantle. The forces pushing the plate keep pushing, until there is so much force that it overcomes friction and the plate suddenly jerks forwards a bit. That's the earthquake.

Earthquakes can happen at different sorts of plate margin.

Key

Direction of plate movement

Friction here makes earthquakes

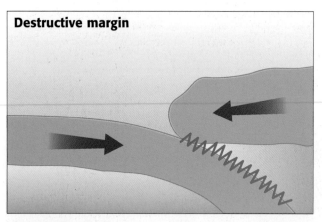

Destructive margin

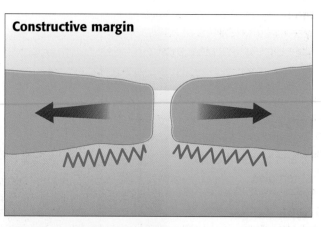

Constructive margin

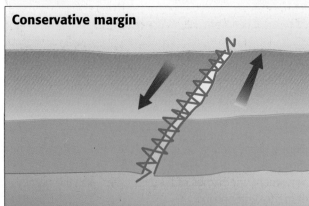

Conservative margin

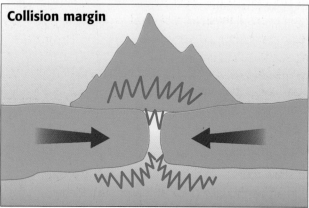

Collision margin

Where the plate moves – underground – is called the **focus**. The point on the surface straight above the focus is the **epicentre**. Earthquakes near the surface cause more damage than deep ones.

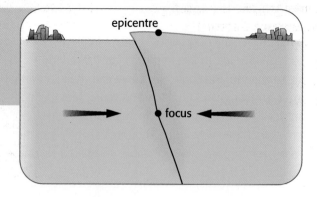

How big?

Earthquakes are measured on a scale called the **Richter scale**. If you go up 1 point on the scale it means the quake is 10 times bigger (it's a **logarithmic scale**), and about 30 times more energy is given out.

The amount of energy an earthquake gives out is called its **magnitude**.

When?

We don't know exactly when an earthquake is going to happen. Scientists who study earthquakes (called **seismologists**) do make predictions, but they're just probabilities of an earthquake happening, rather than an exact time and date.

The methods that seismologists use are:
◆ putting laser beams across the fault, so that they can see any initial small movements
◆ monitoring to see if radon gas is escaping from the fault
◆ checking to see if water levels in wells are falling – the water might be going into small tension cracks that develop just before an earthquake
◆ using sensitive instruments called **seismometers** that measure the movement of the ground to see if there are small foreshocks just before an earthquake
◆ graphing the magnitude (size) of earthquakes in specific places from the past to see if there's a pattern (the gap between earthquakes of similar magnitude is called the **recurrence interval**)
◆ watching for strange animal behaviour – Chinese research suggests that this may indicate an earthquake is imminent.

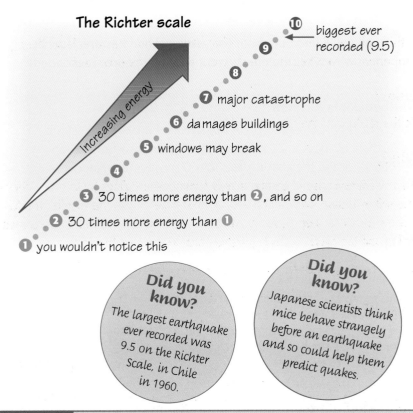

The Richter scale

10 biggest ever recorded (9.5)
9
8
7 major catastrophe
6 damages buildings
5 windows may break
4
3 30 times more energy than ❷, and so on
2 30 times more energy than ❶
1 you wouldn't notice this

Increasing energy

Did you know?
The largest earthquake ever recorded was 9.5 on the Richter Scale, in Chile in 1960.

Did you know?
Japanese scientists think mice behave strangely before an earthquake and so could help them predict quakes.

Activities

1 What is the basic cause of earthquakes?
2 Explain how earthquakes happen at collision zones.
3 Draw a diagram to show why earthquakes happen at destructive margins.
4 Why are there earthquakes in California? (Hint: look back to Unit 1.2!)
5 What do these words mean:
magnitude, focus, epicentre, recurrence interval, seismometer, seismologist?
6 **a** How are earthquakes measured?
 b What is special about this scale?
7 Use this writing frame to make notes about earthquake prediction:

> Scientists attempt to predict earthquakes. They use lots of methods, including . . .
> I (do/do not) think these predictions are accurate and detailed. My reasons are . . .
> I (do/do not) think these predictions give lots of advance warning . . .

8 **a** Make rough notes of your ideas about:
 ◆ How you think people would respond to warnings given by seismologists.
 ◆ Why they would react like that.
 ◆ What the implications could be of the ways people react.
 ◆ If predictions could be given that were accurate and time-specific, how would people react? What implications would the public's actions have?
 b Use your ideas to answer this question as a long piece of writing:
 'Are predictions of earthquakes a good thing?'

Kashmir earthquake – an LEDC case study

In this unit you'll find out about the earthquake in Kashmir – what happened, why, what the effects were and how people responded.

Earthquake in Kashmir

8.40 a.m. on 8 October 2005. A massive earthquake hits Kashmir in Pakistan. Its focus is 26 km down. The quake measures 7.6 on the Richter scale. The shaking lasts for 60 seconds. Aftershocks (some up to 6 on the Richter scale) continue for 2 days.

Why?

1 Kashmir is on the border of India and Pakistan. It's a mountainous area – in fact, its part of the Himalayas. The people who live here earn a living by farming on the fertile soils, and by tourism. Most people live in the towns of Muzaffarabad and Srinagar, but some also live in very remote villages.

2 This area is right where two plates are colliding. Its called a **collision zone**. The Indian plate is squashing into the Eurasian plate. That's what made the Himalayas in the first place, and it's still going on.

3 On 8 October, the strain got too much – one mass of rock suddenly slid upwards and set off the earthquake.

The primary effects

The shaking caused buildings to collapse, signs to fall off walls, windows to shatter, furniture to fall over, roads to crack, bridges to topple. All these are primary effects. They caused injury and death.

In Kashmir, over 79 000 people were killed, 100 000 were injured, and 3.3 million homes were destroyed by the primary effects. There were large cracks in the ground surface, and landslides. The effects were so serious in Kashmir because the buildings in the towns and villages weren't built very strongly.

As Saturday is a normal school day in the region, most students were at school when the earthquake struck. Many were buried under collapsed school buildings.

The secondary effects

These are effects that happen later. They can be fires caused by broken gas pipes, or disease caused by dead bodies that aren't buried, and also by sewerage pipes bursting and contaminating water supplies.

In Kashmir, the secondary effects included diseases (mainly diarrhoea) spread from contaminated water supplies, and also respiratory infections like pneumonia. People also died of cold in the harsh winter, because they only had thin tents to live in.

Deaths due to secondary effects were lower than they might have been, because helicopters were able to keep flying supplies in and the sick out. This cost $500 000 a day.

The long-term effects

These are things that continue to be a problem for a long time. They can be social, economic and environmental. In Kashmir, the main long-term effects were:

◆ In rural areas the crops mostly survived and so did the animals. So farmers could continue their jobs and the markets re-opened quickly. But in the urban areas, lots of people lost their jobs as their offices or shops were damaged.

◆ Electricity lines were brought down, so reconstruction was made harder.

◆ Schools were damaged and students lost their books.

◆ 3.3 million people lost their homes and were forced to live in temporary shelters until rebuilding could start in the spring.

◆ The overall cost of the damage is expected to be over $5 billion.

How did people respond?

Responses can be divided into the immediate and more long term.

Immediate responses

- Local people started trying to rescue those who were trapped.
- The Indian Red Cross distributed 21 500 blankets, 300 kitchen sets, and medical supplies.
- The army and emergency services arrived to help dig people out.
- Helicopters from the military were used to take the injured to first aid centres on flatter ground (see top photo).
- The border between India and Pakistan was opened in a few places to allow food and emergency supplies to cross (see right).
- Tents were given out by charities like Muslim Aid and the Pakistani and Indian armies.
- Pakistan Airways carried emergency food and supplies from other countries for free.
- Military hospitals were opened for civilian casualties.
- Rescue and medical teams arrived from other countries (e.g. Russia and the UK) to try to find survivors and treat the injured.

Probable long-term responses

At the time of writing, the earthquake was recent – so it was too soon to say what all the long-term responses will be.

- The Red Cross re-established water supplies in Muzaffarabad.
- The tents weren't enough for the cold winter, so the army and the Red Crescent built pre-fabricated homes using corrugated tin for people to live in until they had rebuilt their houses (see right).
- Schools will need to be re-built and re-supplied.
- Teachers may be trained in counselling to help traumatized children.
- Sanitation will be needed for the temporary houses.
- Building laws will be tightened up to make sure that next time there will be less damage and fewer deaths.

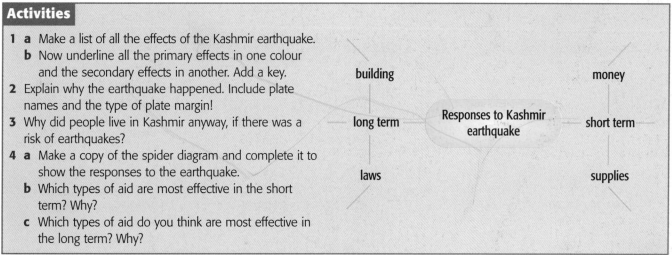

Activities

1 **a** Make a list of all the effects of the Kashmir earthquake.
   b Now underline all the primary effects in one colour and the secondary effects in another. Add a key.
2 Explain why the earthquake happened. Include plate names and the type of plate margin!
3 Why did people live in Kashmir anyway, if there was a risk of earthquakes?
4 **a** Make a copy of the spider diagram and complete it to show the responses to the earthquake.
   b Which types of aid are most effective in the short term? Why?
   c Which types of aid do you think are most effective in the long term? Why?

building
money
long term — Responses to Kashmir earthquake — short term
laws
supplies

Los Angeles earthquake – an MEDC case study

This unit is about the LA earthquake – what happened, why, what the effects were, and how people responded.

What happened?

At 4.31 a.m. on Monday 7 January 1994, an earthquake struck the Los Angeles suburb of Northridge. It measured 6.7 on the Richter scale. The focus was 18.4 km deep. The shaking lasted 15 seconds. Some areas were permanently lifted 50 cm higher. 14 people were crushed as their apartment block collapsed. Highways broke apart and one man fell to his death down a 25-foot crack. 9 bridges collapsed. Cars were thrown off bridges, landslides moved houses down slopes. Motorists were trapped in their cars under mounds of rubble.

Once the shaking stopped, the broken gas mains caught fire, shooting fireballs into the sky. Cars exploded in the intense heat. 22 000 people have been left homeless. The final death toll is 57 people, with 12 500 buildings damaged. The cost of the damage is estimated at $15 billion.

What caused the earthquake?

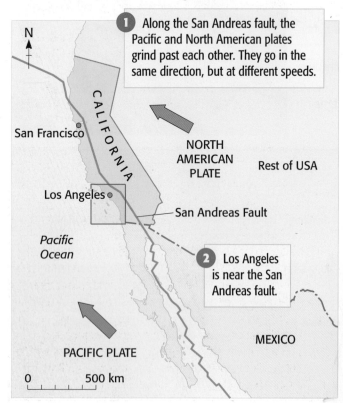

1. Along the San Andreas fault, the Pacific and North American plates grind past each other. They go in the same direction, but at different speeds.

2. Los Angeles is near the San Andreas fault.

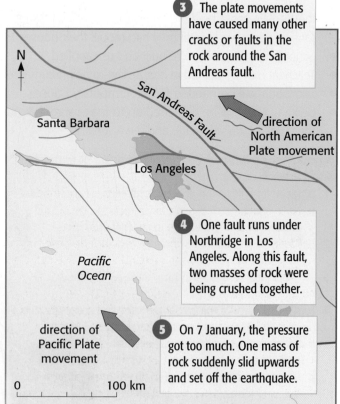

3. The plate movements have caused many other cracks or faults in the rock around the San Andreas fault.

4. One fault runs under Northridge in Los Angeles. Along this fault, two masses of rock were being crushed together.

5. On 7 January, the pressure got too much. One mass of rock suddenly slid upwards and set off the earthquake.

18

Why do people live there then?

There are lots of reasons. For example:

◆ **Economic**: People work in the area and can't afford (or don't want to) lose their jobs by moving. LA is a rich city with (for most people) a good lifestyle, and well-paid jobs.

◆ **Technological**: People feel secure that prediction will give them enough warning and, even if it doesn't, that technology will mean their homes are safe and the emergency services will be able to cope.

◆ **Perception**: People don't see relatively uncommon events like earthquakes as big risks. Regular things like car accidents and crime are often seen as being more likely to happen to you, so are more 'dangerous'.

◆ **Social**: People have their families, friends, schools, and favourite places nearby, and don't want to lose them.

▲ *Trapped!*

How did people respond?

The Los Angeles Recovery and Reconstruction Plan was written in the light of lessons learnt from the 1994 earthquake. It includes plans to have more emergency crews based in the city and plans for places where people can be housed immediately after an earthquake, and for the re-opening of essential financial services like banks. Also, more practice for emergency crews and medical staff so they know what to do, and stricter building codes.

Almost all schools were re-opened after one week, and all by three weeks after the earthquake.

More people have earthquake kits at home, with water, torches, and radios.

Electricity supplies were repaired within hours.

The government compensated home owners.

The LA earthquake, 1994

80 000 new housing units have been built in the area.

The Red Cross established emergency food and shelter in nearby schools within hours.

The Fire Department rescued 30 people from collapsed buildings and freeways.

Food was handed out from Dodger Stadium.

The public is now given leaflets and training on how to respond to an earthquake in future.

Activities

1 Why do people live in LA despite the risks? Give at least three reasons.

2 **a** Write a fact-file about the LA earthquake. Include time, date, magnitude, and primary and secondary effects.
  b Explain why the LA earthquake happened. (Remember plate names and the type of margin.)

3 The spider diagram shows responses to the LA earthquake. Put them into three lists. The headings for the lists should be: Short-term responses, Medium-term responses, and Long-term responses.

4 This is an examination-style question:
  a For an earthquake you have studied, explain 3 ways in which it affected people or their environment. (*3 marks.*)

  b How do people attempt to manage the risk of earthquakes? (*5 marks.*)

5 **a** Make rough notes about the LA and Kashmir earthquakes. Include:
  ◆ similarities and differences in the primary effects at each place
  ◆ similarities and differences in the secondary effects at each place
  ◆ differences in deaths and injuries
  ◆ differences in short- and long-term responses.
  b Use your rough notes to produce a long piece of writing entitled 'A comparison of the Los Angeles and Kashmir earthquakes.'

Volcanoes

In this unit you'll learn what volcanoes are.

What?

A volcano is essentially a place on the Earth's surface where lava erupts. Not always a lot of lava though.

Did you know?
The word 'volcano' comes from the name of the Roman god of fire.

Did you know?
Kilauea on Hawaii is the world's most active volcano – it has been erupting since 1983.

A hot avalanche or pyroclastic flow (a glowing cloud of hot ash, rocks, steam, and gases) – may move at over 200 mph. Very dangerous.

Ash cloud – can be blown a long way. Can cause death by asphyxiation.

Lava is usually the last thing to be erupted. It doesn't flow far. Not that dangerous.

Volcanic rock weathers to produce fertile soil ideal for farming. This is why people live near volcanoes.

A mudflow or lahar – made of water (from melted snow or a crater lake) mixed with volcanic ash. Follows river valleys for quite a way at high speed. Very dangerous.

Did you know?
1 in 10 of the world's people live within 'danger range' of volcanoes.

Volcanoes come in different shapes. It all depends on the type of lava that makes them.

Composite volcanoes

Composite volcanoes happen when the lava is **acidic** (also called felsic). You get these along **destructive** plate margins. This lava is sticky so it makes steep-sided mountains. Mount Mayon in the Philippines is like this.

A rock plug may be left from a previous eruption. This can be blown off in a future eruption, producing a hail of ash and rock. The top of the cone might collapse.

crater

parasitic cones

Alternate layers are formed because each eruption first produces rock fragments which are later covered by lava.

magma

The sticky acidic lava pours slowly down the side of the cone like toothpaste and cools quickly – this produces the cone's steep sides.

The viscous (sticky) magma traps hot gases within it, releasing them suddenly in an eruption. As it was originally oceanic crust, the magma also contains a lot of water which, as steam, increases the pressure in the lava tube. This makes a violent eruption more likely.

Shield volcanoes

Shield volcanoes form when the lava is **basic** (that's the opposite to acidic; it's also called mafic). You get these along **constructive** plate margins, like in Iceland, and also where there are **hot spots**, like Mauna Loa in the Hawaiian islands.

Because the magma isn't viscous, it releases its gases, preventing a build-up of pressure. Eruptions therefore tend not to be explosive.

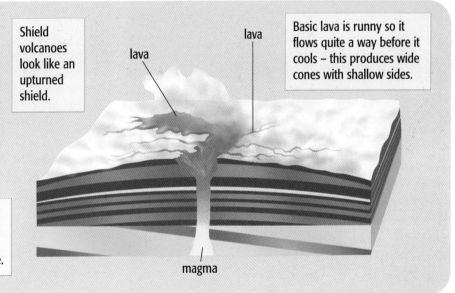

Shield volcanoes look like an upturned shield.

lava

lava

Basic lava is runny so it flows quite a way before it cools – this produces wide cones with shallow sides.

magma

Activities

1 An ICT activity.
   a Make a presentation about volcanoes. You will need to include:
      ◆ what a volcano is
      ◆ where they happen and why (destructive margins, constructive margins, and hot spots)
      ◆ the two types of volcanoes and why they are like that
      ◆ some extra research of your own.
   b Make your presentation either to the whole class or to small groups.
   c Print your presentation as a handout and stick it in your book.

Volcanoes continued

In this unit you'll learn more about volcanoes – why they're there, and how we can predict eruptions.

Why?

Volcanoes form when magma is forced up through the crust. This happens at **destructive margins** because the melted crust is less dense than the rest of the mantle. If there are gases dissolved in the magma they can escape as the magma gets higher up. These gases can make an explosion. If there is old solidified lava (called a **plug**) blocking the way out, the gases and magma either force it out of the way or they break out of the side of the volcano.

At **constructive margins** there are volcanoes because the plates are moving apart and leaving a gap that the magma can rise up into. Eruptions here are quite gentle.

Volcanoes also happen at **hot spots**. These aren't plate margins. These are where there is a really strong upward convection current in the mantle which forces some of the magma through the crust to make volcanoes.

Did you know?
If the volcano on La Palma in the Canaries explodes, a 500-metre-high mega-tsunami could engulf low-lying parts of the UK.

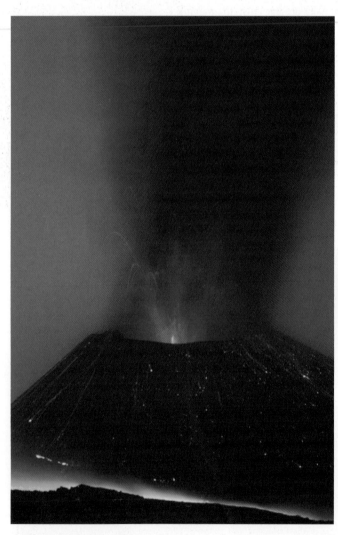

▲ *Mount Etna in Sicily, Italy.*

▲ *Mount St. Helens, north-west USA.*

When?

When a volcano is becoming active, it gives out signs. If you watch or **monitor** it, you can predict when it will erupt – and this means you can warn people.

1 When magma is on the move, it causes hundreds of tiny earthquakes. You can set up **seismometers** to detect these.

2 Days before an eruption, hot magma starts moving upwards. You can 'see' the ground getting warmer, on satellite images. (Satellite cameras detect heat!)

3 The rising magma causes the volcano to swell and bulge. So you could use . . .

a **tiltmeter** to detect changes in the slopes of the volcano

a **global positioning system** (GPS) which uses satellite signals to detect movement.

4 Gas seeping from the volcano is another sign. The more sulphur dioxide the volcano gives out, the closer it is to eruption.

In this photo, geologists are collecting gas samples on the Mount St. Helens volcano.

5 When magma is moving, it gurgles and belches. Now scientists are starting to use these sounds as warning signals.

The more closely scientists monitor the volcano, the better their predictions are likely to be.

Activities

1 Write out and complete this paragraph by filling in the gaps.

_____ form when _____ is forced up through the crust. This happens at destructive _____ because the melted crust is less dense than the rest of the mantle. If there are gases dissolved in the magma they can make an explosion. At constructive margins there are volcanoes because the plates are moving _____ and leaving a _____ that the magma can rise into. Eruptions here are quite _____. Volcanoes also happen at _____ _____. These aren't plate margins. These are where there is a really strong upward convection current in the mantle which forces some of the magma through the crust to make volcanoes.

2 a How can seismologists (scientists) predict volcanic eruptions?
  b Which methods do you think are best? Why? (Think about the length of time needed for warning, the accuracy of the technique, and the danger for the scientists.)
3 A research activity: Find out about Mount Fuji – it's Japan's biggest tourist attraction.
  a Suggest why tourists visit there.
  b How does this contribute to the economy of the area around the volcano?

Montserrat – an LEDC case study

In this unit you'll learn about the volcanic eruption on the island of Montserrat.

What happened?

I'm Joe . . .

That's me, mowing the lawn in August 1997. And that's Chances Peak behind me.

We thought it was extinct! Turns out it was only dormant. It started erupting in July 1995. The dust and ash were our warning. Scientists came and started monitoring the gases coming out and the changes in the shape of the mountains. They also had machines called seismographs to measure tiny vibrations underground.

In August 1995 they evacuated people to the north of the island – they had to live in halls and churches, sharing toilets, with nothing to do. In April 1996 everyone had to leave Plymouth, our capital city.

Starting in June 1997 the south of the island was covered by rivers of hot ash, gases, mud and rock. Scientists call these pyroclastic flows. The fires were huge! 19 people were killed, because they'd decided to stay behind in the south.

We've lost two-thirds of our houses and three-quarters of our infrastructure.

More than half of us are leaving to go to Antigua, the USA, and the UK – we're a UK colony. Before the eruption there were 11 000 of us living here – people have lived on Montserrat for thousands of years.

We're losing lots of money because there aren't any tourists any more. There used to be about two thousand every year.

So, why did it happen?

◆ The North and South American Plates are being subducted under the Caribbean Plate.

◆ The melted plate, mixed with sea water, is less dense than the rest of the mantle. So the melted magma rises upwards.

◆ The dissolved gases are released when the magma gets higher up. That's because the pressure is lower in the crust.

◆ The released gases pushed out the dust and ash from previous eruptions. That's what made the first eruptions in July 1995. And the volcano has been active ever since.

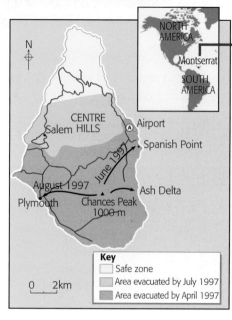

Montserrat is part of an island arc – a curved string of islands created by volcanic eruptions

Key
☐ Safe zone
▨ Area evacuated by July 1997
▓ Area evacuated by April 1997

Responding to the eruption

Immediate responses

◆ Scientists monitored the volcano and set up warning systems via radio, loudhailer, and sirens.

◆ The UK government sent £17 million of emergency aid, including temporary buildings and water purification systems.

◆ Charities like the Red Cross set up temporary schools.

◆ People evacuated to the north of the island, and then to other countries. By November 1997 the population had fallen to 3500.

◆ Some people evacuated on boats paid for by the governments of the UK and USA. The British navy took some people. Other people used their own boats.

◆ The USA sent troops for the evacuation.

◆ Charities also sent emergency food for farm animals.

▲ *Plymouth after the eruption.*

Long-term responses

◆ Ten years later, in 2005, the south of the island remained out of bounds and scientists were still monitoring the volcano.

◆ People moved back. By 2005 the population was over 8000.

◆ The Red Cross built a home for the elderly.

◆ The UK government funded a three-year redevelopment programme for houses, schools, medical services, infrastructure, and agriculture. People were also offered mortgages so they could start new businesses. It cost £122.8 million.

◆ The population structure changed, because more of the younger people made new lives elsewhere, and more of the older people either never left the island, or moved back.

◆ Some vegetation began to re-grow in the south of the island. The soil will eventually become fertile as the ash and lava break down.

◆ Tourists may come back and the volcano itself may become a tourist attraction.

Activities

1 a Where is Montserrat?
  b Make a time-line to show the main events in Montserrat from 1995 to the present.
2 Make a table to show the effects of the eruption. Have columns for effects on people, the environment, and the economy.
3 Why did the eruption happen?
4 a What is a pyroclastic flow?
  b Why is it so dangerous?

5 Cut up sheets of card to make 14 cards (about the size of a bus pass). They need to be all the same colour. Write each of the responses onto one card. You have now made a sorting game that you can use as part of your revision. Sort the cards into short and long term responses. You can always check in your textbook.
6 Why do you think people are returning to Montserrat? What does this say about people's attitudes to the volcano risk?

Mount St. Helens – an MEDC case study

In this unit you'll look at the causes and effects of the eruption of Mount St. Helens.

Where?

Washington State, USA. Mount St. Helens is a volcano in the Cascade Range of mountains. They are fold mountains (remember them? – see Units 1.2 and 1.3).

When?

◆ On 20 March 1980 there was an earthquake under the mountain. It was caused by the magma beginning to move.
◆ On 25 March there were 47 earthquakes!
◆ So, on 26 March, scientists issued a warning to the local people that they might have to evacuate the area.
◆ On 27 March gas and steam belched out of the top of the mountain.
◆ On 3 April a bulge started to appear on the side of the mountain. It kept growing and by 12 April it was 100 metres high.
◆ On 30 April scientists gave another warning and the local authorities put a 30-km danger zone around the volcano that people weren't allowed to enter.
◆ On 10 May there were several earthquakes under the mountain and the bulge kept growing, up to 1.5 metres a day.
◆ On 18 May the volcano erupted.

What?

The volcano didn't just erupt out of the top, as expected. It erupted out of the side too! That was because the top was partly blocked by a plug of old solidified lava.

Because the volcano is over a destructive margin there was a lot of gas and steam in the magma chamber. When the volcano erupted, the gas, steam, and ash burst out and flowed down the side of the volcano like a rolling cloud of burning gas. This is called a **pyroclastic flow**. It moved at 300 km/hr. It flattened and burnt trees over 360 square kilometres! 7000 animals were killed in the forests. 12 million salmon in a fish farm were killed. 61 people died, mainly scientists and photographers.

The hot magma came to the surface next, and melted the snow that had been on the top of the mountain. This made mudslides that flowed down river valleys at 35 metres per second.

Some of the smoke and dust and ash went upwards and made a cloud 24 km up into the sky. (See photo in Unit 1.8.) Planes had to be diverted. When the ash settled, it made a layer 15 cm deep. This made the roads unusable and ruined crops and farm machinery. The cost of the damage caused by just the ash was $175 million!

After the eruption, the mountain was very different. The side had blown out and the top had collapsed – it was 365 metres lower than it used to be.

Did you know?
Ash blown high into the atmosphere caused colourful sunsets in Europe for several months after the Mount St. Helens eruption.

Did you know?
About 90% of the world's 1900 active volcanoes are in the Ring of Fire, a band of volcanoes circling the Pacific Ocean.

The long-term effects

- The US government gave $951 million in aid to rebuild industry in the area and compensate people.
- The area is now a tourist attraction. This means the local economy is wealthier than it was before the eruption.
- There is now an increased risk of flooding, due to the new landscape.

▲ *Mount St. Helens after the eruption.*

Activities

1 Make a time-line of the events at Mount St. Helens in 1980. Start like this:

20 March ┬ *earthquake under the mountain*
          │
25 March ─┤

2 Why are there volcanoes in the Cascade Range?

3 Make a copy of this mind map. Complete it using the information about the eruption from these pages. You may need to add more legs!

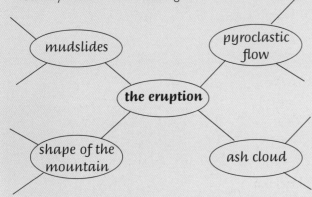

4 The area around Mount St. Helens is a rural area with an economy based on forestry and farming. The population of the area was very low. How did this affect the number of deaths and injuries?

5 Make a table to show the short-term and long-term effects of the eruption.

6 a The Montserrat and Mount St. Helens volcanoes were similar types of eruptions. Make rough notes about the:
- similarities and differences in the processes at each place.
- similarities and differences in the effects on people, the economy, and the landscape. Try to explain the differences.
- differences in the short- and long-term responses.

b Use your rough notes to produce a long piece of writing entitled 'A comparison of the Montserrat and Mount St. Helens eruptions.'

7 Now that you have learnt about the structure of the Earth, fold mountains, and volcanoes and earthquakes, you need to make revision cards for all of this chapter. Keep the cards in an envelope stuck into your book.

2 Rocks and landscape

The big picture

This chapter is about rocks, landscapes and land use. These are the big ideas behind the chapter:

◆ There are lots of different types of rocks, but they are grouped into three categories – sedimentary, igneous and metamorphic.

◆ Sedimentary, igneous and metamorphic rocks are formed in different ways.

◆ Different types of rock produce their own distinctive landscapes.

◆ The land use found in an area depends on what type of rock there is.

◆ Some types of land use – like quarrying – lead to conflict.

Your goals for this chapter

By the end of this chapter you should be able to answer these questions:

◆ Give an example of igneous and sedimentary rocks and say how they were formed.

◆ How does granite affect the landscape?

◆ Name one granite area and list the ways it is used.

◆ Give four examples (or six if you can) of limestone features in the Yorkshire Dales and explain how they were formed.

◆ What jobs do people do in limestone areas like the Yorkshire Dales? And what do people think about quarrying?

◆ What type of landscape does chalk make? Name an example of a chalk area, and say how it is used.

◆ Give an example of a clay area. How does clay affect the landscape?

◆ What do these terms mean?
magma, calcium carbonate, porous, solution, slumping, impermeable

And then . . .

When you finish the chapter, come back here and see if you've met your goals!

Did you know?
The word 'granite' comes from the Latin *granum* – a grain – and refers to the coarse-grained structure of the rock.

Did you know?
The White Cliffs of Dover, on the coast of Kent, are made of chalk.

Did you know?
◆ Many figures have been carved into Britain's chalk hillsides.
◆ Perhaps the most famous is the White Horse at Uffington. It's thought to be 3000 years old.

Did you know?
The Mohs scale measures how hard a rock is.

Your chapter starter

Look at the photo on page 28.
Do you think this is a natural feature or do you think someone made it?
Have you ever seen anything like it?
Do you think it's made of a hard or soft rock?
What types of rock can you name? (No marks for saying 'Blackpool Rock'.)

This place rocks.

It's just a rock isn't it?

In this unit you'll learn about the three main types of rocks, and how they were formed.

Rock types

There are lots of different types of rocks. But they can be fitted into just three categories. These are **sedimentary**, **igneous**, and **metamorphic**.

Sedimentary rocks

Sedimentary rocks are formed from things (sediments) that have fallen to the bottom of a lake or sea. These sediments could be sand, shells, or even skeletons! Examples of sedimentary rocks are limestone, chalk, clay, and sandstone.

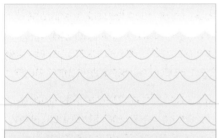

Once upon a time, over 300 million years ago, the land that forms the UK lay under the sea.

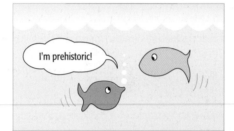

Fish and other sea creatures lived in the sea.

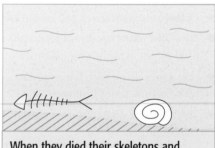

When they died their skeletons and shells fell to the sea floor as sediment.

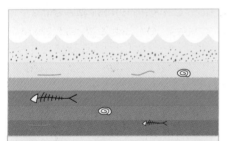

Millions of years went by. The sediment layer grew as high as a skyscraper – and very heavy.

It was so heavy that the sediment got squeezed and cemented. It slowly turned into limestone rock.

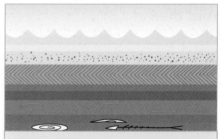

Often, too, rivers carried sand and grit to the sea. These fell to the bottom – and became sandstone and gritstone rock.

After millions of years, strong forces inside the Earth began to punch the sea bed upwards.

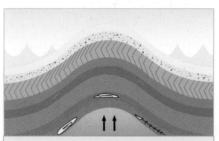

So the sea drained away. The rock that had formed on the sea bed now became land.

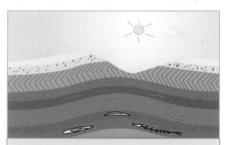

Today you can see the limestone (and sandstone and gritstone) in places like the Yorkshire Dales.

It's sedimentary my dear Watson.

Metamorphic rocks

Metamorphic rocks have been heated or squashed (put under pressure) until they have changed to make a new type of rock. These rocks are usually very hard and don't get eroded or weathered very much.

Schists (left) are formed from basalt (an igneous rock) or shale (a sedimentary rock) that has been pressurised. Marble is made from limestone that has been subjected to moderate heat and pressure.

Igneous rocks

Igneous rocks have come from magma – that's molten rock from under the Earth's crust. Igneous rocks are either from lava that erupted from a volcano (like basalt) or from magma that cooled inside the Earth (like **granite** below).

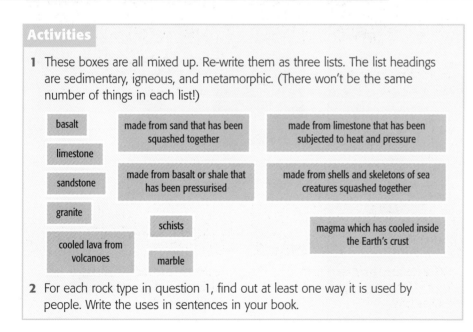

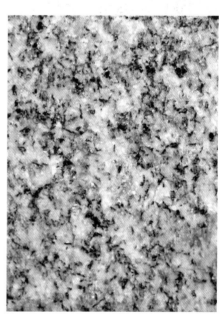

Activities

1 These boxes are all mixed up. Re-write them as three lists. The list headings are sedimentary, igneous, and metamorphic. (There won't be the same number of things in each list!)

basalt

limestone

sandstone

granite

cooled lava from volcanoes

schists

marble

made from sand that has been squashed together

made from basalt or shale that has been pressurised

made from limestone that has been subjected to heat and pressure

made from shells and skeletons of sea creatures squashed together

magma which has cooled inside the Earth's crust

2 For each rock type in question 1, find out at least one way it is used by people. Write the uses in sentences in your book.

Granite

This unit is about granite – what it is, how it was made, and how it affects the landscape.

What is granite?

Granite is an **igneous** rock. That means it was made from molten rock from inside the Earth (the mantle, in fact). If the **magma** doesn't quite make it out of the crust, but cools down inside the crust, it makes granite. Where the magma intrudes (goes into) the crust it makes **granite intrusions**. This diagram shows the different types of intrusions:

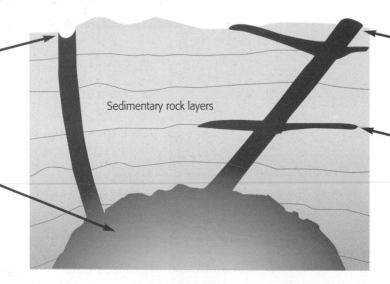

A vertical intrusion is called a **dyke**. If it's softer than the rest of the rock, it makes a dip called a **trench**.

If it makes a big, dome-shaped intrusion, it is called a **batholith**.

Sedimentary rock layers

If the dyke is harder than the surrounding rock it sticks up leaving a **ridge**.

A sideways intrusion that goes along a bedding plane is called a **sill**.

Granite areas in Britain. ▶

Land's End

What's it like on top of a batholith?

1 The top of the granite might be exposed if the rock on top gets eroded away. Granite is quite hard to erode, so it gets left sticking up.

3 The top of the batholith isn't smooth, there are bits that stick up more. These bits are called **tors**.

2 This is what has happened in Devon and Cornwall – Dartmoor, Bodmin Moor, and Land's End are all part of a huge batholith.

What's a tor like?

Granite is a **jointed** rock. That means it has small cracks in it. These joints are lines of weakness. Granite doesn't get weathered or eroded very easily, but these joints can be weathered by **frost-shattering**.

Frost-shattering is when water gets into cracks and then freezes. When it freezes it expands. This forces the joint to get bigger. So a tor is a rocky peak with expanded joints. Eventually bits break off the tor. The bits fall to the bottom and make a **blockfield**.

Did you know?
- Granite makes good building stone because it's so strong.
- Aberdeen in Scotland is known as 'the granite city' because many of its old buildings are made from local granite.

Activities

1 Make a larger copy of the mind map in your book. Add extra legs to put all the information from this unit onto it.

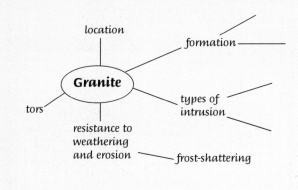

location
formation
Granite
tors
types of intrusion
resistance to weathering and erosion
frost-shattering

2 Copy the paragraph below about frost-shattering. Use the words from this box to complete it.

0 °C		joints
	bigger	
blockfield		expands

Rocks like granite have many _____. This means water can get into the cracks. When the temperature falls below _____ the water turns to ice and _____. This forces the joint to get _____. Eventually pieces fall off making a _____ at the bottom of the tor.

Dartmoor – a granite area

In this unit you'll find out about Dartmoor – its physical features and its use by people.

Wild moorland and windswept tors

This is Dartmoor ...

Dartmoor

Dartmoor is the top of an exposed batholith. The land around it is lower because Dartmoor's granite is more resistant to erosion and so sticks up. Dartmoor is the largest area of exposed granite in the south of the UK. It covers 625 square kilometres. The landscape is hilly and uneven with over 160 tors sticking up. The highest tors are in the northern parts. The vegetation cover is grass (but it would have been trees until prehistoric people cut them down!). There are deep river valleys where the rivers have eroded the jointed rock. Because the granite holds together well, the sides of the valleys are steep.

▲ *The view from Hay Tor.*

How is Dartmoor used by people?

Nice view.

Some of the granite underground gets chemically weathered to make china clay. China clay is mined – it's used for making ceramics and in paper-making.

Dartmoor is very popular with tourists – over 10 million a year! They come for walking and camping and to see the beautiful scenery.

As the granite cooled, minerals got concentrated into layers. These layers are called veins. There are veins of copper and tin, so mining used to be a big employer around here.

Granite soils are quite poor and acidic – OK for grass, but not for crops. The soil isn't good enough for the rich grass cows need. So they farm us sheep on the hills here.

Dartmoor's a National Park, you know.

Does anyone come to see us?

China clay

China clay is mined in open-cast mines (see above). The overlying rocks are removed, and then the clay is washed out with giant hoses. The clay-and-water mixture runs down the pit to form a pond, where the clay settles. The sand and other unwanted material is removed and dumped as tips around the mine.

The china clay industry is worth over £120 million a year to the Cornish economy. It employs 2500 people.

Did you know?
- Dartmoor Prison was built in 1809 at one of Dartmoor's highest and most remote places.
- People thought it would be hard for prisoners to escape over the rugged moorland!

Activities

1 This is an examination-style question.
   Describe the physical features of a granite landscape you have studied. (*4 marks.*)
2 Make a larger copy of the table below and use the information on these pages to complete it.

3 Look at the photo above. It shows a china clay mine in Dartmoor.
   a Describe the appearance of the China clay mine.
   b What good things are there about china clay mining in Dartmoor?
   c What problems might china clay mining cause for tourists and people who rely on income from tourism?

Land use in Dartmoor	Why is it there?	What happens?
sheep farming		
mining		
tourism		

Limestone

This unit is about limestone – what it is, how it was formed, its properties, and where it's found in the UK.

What is it professor?

Limestone is a sedimentary rock. It was made by lots of skeletons and shells of sea creatures falling to the bottom of clear tropical seas and getting compacted (squashed) there (look at the photo).

Where can I find some?

There's quite a bit of limestone in the UK. A famous area of limestone is the Yorkshire Dales.

What's it like?

Limestone is:

◆ made of **calcium carbonate** – this means it can be dissolved slowly by rain-water or sea water (they are both slightly acidic).
◆ usually jointed – the joints are lines of weakness so they get weathered more.
◆ quite strong – so it can make steep hills and cliffs without collapsing (like clay would).

There are lots of features you can only find in limestone areas.

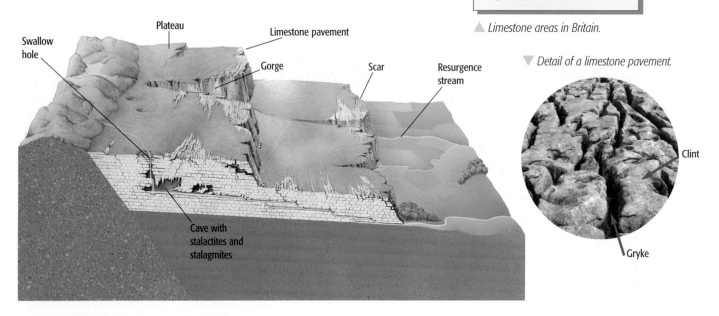

▲ Limestone areas in Britain.

Yorkshire Dales

▼ Detail of a limestone pavement.

Swallow hole
Plateau
Limestone pavement
Gorge
Scar
Resurgence stream
Cave with stalactites and stalagmites

Clint
Gryke

Activities

1 Make a larger copy of the mind map in your book. Add extra legs to put all the information from this unit on to it.
2 Make a table with these headings: Feature, Example, Description, Formation, Diagram, and complete it using information from these pages.

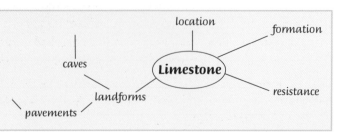

location
formation
caves
Limestone
resistance
landforms
pavements

Limestone features in the Yorkshire Dales

Swallow holes

These happen when a stream dissolves a joint and then flows down it rather than over the ground. The hole 'swallows' the stream! This photo shows a famous swallow hole – Gaping Gill near Ingleborough.

Dry valleys

These are old river valleys. When there was a lot of water around, and the ground was saturated after the last ice age, the rivers flowed over the surface and made these valleys. Now the ground isn't saturated, the water can permeate into the limestone (down swallow holes) and so the valleys are left dry. This dry valley is above Malham Cove.

Caves

These happen when the underground stream dissolves an underground hole called a cave, like the ones leading from Gaping Gill. Inside caves, the dripping water deposits pure limestone in hanging **stalactites** (which hold 'tite' to the roof of the cave) and standing **stalagmites**.

Gorges

If a cave system (a group of caves) collapses, it leaves a stream in the bottom of a steep-sided narrow gorge, like Trow Gill gorge near Clapham, shown here. Some people think there's another reason for gorges: powerful rivers of meltwater from the glaciers that melted at the end of the last ice age.

Limestone pavements

These are areas where the limestone is exposed. The joints are weathered by solution and this leaves a pattern of dips (enlarged joints called **grykes**) and flat surfaces (called **clints**). This looks like a pavement! This one, near Malham, is a good example.

Dolines

These are hollows in the limestone that don't have a stream going into them. They are formed either by water dissolving the limestone near the surface or by a cave collapsing. There are a lot of them just north of Malham Tarn.

Making a living in the Yorkshire Dales

In this unit you will find out about the jobs people do in limestone areas like the Yorkshire Dales.

The Dales economy

Quarrying

There are eight large quarries in the Southern Dales, producing 4.7 million tonnes of limestone each year. 93% of this goes out of the Dales by road, 7% by rail. Limestone has many uses. It's used as a building stone, for making cement, and as a cleanser in the steel industry. Quarrying earns £6 million a year for the Dales economy. This quarry is at Castle Bolton.

Tourism

Some come for the day and some come to stay. 93% come by car! People come to the Dales to see the landscape – with its caves and limestone pavements and traditional villages. There are nearly 1500 km of footpaths. Tourism gives jobs in hotels, bed and breakfasts, restaurants, and shops. 8.3 million visitors a year bring in about £175 million!

Farming

Limestone soils are thin – because the weathered material is dissolved, it doesn't build up to make a deep soil. This means you can't grow crops or good grass for cows, but the grass is OK for sheep. Sheep can also cope with the cold winters out in the fields.

60% of the land in the Yorkshire Dales National Park is farmland, and 20% of the people rely on farming for their livelihoods. The farmers are supposed to farm in a traditional way, so they don't spoil the National Park.

So everything's rosy then?

Not always. Tourism is obviously important to the Dales economy, but it brings some problems:

◆ The most popular places – called 'honeypots' – become crowded with people and congested with traffic, and local people sometimes resent the tourists.

◆ Farmers complain that some tourists damage their walls and gates, harm their animals, and leave litter.

◆ The main footpaths, and parts of the famous limestone pavements, have been eroded by millions of tramping feet.

◆ House prices in some villages are rising as tourists buy holiday homes – this can make them too expensive for local people, which means young people have to move away.

There are also problems with quarrying, and you'll find out about these in the next unit.

Did you know?
There is evidence that people have lived and farmed in the Dales for the last 10 000 years.

Did you know?
The soap opera 'Emmerdale' is filmed in the Yorkshire Dales.

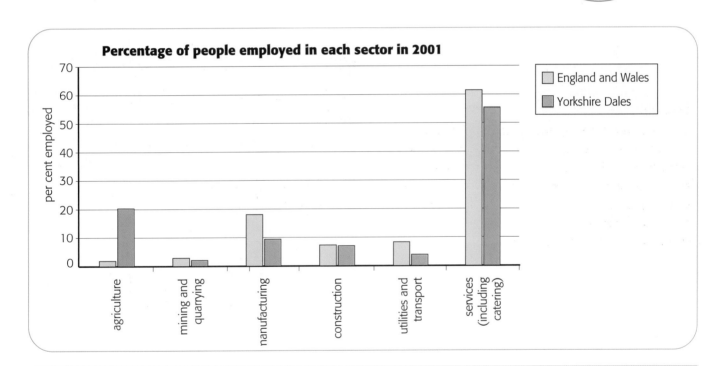

Percentage of people employed in each sector in 2001

Legend: England and Wales; Yorkshire Dales

y-axis: per cent employed (0–70)

x-axis: agriculture, mining and quarrying, manufacturing, construction, utilities and transport, services (including catering)

Activities

1 Use the writing frame on the right to make a detailed case study about the Yorkshire Dales.

2 Look at the graph above of the jobs that people do. It shows both the average for the whole of England and Wales and the figures for the Dales. The data is from the last census in 2001.

   a Describe the graph. (That means say what the biggest and smallest sectors are and give numbers, say what is similar and different between the two data sets.)

   b Explain the pattern of employment in the Dales. (That means give possible reasons for the data about the Dales.)

Title: _____

This area is located . . .

The geology of the area is . . .

The three main economic activities in the Dales are . . .

Quarrying is . . .

Farming in this area is . . .

Tourism is . . .

Good things about tourism are . . .

Possible negative effects of tourism are . . .

Ingleton quarry

In this unit you'll find out that people have different views about quarrying in the Yorkshire Dales National Park.

As I was saying . . .

The quarry ruins the view for tourists. It's noisy too, and then there's those huge trucks on these narrow country roads! I might not come here again. I'll go somewhere else instead – no noisy quarries to spoil the landscape and the peace and quiet.

Limestone is a non-renewable resource – once it's gone, it's gone for good. And if they take the limestone out, will the rare plants that live on the limestone soils ever come back? Is it sustainable to use the land like this? Is the land being used in a way that doesn't harm the ecosystem and environment in the long term?

Ingleton quarry is good for the local area. On top of that, the country needs our stone. We've spent over £1 million reducing the dust and noise. And we've planted lots of trees. We have a plan to landscape the area and plant more trees when the quarry is exhausted. So, it will go back to looking like it did before the quarry started.

I work in the quarry – have done for years. There's fifteen of us working here, but other local people have jobs because of the quarry too – electricians, lorry drivers, local cafes, and so on. It would have a big impact on the local economy if we had to close now instead of when the stone's all gone, many years from now. And where else could I get a job round here? There's nothing!

What and where

Ingleton quarry

◆ Employs 15 people.

◆ Has won two awards for environmental sensitivity.

◆ Has already planted 29 000 trees to screen the quarry (see main photo).

◆ Limestone from here is mainly used in construction – it's broken up and mixed into aggregates for roads.

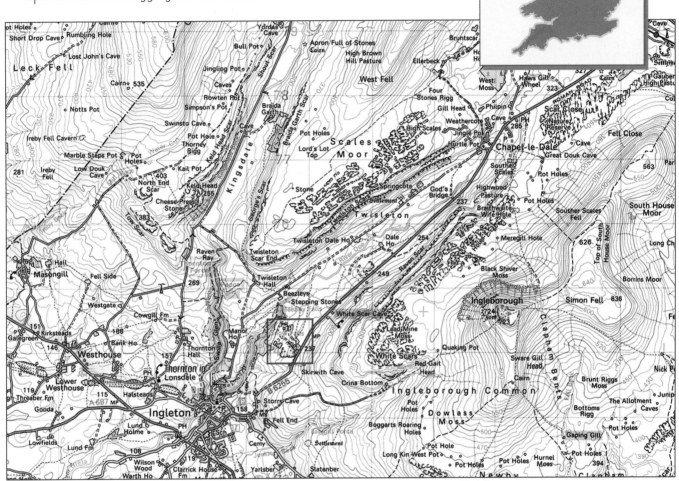

Yorkshire Dales National Park

1 Read the opinions about Ingleton quarry. Make a fact-file about the quarry, covering its location, and the advantages and disadvantages of the quarry. Include a sketch map of its location. Think about what you should show on your sketch map, before you start drawing it.

2 Quarries can cause a lot of conflict. People can't agree on whether they are good or bad things. Local councils might well have meetings about local quarries. You need to consider three possible options for the future of Ingleton quarry.

These are:

Option 1: Let the quarry carry on as it is.

Option 2: Limit the quarry to another three years of production. Some quarries in the Dales are time-limited. In other words they are told they can only use the land for so many more years.

Option 3: Close the quarry down now.

a Make a list of the advantages and disadvantages of each option.

b Decide which one you favour.

c Prepare a presentation or short statement outlining your case.

Chalk

This unit is about chalk – what it is, how it was made, how it affects the landscape, and how it is used.

What is chalk?

It's a sedimentary rock; a type of soft limestone in fact. It's made of calcium carbonate.

How was it made?

By lots of shells of sea creatures (mainly ones called foraminiferans) falling to the bottom of the sea and then getting compacted over the centuries.

What's it used for?

Chalk is used in making plaster, putty, cement, mortar, and rubber. Strong types of chalk can be used for building. And it is also used for blackboard chalk.

What sorts of landforms does chalk make?

Chalk is very **porous** so it lets water through. This means there aren't many rivers on chalk – but there are **dry valleys**, like those found on limestone. Chalk gets eroded mostly by **solution**, which is a slow process. This is why chalk tends to stick up above other rocks that have been eroded more quickly.

Chalk doesn't have joints like limestone, so it doesn't make pavements and caves. It tends to make **steep cliffs** like the Seven Sisters, and rolling **hills** like the Downs.

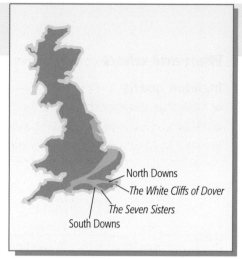

North Downs
The White Cliffs of Dover
The Seven Sisters
South Downs

▲ Chalk areas in Britain.

Did you know?
◆ Great Bustards are the heaviest flying bird in the world – they can weigh up to 25 kg.
◆ They became extinct in Britain in the 1830s, but are now being re-introduced to chalk downland in parts of southern England.

Did you know?
Watership Down (the book about rabbits you might have read) is a real place – it's part of the South Downs.

◀ Land ahoy! The Seven Sisters – chalk cliffs along the south coast of England, where the South Downs meet the sea.

The North and South Downs

The North and South Downs are areas of chalk that aren't by the coast. The chalk sticks up above the other rocks in the area to make gentle hills. Originally the North and South Downs were part of the same dome of chalk, but the middle part has been eroded to form the Weald.

The soil is thin so there aren't many trees. The vegetation is mostly grasses and some herbs like trefoil. The land is used mainly for grazing animals like sheep, and sometimes cows. In fact, the animals stop scrub plants like hawthorn and privet coming in and taking over, so they protect the **downland habitat**. There are lots of rare insects and flowers, like orchids. There used to be Great Bustards in the chalk hills too – birds of prey up to a metre tall!

▲ *The South Downs in West Sussex.*

I'm preserving the environment as I eat.

I'm part of the unique downland habitat.

Activities

1 Make a larger copy of this mind map. Add extra legs to put all the information from this unit on to it.
2 This is an examination-style question.
   a Describe the physical landscape of one named area of chalk. (*4 marks.*)
   b What is the main land use in this area? Why? (*6 marks.*)

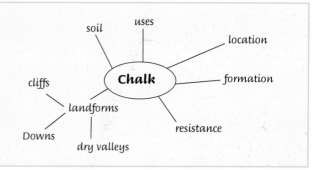

Clay

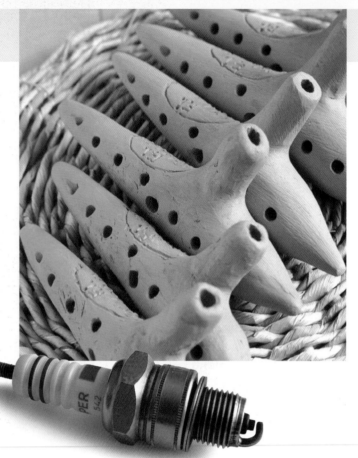

This unit is about clay – what it is, how it was made, how it affects the landscape, and how it is used.

What is it?

Clay is a fine-grained sedimentary rock. The particles are 0.02 mm across or smaller!

How is it formed?

Clay is made from the chemical weathering of other rocks and minerals. It builds up in layers on top of these rocks, or it can be transported by rivers and glaciers and then deposited in lakes and seas.

What's it used for?

Making pots is one obvious use! But clay is also used in paper making, for the tips of spark plugs (see right), in chemical filters, and even in a musical instrument called the ocarina (see above right).

Where can I find some?

In the UK there are lots of areas that have clay geologies. One is around Lough Neagh in Northern Ireland. The clay here was deposited by glaciers in the last ice age.

How does it affect the landscape?

Clay isn't strong enough to make steep slopes. It collapses under its own weight. If clay gets wet the water acts like a lubricant and the clay slides downhill. This is called **slumping**.

Clay is **impermeable** – this means it doesn't let water in. So the area around Lough Neagh:

◆ is flat
◆ sometimes gets waterlogged (the waterlogged areas are called bogs)
◆ has lots of rivers
◆ is a mixture of farmland, grasses, and woodland (and marshes in the boggy areas).

▲ Clay areas in Britain.

NORTHERN IRELAND

Key

■ Area of clay deposits

Lough Neagh

Belfast ●

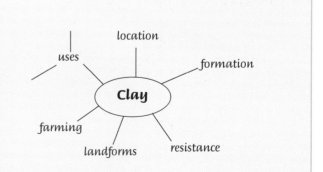
▲ Another area with a clay geology – the Fenland of East Anglia.

How do people make a living around Lough Neagh?

The main land use is farming.
- Clay is high in nutrients for plants.
- Clay soils don't get eroded easily.
- The land is flat so it's easy for machinery to get around.
- Clay soils can be used for arable farming (crops), usually wheat because the weather's right for that.

Around Lough Neagh they also grow fruit in market gardens. There are also some dairy farms, because the cows love the rich grass that the clay soil gives.

The clay itself can also be useful. It can be dug up and used in making clay bricks, and in waterproofing landfill sites.

Did you know?
Clay is used in water treatment works to absorb organic pollutants.

Activities

1 Make a larger copy of the mind map in your book. Add extra legs to put all the information from this unit onto it.
2 This is an examination-style question.
   Describe and explain the physical landscape of one named area of clay. (6 marks.)
3 Now you've looked at all the rocks in this chapter, go back through your notes and check you have completed everything your teacher set. Then make revision cards on:
   - Rock types
   - Granite (geology, landscape, land uses)
   - Limestone (geology, landscape, land uses, quarries)
   - Chalk (geology, landscape, land uses)
   - Clay (geology, landscape, land uses)

uses · location · formation · **Clay** · farming · landforms · resistance

3 Glacial landscapes

The big picture

This chapter is about glaciers and the landscapes they create. These are the big ideas behind the chapter:

◆ Glaciers are like rivers, except they're made of ice and they flow very slowly.

◆ Glaciers erode, transport and deposit material.

◆ Glaciers create lots of different landforms by erosion and deposition.

◆ You can recognise glacial landforms on maps.

◆ People make a living in upland glaciated areas from forestry, farming and tourism.

◆ Tourism can create problems which need to be managed.

Your goals for this chapter

By the end of this chapter you should be able to answer these questions:

◆ What is a glacier? Where do you find them? How do they change the landscape?

◆ How are these formed?
corries, arêtes, pyramidal peaks, glacial troughs, truncated spurs, hanging valleys, drumlins, eskers, kames

◆ Name five landforms created by glacial deposition.

◆ What do these terms mean?
melt-water, crevasse, plucking, abrasion, striation, moraine, freeze-thaw weathering, U-shaped valley, misfit stream, till

◆ Which glacial landforms can you recognise on an OS map?

◆ Why is farming difficult in areas like Snowdonia?

◆ How important is tourism in Snowdonia? Give some facts and figures.

◆ What problems does tourism cause?

◆ Give some examples of solutions to the problems that tourists cause. At least six, and ten if you can.

◆ What do people think about some of the solutions?

And then . . .

When you finish the chapter, come back here and see if you've met your goals!

Did you know?
◆ The last ice age ended about 10 000 years ago.
◆ Most of Britain was covered by ice, and much of our landscape is the result of ice erosion and deposition.

Did you know?
◆ Today, glacial ice covers about 10% of the Earth's land surface.
◆ During the last ice age, it probably covered about 30%.

Did you know?
◆ A glaciation or ice age is when massive amounts of ice spread over the Earth.
◆ We are currently in what's called an inter-glacial – a non-ice age.

Did you know?
The most severe ice age in the history of the Earth occurred 800 million years ago, when glaciers got close to the equator.

Your chapter starter

Look at the photo on page 46.
What is it? What's it made of?
Where could it be? Have you ever seen anything like this?
What could the person (or their dog) be thinking?
What's the link between glaciers and global warming?

That's a long way for his little legs.

Introducing glaciers

In this unit you'll learn what glaciers are, where they're found, and how they shape the landscape.

What is a glacier?

A glacier is like a river – only it's made of ice and it flows much, much more slowly. A glacier is made when lots of snow gets squashed into ice and then slides downhill. The ice goes down the easiest route, so it follows old river valleys down from the mountains.

Glaciers are really big so they make massive impacts on the landscape.

▲ The Russell glacier, Alaska.

Where are glaciers found?

Today we can find glaciers anywhere it's cold enough. Most big mountain ranges have glaciers, like the Alps, the Rockies, the Andes, and the Himalayas. Places that get lots of snow have huge masses of ice that form an **ice sheet**, like Greenland, Iceland, and Antarctica. But in the past other places had glaciers too.

Where did they used to be?

There have been many **ice ages** since the formation of the Earth. In the last Ice Age, lots of the UK was covered by ice, and that means there were lots of glaciers!

The map shows where the ice was. The ice didn't melt until 10 000 years ago. We can still see the effects of this ice in the landscape of the UK.

How do they move?

Slowly. But with great power. Glaciers move between about 7 and 10 km a year. Much slower than a river, but wow do they make a difference to the landscape! There is usually some **melt-water** at the bottom and this helps them move. The middle moves faster than the edges, and sometimes the glacier hits an obstacle so it slows down. All this means the ice gets stretched and squashed, so it cracks. These cracks are called **crevasses**.

How do glaciers change the landscape?

Just like waves and rivers, glaciers have energy. That means they can do work. The work they do is eroding and transporting material.

Glaciers can erode rocks in two ways – by **plucking** and by **abrasion**. Plucking happens when the ice freezes on to a rock. Then when the ice moves again it pulls (plucks) the rock with it. This rock is then stuck underneath the glacier.

Did you know?

The world's longest and largest glacier is the Lambert Glacier in Antarctica – it's 400 km long and covers 1 million sq km.

Did you know?

About 75% of the world's freshwater is stored in glacier ice.

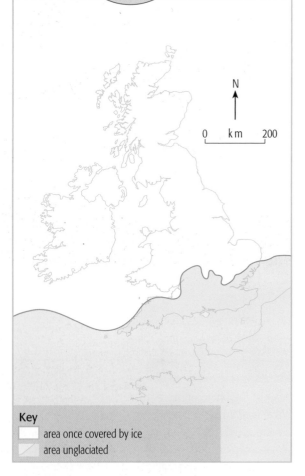

N

0   km   200

Key

area once covered by ice

area unglaciated

▲ Mind the ice!

Abrasion is like the action of sandpaper. It takes place when rocks and pebbles stuck in the bottom of the ice grind over the bedrock. This can make scratches in the rock, called **striations**.

The glacier carries lots of material with it. This material is called **moraine**. Some moraine is under the ice (**ground moraine**). Moraine can also be inside the glacier if it has fallen into crevasses, or fallen from the surrounding mountains and then been covered by new snow. Moraine can also be on top of the glacier if it has fallen off the mountain slopes above the ice. It gathers at the side of the glacier to make **lateral moraines**. If two glaciers join up, one lateral moraine will get stuck in the middle. Then it's called a **medial moraine**. The drawing below and the photo on the left show moraines on a glacier.

There's lots of surface moraine because there's a weathering process going on. This is called **freeze-thaw weathering**. On the slopes above the ice, water gets into cracks in the rock. Then when the water freezes, it gets bigger. This forces the crack wider. Eventually the rock breaks off where the crack is.

Did you know?
The world's fastest-moving glacier is the Columbia Glacier in Alaska – it covers 35 metres per day.

Did you know?
Many of the world's glaciers are retreating – getting shorter and smaller – because of global warming.

▼ *A slice through the ice.*

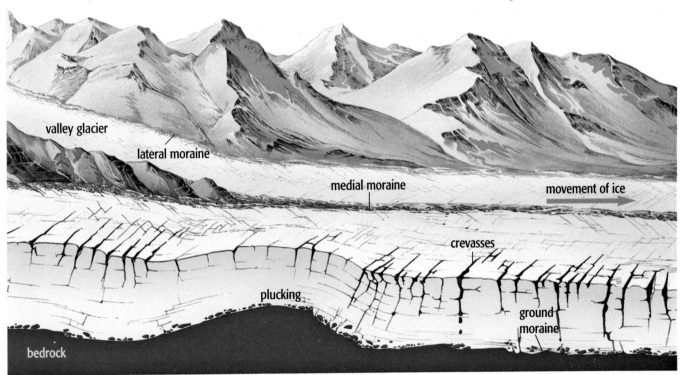

Activities

1 a Make a large copy of this mind map. Use a whole page.
  b Add to it using the information on these pages. You may need to add more 'legs'.
  c Extra research from books or the Internet could make this more detailed. Think about examples, or facts and figures.
2 Answer in full sentences in your book:
  a What is freeze-thaw weathering?
  b How does it work?
  c What do you think the effects of this process might be on the landscape? Why?

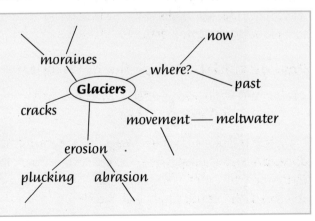

Glacial landforms – erosional features

In this unit we'll look at some glacial landforms and how they were made.

What landforms do glaciers make?

Glaciers make lots of features, some of which have strange names! The ones we will be studying are corries, arêtes, pyramidal peaks, troughs, truncated spurs, hanging valleys, ribbon lakes, till, drumlins, eskers, and kames. Some are made by erosion and some by deposition.

The Lake District was covered by ice during the last Ice Age, so it has lots of examples of glacial features.

The first three erosional features are …

Corries

These can also be called **cirques** or a **cwms** – they're all names for the same thing, so don't get confused.

- Corries start as sheltered hollows near the top of a mountain.
- Snow collects there.
- The snow fills up the hollow and gets squashed to make ice.
- The ice moves downhill because it is pulled by gravity.
- But it doesn't move straight down. It moves in a rotational (curved) way.
- As it moves, it is plucking and abrading, so it makes a deep semi-circular hollow – this is the **corrie**.
- Plucking and freeze-thaw mean that the **back wall** of the corrie is very steep.
- The ice erodes less at the front edge, so a **lip** is left.
- When the ice melts, a small lake might be left behind the lip. This is called a **corrie-lake** or a **tarn**.

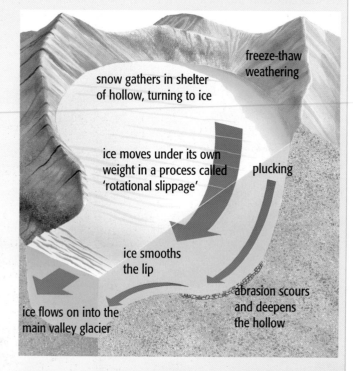

snow gathers in shelter of hollow, turning to ice

freeze-thaw weathering

ice moves under its own weight in a process called 'rotational slippage'

plucking

ice smooths the lip

abrasion scours and deepens the hollow

ice flows on into the main valley glacier

▼ *Helvellyn, an example of a corrie in the Lake District.*

steep back wall

corrie

tarn

lip

Arêtes

If two corries form next to each other they will leave a sharp ridge between them. This is called an **arête**. ('Arête' is French for stop!) This photo shows Striding Edge, a famous arête in the Lake District.

the arête

Pyramidal peaks

These are made when three or more corries form around a mountain. They cut backwards to leave a **'horn'** or **pyramidal peak** in the middle. There isn't a good example of a pyramidal peak in the Lake District, but there is in Wales – Mount Snowdon, shown in this photo.

the peak

Activities

1 Make a flow diagram to show how corries are made. Start like this … ⟶
2 Use these beginnings to makes notes on arêtes and pyramidal peaks:
   ◆ An arête looks like …
   ◆ An arête is formed when …
   ◆ An example of an arête is …
   ◆ A pyramidal peak is made when …
   ◆ An example is …
3 Draw a diagram of one of the photos on these pages. Add explaining labels (annotations) to explain how the feature was formed.

Snow collects in a sheltered hollow at the top of a mountain …

Erosional features continued

Now you'll learn about the other erosional features.

The final three erosional features are …

Glacial troughs, truncated spurs, and hanging valleys.

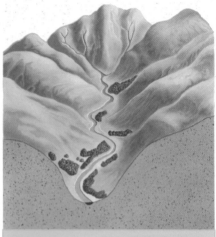

When a glacier moves downhill it usually takes the easiest way. That often means down an old river valley. See the interlocking spurs and the tributaries?

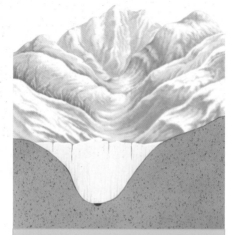

The glacier carves its way through the rock. It erodes a deeper and wider valley by **abrasion** and **plucking**.

When the ice melts, a **glacial trough** is left behind. You can see that the old interlocking spurs have been cut-off to leave **truncated spurs**. The old tributaries are left hanging high up on the valley sides – so they're called **hanging valleys**.

Glacial trough

This is Martindale Valley in the Lake District.

Glacial troughs can also be called **U-shaped valleys** – because they're shaped like a U!

Steep valley sides. Some material has slumped down to make the sides a bit gentler over the years.

Misfit stream. This is a small stream in the bottom of a glacial trough – it looks too small to have made the valley.

Flat valley floor.

Truncated spurs

When the glacier erodes the old river valley, it cuts off the **interlocking spurs**. This leaves **truncated spurs**. Truncated is really just another word for 'cut-off'. This photo shows Wast Water in the Lake District. You can see the ends of the spurs that have been truncated on the left-hand side of the photo.

truncated spurs

Hanging valleys

This photo shows a hanging valley in Norway. You can clearly see the high-level tributary valley, from which there's a sharp fall to the level of the lower, main valley. The extra depth of the lower valley is due to more severe glaciation, because it contained more ice. To the left of the hanging valley is a truncated spur – so this photo's got it all!

hanging valley

Activities

1 **a** Draw a field sketch of the photo of the hanging valley.
  b Annotate it with explaining labels about the hanging valley, truncated spurs, and glacial trough.
2 Match up these beginnings and endings and write them out correctly.
  A glacial trough is . . .
    . . . the ends of interlocking spurs that have been cut off by the glacier.
  A hanging valley is . . .
    . . . a tributary valley that enters a main valley part way up the valley side.
  Truncated spurs are . . .
    . . . the eroded valley left by a glacier.
3 Write down this beginning: 'Misfit streams are . . .' and then finish off the sentence.
4 A thinking question! Why do you think there's a lake at the bottom of the valley of Wast Water? Make rough notes of your ideas.

Did you know?
The ice covering Antarctica is over 2.6 miles thick in some places!

Glacial landforms – depositional features

In this unit we'll look at some more glacial landforms and how they were made.

Depositional features

Deposition is when material is dropped by the glacier. This material is a lot of jumbled up bits of clay, sand, gravel, and boulders. It is called **till**.

Terminal moraine and ribbon lakes

As a glacier moves, it pushes material in front of it and then leaves it there when the ice melts. This is called the **terminal moraine**. It shows the furthest point a glacier reached. Sometimes water gets trapped behind the terminal moraine, in the glacial trough. This makes a **ribbon lake**. This one is Derwent Water in the Lake District, with the town of Keswick next to the lake.

Drumlins

When a glacier is moving slowly, it doesn't have very much energy. This means it can't erode and transport material – it can only shape the clay underneath it. This makes smooth hills. Some people say they look like eggs – and a basket of eggs where there are lots together.

What happens when the ice melts?

The glacier drops its load! This makes lots of features.

Eskers and kames are quite small features, so they don't get given individual names.

Eskers
Any material that was being carried in a stream under the glacier gets left as a long wiggly ridge called an **esker**.

Kames
Any debris that was in a crevasse gets dropped to the valley floor in a heap called a **kame**.

esker

kame

lake dammed by terminal moraine

terminal moraine (unsorted) deposits)

drumlins

till

Activities

1 a What is a terminal moraine?
   b What is a ribbon lake?
   c How can a terminal moraine tell us about global warming?
2 Look at the photo of Derwent Water. Why do you think the settlement (Keswick) was built there? Try to come up with three reasons.
3 Write a series of true and false statements based on this chapter so far. Take turns with the rest of the class to read

out your statements for the other students to decide if they are 'true' or 'false'.
4 Make revision cards of all the features you have learnt about in this chapter. For each card, write the feature on one side and on the other write:
   ◆ a description of it
   ◆ how it was formed
   ◆ an example.

Glacial landforms on maps

In this unit you will see what glacial landforms look like on maps.

▼ This map extract is from the Ordnance Survey Landranger series, Map 90, Penrith and Keswick. 1 : 50 000 scale (2 cm to 1 km, 1.25 inches to 1 mile).

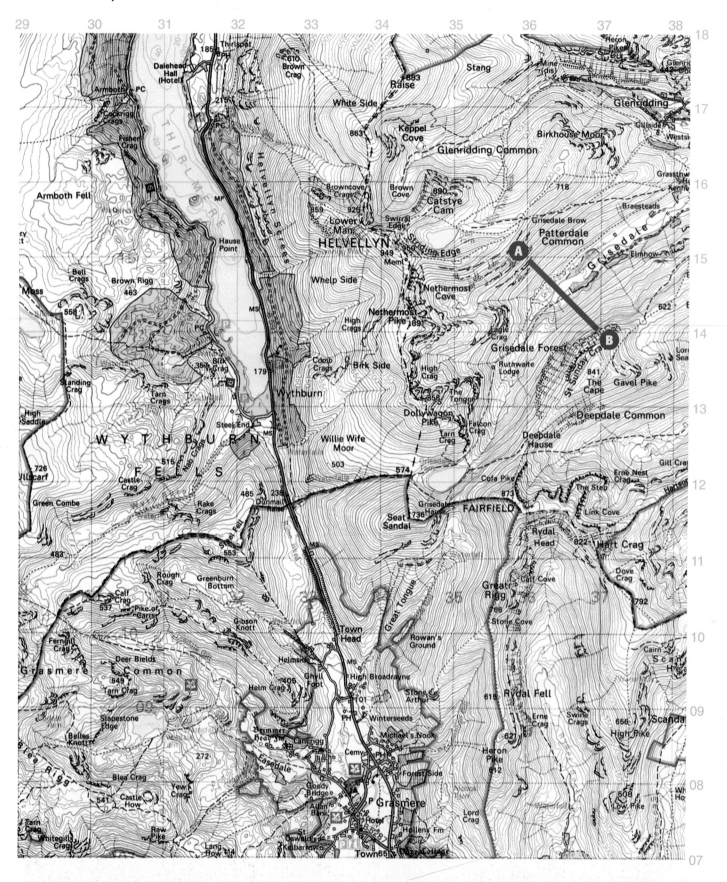

Activities

1 a How is height shown on an OS map?
  b How is steepness shown on an OS map?
  c Describe the overall **relief** of the area in the map.

2 Match up these grid references with the place names:

342151	Alcock Tarn
321131	car park
349079	spot height 949 on Helvellyn

3 Match up these places or locations with the correct landform type.

Brown Cove   ribbon lake   corrie lake   truncated spurs

glacial trough   hanging valleys   Thirlmere   Striding Edge

along the eastern edge of Thirlmere   Red Tarn   corrie   along the eastern edge of Thirlmere

Grisedale   arête

4 Draw a cross-section of the transect A-B marked on the map. (Hint: the bolder contour lines go up in 50-metre gaps.)

5 Why is Grasmere Village built in square 3307?

6 Why is the A591 built where it is?

7 What type of forestry has been planted on the shores of Thirlmere? Why do you think that is?

8 a Look at the photo below. What grid reference was the photographer standing at?
  b Which direction was the camera pointing in?

9 Make a large copy of the table below. Use the map and the previous pages to complete it.

feature	example	description	explanation of how it was formed
corrie			
tarn			
arête			
pyramidal peak	*Snowdon*		
glacial trough			
truncated spur			
hanging valley			
terminal moraine			
ribbon lake			
drumlins	-----		
esker	-----		
kame	-----		

Thirlmere viewed from Helvellyn

Snowdonia: people in upland areas

In this unit you'll learn how people make use of the land in an area that was glaciated.

People have to make a living

Snowdonia was glaciated in the last Ice Age. It's an upland area, in North Wales.

But there aren't just glacial landforms in Snowdonia. There are people too! Over 26 000 of them. And they have to make a living. So what do they do?

Snowdonia

The higher land is colder and has thinner soils so it is used for grazing sheep.

The lower land is warmer so there are some dairy farms here.

Dry-stone walls are still built in the traditional way to separate the fields.

Forestry

16% of the land in Snowdonia is forested, usually with coniferous trees (usually pine trees). These were planted because they grow fast and can be sold for timber and paper-making. The steep slopes and the hilltops aren't very useful for agriculture so forestry is an efficient use of the land.

But recently there has been concern about the coniferous plantations. Native insects, birds, and mammals can't cope easily with the pine trees, because there's less food and the leaf litter is acidic. The trees are also planted in straight rows – this is very unnatural, and they spoil the view. So now woodlands are being changed to include native tree species, planted in a more random way.

Farming

Merthyr Farm is a hill farm in Snowdonia. It is 140 hectares in area. It is high up, between 180 and 360 metres above sea level. They get lots of rain – up to 1500 mm a year.

100 hectares is grassland for the sheep and cows. 40 hectares is rough grazing – this is on top of the hills, and isn't very nutritious for the animals. The farm has over 700 sheep and more than 60 cows.

The climate is too cold and the soil is too thin for crops to grow. The lower slopes get waterlogged because the soil doesn't drain well.

Lambs don't fetch much money in the market now, only about £25 each. This is because there's less demand for red meat generally in the UK, and because meat is imported more cheaply from other countries. Even wool doesn't make much money – it costs the farm more to shear the sheep than they make by selling the wool! But if they don't shear the sheep they get infested with maggots.

The farmer does get some extra money from the government because the area is so hard to farm. This is called a subsidy. They also have a 'bed and breakfast' business and rent space for caravans. The owner of the farm even teaches people how to do dry-stone walling to earn a bit of extra money.

▲ Caerwyn Roberts – the farmer.

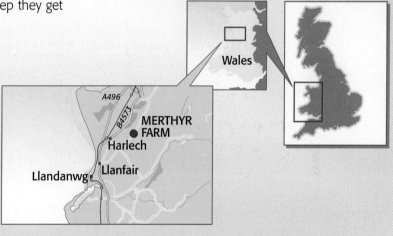

Activities

1 Make a copy of the tree diagram on the right in your book, then add facts in each branch.
2 Use this writing frame to make a case study about Merthyr Farm.

> **Title:**
> This farm is in …
> The size of the farm is …
> The type of farm is …
> Animals are …
> It is difficult to farm in upland areas because …
> Ways round the problems are …

3 Add a sketch map showing the location of the farm.

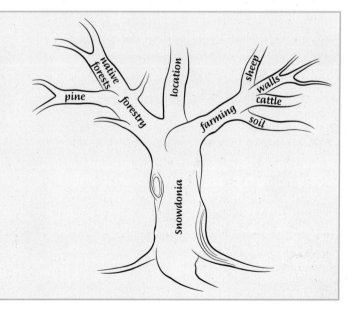

Tourism in Snowdonia

In this unit you'll find out more about economic activity in an upland area of an MEDC.

Thanks for visiting

Tourism is really important to the economy of Snowdonia. There are about 8 million visitors a year, and just over half of them stay overnight. This means jobs in hotels and B&Bs, cafes and restaurants, shops, and transport. And of course farmers and other local businesses can sell their produce either directly to the tourists or to local shops so that they can sell it on to the tourists.

5000 people have jobs linked to tourism. Tourism makes about £180 million a year for Snowdonia. A day-visitor spends an average of £22 and an overnight visitor spends nearly £80! – this shows how important tourism is.

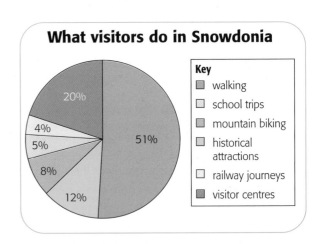

What visitors do in Snowdonia

51% 20% 4% 5% 8% 12%

Key
- walking
- school trips
- mountain biking
- historical attractions
- railway journeys
- visitor centres

Welcome to Snowdonia Mountains and Coast

Snowdonia National Park, the Llyn Peninsula, and the Cambrian Coast – an area of striking contrasts.

Snowdonia is a land of breathtaking beauty and fantastic scenery. Climb the highest mountains in England and Wales. Walk or mountain–bike in one of Britain's most beautiful National Parks. Visit the picturesque surroundings of Dolgellau, Porthmadog, Beddgelert, and Llanberis to find that ideal gift for family and friends or just relax by a quiet street corner sipping Welsh tea and tasting 'bara brith' – our famous Welsh cake.

Snowdonia is also a land of castles – Caernarfon, Conwy, and Harlech, built by Edward I, are three of the best-preserved mediaeval fortresses in Britain. They are World Heritage Sites.

Snowdonia is fringed with a coastline designated a Heritage Coast and part of an Area of Outstanding Natural Beauty. The magnificent coastline is home to numerous blue flag beaches to suite all tastes. If you're looking to spend the day on the beach or just take a stroll the ideal beach is only a short distance away. Along Cardigan Bay there's Aberdyfi, Barmouth, Tywyn, and Harlech and all around the Llyn you have beaches from Pwllheli to Aberdaron and Nefyn.

So, tourism's good then?

Well, not all good . . .

◆ Footpaths get eroded by all the walkers. Feet trample the soil and damage the vegetation. This means that when it rains the water can't soak in. So it runs off the slopes and takes soil with it. The paths get deeper and that makes even more run-off. The paths end up rocky and dangerous for people, and they look ugly – like big scars. The vegetation takes a long time to grow back as the climate is cool. It costs about £100 per metre to mend a path.

◆ Obviously most tourists only come in the summer, so 19% of the people in Snowdonia have seasonal jobs – this means they only get work for part of the year.

◆ Snowdonia National Park Authority has parking for nearly 2000 cars and local councils have other car parks, but it's not enough. Traffic on narrow country roads is a big problem too. That means local people can't get around easily, and emergency vehicles might not get through. 92% of visitors come by car.

◆ Litter is a big problem. It spoils the view and can also be dangerous for small wild animals. In Betwys-y-Coed, volunteers filled a whole skip with litter in just 4 hours!

◆ Salaries for workers in tourism are low, but the attractive location and all the tourists visiting and then wanting to buy a holiday home, means house prices are really high.

◆ Some villages get swamped by visitors. They are called 'honeypot' villages, with the tourists like the bees around them! Examples are Betws-y-Coed and Beddgelert.

◆ Farmers get annoyed when gates get left open allowing sheep and cows to escape. Dogs owned by tourists often worry sheep (this means they chase the sheep). In lambing season that could mean a ewe (a female sheep) miscarries.

Did you know?
◆ Snowdon is the highest mountain in Wales and England. It is 1085 metres (3560 feet) high.
◆ It usually takes 5 to 10 hours to walk up and down.

Activities

1 Make a mind map about tourism in Snowdonia. Include why people go there, some numbers (hint: use the pie chart), and how tourism is important for jobs and income.

2 Make up a scene where there is conflict between tourists and locals. Include the reason for the conflict. Write it as a role play.

3 Create a newspaper article for a local paper called *Tourists – they're loving us to death* and include all the problems that tourism causes in Snowdonia.

4 A research task: find out these things about Betws-y-Coed:
   ◆ where it is
   ◆ a map of the village
   ◆ a bit about its history
   ◆ why tourists go there.
   Present your findings on one side of A4 only.
   Remember: no printing straight from the Internet – put it in your own words.

5 Come up with some solutions to the tourist problems. Write your ideas down.

Managing tourists

In this unit you'll find out how problems in Snowdonia can be managed.

Looking for solutions

◆ Fines of £50 for litter louts in villages.
◆ Footpaths mended by planting new grass, or if the path is severely eroded, laying a new path out of quarried stone (see the photo on the right).
◆ The National Park Authority gives planning permission for new homes only if they are cheap and for local people.
◆ Estate agents mainly advertise locally.
◆ New tourist developments like visitor centres have to be within walking or cycling distance of villages, so people don't use their cars.
◆ Three by-passes are planned for villages in Snowdonia.
◆ Lowering speed limits along minor roads.
◆ The Park Authority is considering closing some roads to cars altogether, and only allowing cycles and buses.
◆ Bike hire centres spread out over the park.
◆ Residents-only car parks.
◆ Housing associations like Tai Clwyd and Tai Eryri are building affordable housing for rent in the larger villages.
◆ Altering old country houses for use as modern offices in attractive surroundings to attract new businesses to the area.
◆ Preferential planning approval for light manufacturing and service industries in villages.
◆ Grants for new businesses and help with funding renovations or new buildings from the Welsh Development Agency.
◆ Countryside Code posters in major tourist areas to remind people about gates, dogs, and litter.
◆ Park-and-ride schemes to get tourists to the big attractions without their cars. One example is the Snowdon Sherpa bus service.
◆ Public transport is advertised and timetables are on display, like the Welsh Highland Railway or the Snowdon Mountain Railway (on the right).

CAUTION!
Work in Progress by
SNOWDONIA SOCIETY VOLUNTEERS
01690-720287

How do people feel about the management schemes?

Betwys-y-Coed

Speech bubbles in image:
- These park-and-ride schemes and car bans aren't much good if you don't want to go to the same crowded places as everyone else.
- I'd like to set up a new processing plant to process the local quarried stone, but the Park Authority won't let me – they say it spoils the look of the place.
- The tourists bring in lots of money, and the Park Authority is making sure the villages still get lots of visitors. The new office complex is bringing more workers in too, and they also spend money in my shop.
- We're much happier with the reduced traffic, and we can park in our own village now! And there's more cheap housing, so we're pleased.

Activities

1 Make a larger copy of this table. Use the information on these pages to complete the table.

problem	management solution
litter in Betws-y-Coed	
traffic jams	
car parking	
path erosion	
house prices	
gates being left open	
seasonal jobs	

2 Take three of the management solutions and make consequence maps for them. Start like this:

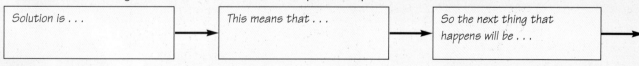

Solution is . . . → This means that . . . → So the next thing that happens will be . . . →

The next two questions are examination-style questions.

3 Explain how footpath erosion can be managed. (*4 marks.*)

4 a Choose a case study of an upland area that has been affected by tourism. Describe three problems that tourists cause in this area. (*3 marks.*)

b Comment on the attitudes of local people to the management schemes that have been introduced. (*5 marks.*)

The big picture

This chapter is about rivers and the landscapes they create. These are the big ideas behind the chapter:

◆ Rivers have energy which means they can erode and transport material. When a river doesn't have enough energy to transport its load it deposits it.

◆ A river changes from source to mouth. You'll find different landforms in the upper, middle and lower courses of a river.

◆ The drainage basin cycle is part of the water cycle.

◆ There are human and physical causes for river flooding.

◆ The effects of flooding are different in MEDCs and LEDCs.

◆ We can try to prevent floods using hard and soft engineering methods. The methods used vary in MEDCs and LEDCs.

Your goals for this chapter

By the end of this chapter you should be able to answer these questions:

◆ How does a river change from its source to its mouth?

◆ Name four ways rivers erode, and four ways they transport their load.

◆ How are these formed?
V-shaped valley, interlocking spurs, waterfalls, meanders, oxbow lake, floodplains, levées, estuaries, deltas

◆ Which river landforms can you recognise on OS maps?

◆ What do these terms mean?
source, mouth, river channel, terraces, distributaries, interception, surface run-off, infiltration, through-flow, percolation, groundwater flow, hydrograph, lag time, rising limb, peak discharge, catchment, hard management, soft management

◆ Give at least three human and three physical causes of the flooding in North Yorkshire in 1999.

◆ What were the short-term effects of the flooding in North Yorkshire?

◆ Give at least two short-term and two long-term causes of the flooding in Mozambique in 2000.

◆ What were the short-term effects of the Mozambique flooding, and what were the long-term effects likely to be?

◆ How can floods be managed?

◆ Why is flood management different in MEDCs like the UK, and LEDCs like Mozambique?

And then . . .

When you finish the chapter, come back here and see if you've met your goals!

Did you know?
The world's longest river is the Nile. It's 6670 km long.

Did you know?
The UK's longest river is the Severn. It's 354 km long.

Did you know?
Less than 1% of the world's water is in rivers. But rivers have helped shape our landscape.

Did you know?
◆ The River Amazon is the world's largest river – it carries the most water.
◆ Its mouth is over 400 km wide.

Your chapter starter

Look at the photo on page 64. It shows the Grand Canyon of the Verdon River, in France. It is Europe's widest and deepest gorge.
Is this near the river's source or mouth?
Where has the river come from? Where is it going?
How would you describe this landscape?
What would happen if the river flooded? Would it matter?

Anyone seen my raft?

Introducing rivers

In this unit you'll learn the basics about rivers and what they do.

From source to mouth

The river near the source:
- narrow
- shallow
- slow-flowing (because of friction)
- has large bedload

The river in the middle:
- wider
- deeper
- faster flowing
- has smaller material in it

The river near the mouth:
- wide
- deep
- fast-flowing
- has mainly suspended load

North Pennines

River Tees

Hartlepool

Newton Aycliffe

Stockton

Redcar

Barnard Castle

Darlington

Middlesbrough

Yarm

Scotch Corner

N

What do rivers do?

Rivers have energy. That means they can do work. The work they do is **erosion** and **transportation**. When they run out of energy they have to stop doing work, so they drop what they're carrying. That's called **deposition**.

Erosion

The material around the river has already been broken down and loosened by weathering.

Some soil and stones have already been carried to the river by rain and gravity.

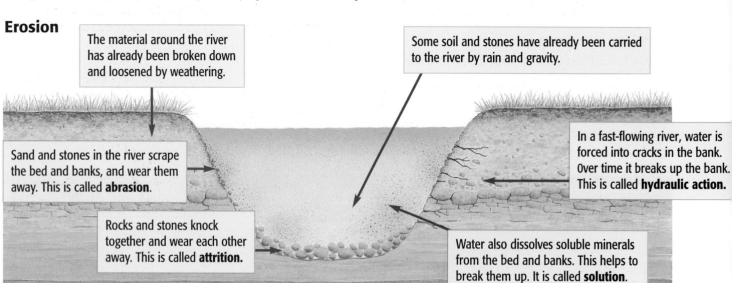

Sand and stones in the river scrape the bed and banks, and wear them away. This is called **abrasion**.

In a fast-flowing river, water is forced into cracks in the bank. Over time it breaks up the bank. This is called **hydraulic action**.

Rocks and stones knock together and wear each other away. This is called **attrition**.

Water also dissolves soluble minerals from the bed and banks. This helps to break them up. It is called **solution**.

The more energy it has, the faster a river can erode.

Transportation

The material a river carries is called its **load**.

The more energy it has, the larger the load a river can carry.

Heavier material is carried along the bottom. It is called the **bedload**.

Sand grains and small stones just bounce along. This is called **saltation**.

Dissolved material is carried along as a solution. You cannot see it.

Larger stones and rocks get rolled along. This is called **traction**.

Small particles of rock and soil are carried along as a **suspension**. They make the water look cloudy or muddy.

Deposition

The deposited material is called **sediment**.

But dissolved material stays in the water and is carried out into the lake or sea.

As the river slows down, it deposits the largest stones and pebbles first, then smaller ones, and finally, the smallest particles.

The less energy it has, the more material a river deposits.

Activities

1 Make a larger copy of this table. Use the map and photo boxes to complete it.

part of the river	description	velocity	width	depth	particle size
upper					
middle					
lower					

2 Use this writing frame to write about the work that rivers do.

Rivers have energy so …
When a river has lots of energy it can erode. Ways it can do this are:
◆ hydraulic action: this means …
◆ …
Rivers can transport the material they have eroded as long as they have enough energy. Material can be carried by …
If a river doesn't have enough energy it drops (deposits) its load …

3 Copy this sentence, but only include the correct word from the brackets.

Rivers have high energy when they are flowing (fast / slowly), or when there is (a lot / a little) water in them.

4 This is an examination-style question.
  a What is erosion? (*1 mark*.)
  b How do rivers erode? (*4 marks*.)

The river's upper course

In this unit you'll learn about the river near its source. Again we're using the River Tees as our case study.

Near the beginning . . .

Near its source the river is in a steep V-shaped valley. The OS map shows part of the upper course of the River Tees. Rivers in their upper course have some typical features you should look out for.

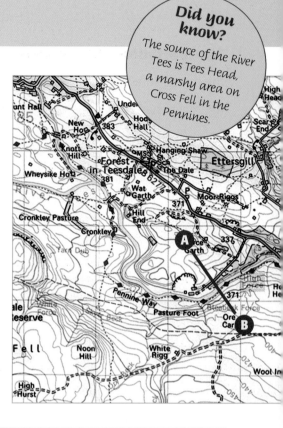

The river channel

Near its source the river flows quite slowly, because there's lots of friction with the **large bedload** it's carrying. The bedload is large because there hasn't been enough time for attrition to make the particles smaller. The channel cross-section (a slice through the river channel) looks like this.

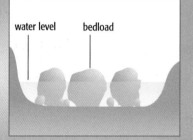

water level   bedload

V-shaped valley

Rivers near their source are a long way above sea level. This means they have a high gravitational potential energy. So they erode mainly downwards (vertically). That makes the steep valley sides. The slopes can't stay vertical because that's not stable, so the soil and rock on the slopes slide down – and that makes the V-shape.

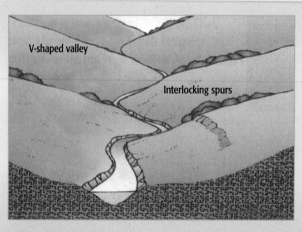

V-shaped valley

Interlocking spurs

Interlocking spurs

These are alternate hills that stick out like the teeth of a zip in the river's path. The river in the upper course doesn't have enough energy to erode the spurs, so it has to flow around them.

Waterfalls

Some rivers have waterfalls in the upper course. High Force on the River Tees (pictured on the right) is a famous one. At over 23 metres high, it's the highest waterfall in the UK!

How waterfalls are formed

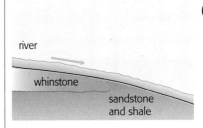

river

whinstone

sandstone and shale

1 Waterfalls happen when the river crosses a band of harder rock. In the Tees valley the hard rock is whinstone.

3 The erosion of the softer rock continues and undercuts the hard rock. The hollow at the bottom is called the plunge pool. It's full of bits of rock from above so there's lots of abrasion here. The force of the falling water means lots of hydraulic action too.

ledge
undercut
plunge pool

whinstone

sandstone and shale

2 The softer rock gets eroded more quickly by abrasion and hydraulic action. This makes a ledge.

4 Eventually the ledge (overhang) collapses. The process keeps going and the waterfall moves backwards. In front of it, it leaves a steep-sided gorge.

Did you know?
The Angel Falls in Venezuela have a total drop of 979 metres – it's the highest waterfall in the world.

Did you know?
Niagara Falls attract about 14 million tourists every year – 50 000 of them honeymooners!

Did you know?
Khone Falls stretch 10.8 km (6.7 miles) across the Mekong River, between Laos and Cambodia – it's the world's widest waterfall.

Activities

1 Use the OS map to make a cross-section along AB of the Upper Tees valley. Add annotations (explaining labels) to explain about the V-shaped valley. This enlargement of part of the OS map will be clearer for making your cross-section.

2 What are interlocking spurs?

3 Make a flow diagram to explain how High Force developed. Remember to include diagrams of each stage too!

4 This is an examination-style question.

   a Draw a sketch diagram of High Force from the photograph opposite. Label the plunge pool, gorge, and name the two rock types. (*6 marks.*)

   b Choose the correct words from the box to complete this paragraph:

Waterfalls are formed where a river flows over a band of hard rock next to a softer rock. The softer rock is eroded by _____ and abrasion. The power of the water creates a deep _____ below the waterfall and undercuts the softer rock until the overhang eventually collapses. This causes the waterfall to _____ upstream, forming a gorge. (*3 marks.*)

| plunge pool | advance | hydraulic action | retreat | traction | meander |

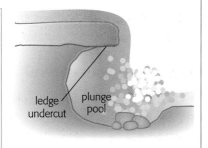

The river's middle course

In this unit you'll learn about the middle course of the river. Again we're using the River Tees as our case study.

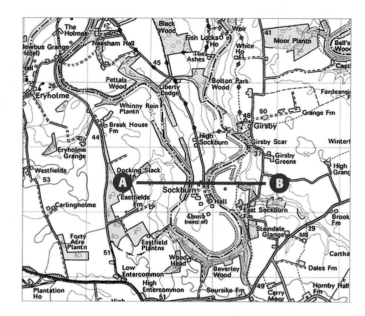

What's happening here?

In the middle course, rivers aren't as high above sea level as they are in the upper course. So they erode sideways (laterally) as well as vertically. This means they are wider and deeper than upstream.

There's more water because tributaries have joined, and because more water has arrived from throughflow and surface run-off. The river **meanders** (twists) from side to side as it erodes laterally.

Meanders

The water in a river flows in a spiral, like a corkscrew. This means that there is variation in the velocity across the river channel. This means more erosion on one side and more deposition on the other.

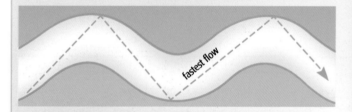

On the side where the fast water is, there is more erosion. This makes the river deeper and cuts into the bank, to make a **river cliff**. On the other side, where the slower water is, there is deposition. This makes a shallower area of sediment called a **point bar**. The gentle slope down to the point bar is called the **slip-off slope**.

The cross-section of the meander looks like this:

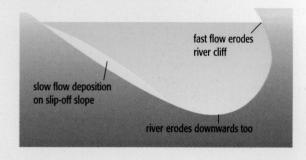

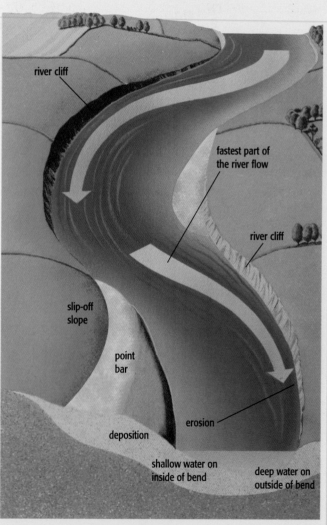

Oxbow lakes

This is how oxbow lakes form.

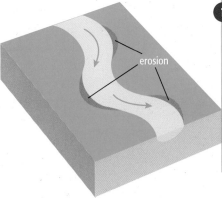

1 The faster water erodes the outside of the bends and there is deposition on the inside. This makes the meanders get more sinuous (wiggly!). This is called meander migration. Sometimes the scars of old meander bends can be seen next to the river.

2 The meander bend gets tighter. A really tight meander is called a **swan's neck meander**.

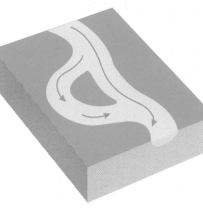

3 When there's a lot of discharge (in a flood or after a storm) the river has more energy, so it erodes a new channel straight across the neck of the meander. It erodes it by hydraulic action and abrasion.

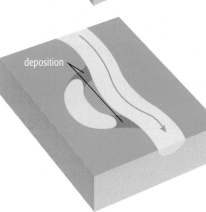

4 The river now uses the new channel because it's easier, even when the water level goes down. The old channel becomes an **oxbow lake** when deposition seals its two ends to separate it from the river. Eventually it gets filled in with debris and soil and might have trees in it.

oxbow lake

swan's neck meander

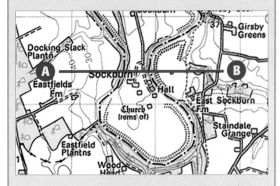

The river's lower course

In this unit you'll learn about the lower course of the river. We're still using the River Tees.

Towards the end

The lower course of the river is the flattest part. Here the river flows in a deep, wide channel. It flows fast because there is much less friction. The load it carries is small, and it carries it by suspension and solution.

The sea comes up the river at the mouth. At low tide the edges are exposed. That leaves **mudflats** at the sides of the river.

The land here is mainly used for industry, like docks and factories that need to import or export heavy goods by sea.

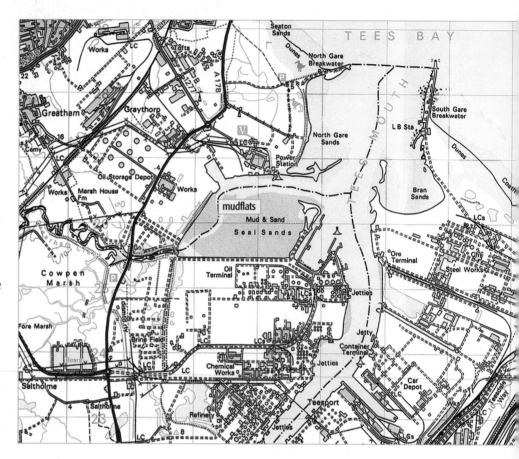

The floodplain

This is the land on either side of the river in the lower course. It is the land that gets flooded – so that's why it's called the floodplain! The floodplain is very fertile for crops because, when the river floods, it leaves behind fine silt called **alluvium**.

Many thousands of years ago, the sea level was higher. That meant rivers didn't have to cut down so far to reach the sea. Then the sea level dropped, and so the river had to cut down further to reach it. This has left **terraces** in the floodplain.

When the river floods, it deposits some of its load. The biggest stuff gets dropped first. It eventually builds up to leave mounds at the sides of the channel. They're called **levées**.

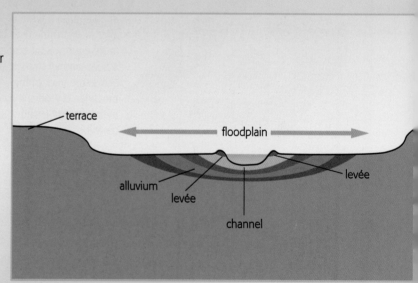

River mouths

Some rivers have estuaries, some rivers have deltas, and some rivers just have a narrow mouth. It all depends on the local rock type, the amount of load the river is carrying, and the strength of the sea.

Estuaries

The River Tees has an estuary. This is a wide, deep mouth. Estuaries are really useful for shipping, so they usually have ports and factories along them.

The Tees estuary. ▶

Deltas

A delta happens when the river has lots of load. When it reaches the sea the water flow slows down, so it drops its load. If the waves or currents aren't too strong and the land doesn't slope too steeply, the load builds up to make a delta. The sediment blocks the river so it has to divide up into lots of different channels called **distributaries**. Deltas can be different shapes, but the two main types are **bird's foot** deltas like the Mississippi delta and **arcuate** deltas like the Nile delta (pictured).

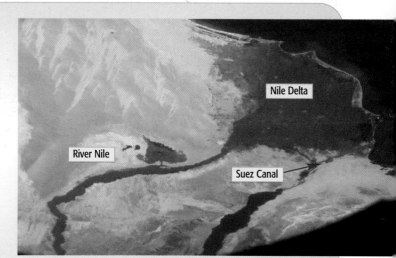

The Nile delta from space. ▶

Activities

1 Use the words from the box to complete this paragraph. (Hint: use the map to help you.)

mudflats	fast	small	flat
industry	marshland	deep	

The lower course of the River Tees is _____. There is a lot of _____ along it. There is also _____ on the northern bank. Here the river flows in a _____, wide channel. It flows _____ because there is much less friction. The load it carries is _____, and it carries it by suspension and solution. The sea comes up the river at the mouth. At low tide the edges are exposed. That leaves _____ at the sides of the river.

2 a What is a floodplain?
   b What is alluvium? How does it get there? What is it useful for?

   c How are terraces formed?
   d What are leveés? How are they formed?
   e Now make a diagram of a floodplain and label the channel, alluvium, leveés, and terrace.

3 a Make a sketch map of the Tees estuary, using the OS map or the photo.
   b Add a suitable title
   c Add labels to show the industry, the flat land, and the wide mouth.

4 Make a sketch map of the delta photo. Give it a title so you know which delta it is. Write annotations (explaining labels) to say what has happened to make the delta.

5 What do you think would happen to the delta if:
   a sea level went up? Why?
   b a dam was built further up the river? Why?

Water – it gets around

This unit is all about the water cycle and how the water gets into rivers.

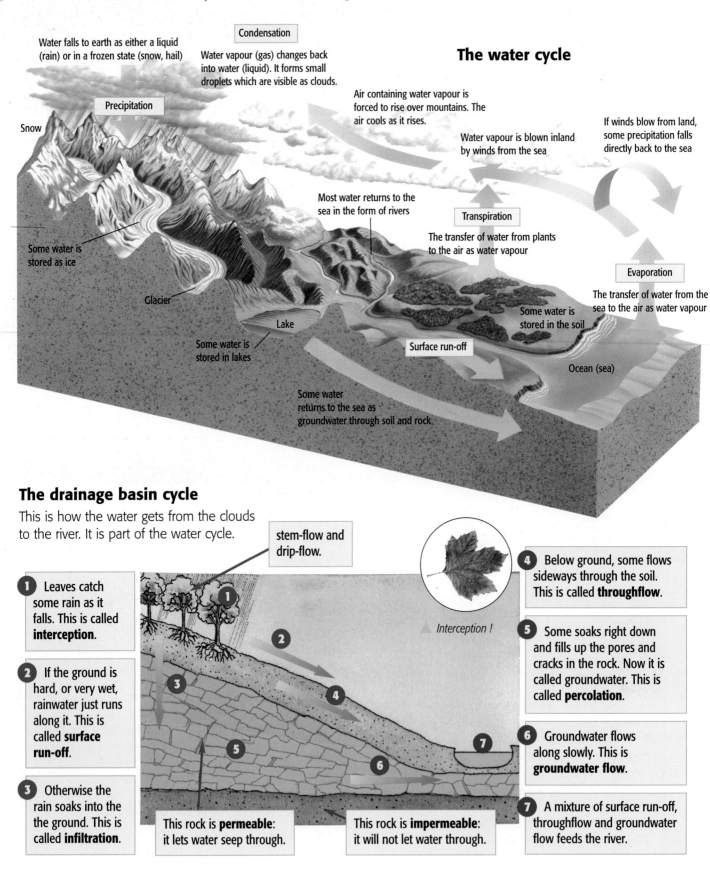

The water cycle

Condensation
Water vapour (gas) changes back into water (liquid). It forms small droplets which are visible as clouds.

Water falls to earth as either a liquid (rain) or in a frozen state (snow, hail)

Precipitation

Snow

Air containing water vapour is forced to rise over mountains. The air cools as it rises.

Water vapour is blown inland by winds from the sea

If winds blow from land, some precipitation falls directly back to the sea

Some water is stored as ice

Glacier

Most water returns to the sea in the form of rivers

Transpiration
The transfer of water from plants to the air as water vapour

Lake

Some water is stored in lakes

Some water is stored in the soil

Surface run-off

Evaporation
The transfer of water from the sea to the air as water vapour

Ocean (sea)

Some water returns to the sea as groundwater through soil and rock

The drainage basin cycle

This is how the water gets from the clouds to the river. It is part of the water cycle.

stem-flow and drip-flow.

Interception !

1 Leaves catch some rain as it falls. This is called **interception**.

2 If the ground is hard, or very wet, rainwater just runs along it. This is called **surface run-off**.

3 Otherwise the rain soaks into the the ground. This is called **infiltration**.

4 Below ground, some flows sideways through the soil. This is called **throughflow**.

5 Some soaks right down and fills up the pores and cracks in the rock. Now it is called groundwater. This is called **percolation**.

6 Groundwater flows along slowly. This is **groundwater flow**.

7 A mixture of surface run-off, throughflow and groundwater flow feeds the river.

This rock is **permeable**: it lets water seep through.

This rock is **impermeable**: it will not let water through.

Hydrographs

When the water gets to the river it adds to the volume of water in it. The discharge is the volume of water flowing past a point in the river in 1 second. It is measured in cubic metres per second (m^3/sec).

After rain, the discharge of the river goes up. This is shown on a hydrograph.

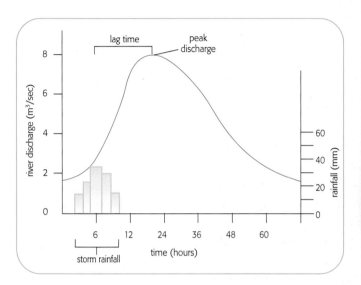

▲ Same point, different discharge.

Activities

1 Copy the simplified diagram of the water cycle and complete it using these labels.

transpiration	precipitation	surface run-off
evaporation	groundwater	condensation

2 Make and label your own simplified diagram of the drainage basin cycle.

3 Match up these definitions and their meanings.

precipitation	water dripping and falling from plants
stem- and drip-flow	water soaking into the soil
infiltration	water flowing through the saturated bedrock towards the river
throughflow	rain, hail, snow and sleet
percolation	water flowing in the river
groundwater flow	water flowing through the soil towards the stream
channel flow	water soaking into the bedrock
transpiration	water vapour breathed out by plants
evaporation	water turning into water vapour

4 What is discharge?

5 a What does a hydrograph show?
   b On the hydrograph above, what is the peak discharge?
   c How long is it from the peak rainfall to the peak discharge? (This is called the **lag time**.)

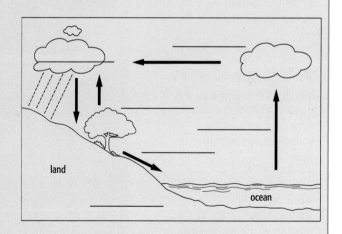

Did you know?
There are 326 million cubic miles of water on Earth, but only 3% is fresh water.

75

In this unit you'll find out what causes flooding
– and how this affects the hydrograph.

What are floods?
Floods happen when a river gets more water than its channel can hold. So water then flows over the banks and on to the floodplain.

What are the causes of flooding?

Anything that stops rain soaking into the ground will increase
the risk of flooding.

Heavy rain means there's more water going to the river.

Snow melt puts more water in the river.

Antecedent rainfall – this means it has rained before, so the surface is saturated. This means rain-water flows straight to the river by surface run-off.

Hot dry weather bakes the top of the soil, meaning water can't soak in when it rains. So it runs off the surface straight into the river.

Deforestation means that the soil can get washed into the river. That takes up space, so there's less space for water. Deforestation also means the rain gets to the surface of the ground faster without the trees, so the ground is more likely to get saturated.

Impermeable rocks mean the rain-water can't percolate into the groundwater, so it flows quickly into the river by throughflow and surface run-off.

Steep slopes mean the rain-water runs straight off the surface before infiltration can take place.

Urbanisation means that water can't soak into the ground because the new surfaces are impermeable. So the water goes straight into the river through surface run-off and through drains.

Ploughing up and down hills makes channels that get the rain-water to the river faster, so it's more likely to flood.

Changes to the hydrograph

If the water gets to the river faster, then that makes the **lag time** shorter. If more water goes over the surface it makes the first part of the hydrograph (the **rising limb**) steeper and the **peak discharge** higher. Look at these hydrographs.

A recipe for flooding is . . .
- snow melting
- heavy rain, after there's already been lots of rain
- chopping the trees down in the **catchment** (the catchment is the area around a river that it gets its water from)
- building in the catchment
- ploughing farmland up and down instead of along the contours.

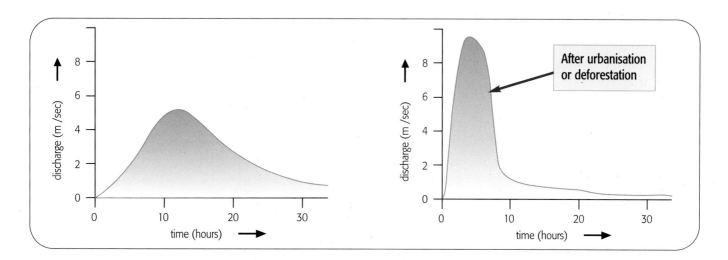

Activities

1 a Make a copy of this table and complete it.
 b Shade the natural factors in green and the human factors in red. Add a key.

Flooding factor	How it increases the chance of flooding
heavy rain	
antecedent rainfall	
long spell of hot dry weather	
steep slopes	
impermeable rocks	
snow melt (thaw)	
deforestation	
ploughing up and down	
urbanisation	

2 If urbanisation increases flood risk, why are buildings still being put on floodplains all over the UK?

3 Write down at least three things that make flooding less likely (like, for example, planting trees).

4 How can hydrographs show the effect that land use has on the chances of flooding?

Flooding in North Yorkshire

This case study is all about the causes and effects of flooding in North Yorkshire in 1999. The UK is an MEDC.

Where?

◆ The River Derwent starts in the North York Moors.
◆ It flows west, then south.
◆ The main towns are Pickering, Norton, Malton, Pocklington, Helmsley, and Stamford Bridge.
◆ The population of the basin is about 100 000.
◆ The basin has an area of 2057 sq. km.

When?

◆ March 1999.

What?

◆ The River Derwent burst its banks.
◆ It was the worst flooding the residents had experienced in 70 years!
◆ Roads and homes were flooded up to 1½ metres deep.
◆ Pickering was flooded first, and towns further downstream were flooded a few days later.
◆ Sewage from flooded drains mixed with the flood waters (nasty!) to make a health hazard.
◆ The rail link between York and Scarborough was cut and the replacement bus couldn't get to the town of Malton.
◆ The main roads A169 and A166 had to be closed.
◆ The hydrograph below shows how the discharge of the river through Buttercrambe changed.

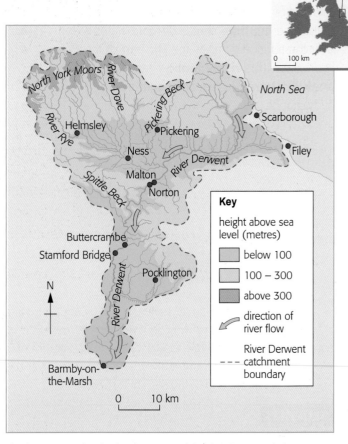

▲ The Derwent river basin. The Derwent joins the River Ouse below Barmby-on-the-Marsh.

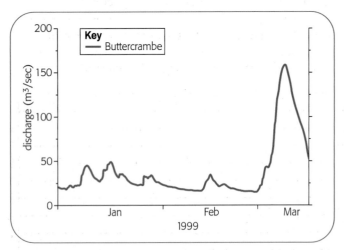

A tractor and trailor had to replace the bus service between Malton ▶ and Norton.

Why?

- Lots of antecedent rainfall so the ground was already close to saturation.
- Between 28 February and 11 March there had been over 250 mm of rain on the North York Moors (about four times the average).
- Melting snow on the North York Moors.
- Steep slopes near the source of the River Derwent.
- Removing peat in the past had lowered the level of the land slightly. Peat also acts like a sponge so it could have stored some of the water.
- Deforestation means the water gets to the ground straightaway, instead of being intercepted, so the top layers get saturated more quickly.
- New building in the floodplain (like a new estate in Malton).
- In Malton, rubbish blocked the channel so the water backed up, making the flood worse here than it would have been.

▲ *Only the ducks were happy at Stamford Bridge.*

Activities

1 **a** Put a big heading *MEDC flooding case study: River Derwent, March 1999* and underline it in a bright colour.
   b Make a simple copy of the location map opposite.
   c Next to it write about the area around the River Derwent.
2 How did the floods affect people's
   - work? (commuters? local workers?)   - homes?
   - health?
3 What do you think the long-term effects of the flood might be? (Think about people's feelings, their jobs, their houses, insurance, future buildings . . .)
4 **a** Make a copy of this table and use the 'Why' section above to complete it.
   b Shade the physical factors in green and the human factors in red.

5 Use this writing frame to describe the hydrograph for Buttercrambe.

> The hydrograph shows the discharge of the River . . .
>
> The pattern for January and February 1999 is . . .
>
> The small peaks are . . .
>
> In March . . .
>
> The peak of the discharge during the flood is . . .

6 **a** Why do places downstream have more warning of a flood?
   b Why does the flood get bigger downstream?

Factor	Human or physical?	How did it lead to flooding?
antecedent rainfall		
heavy rain		
snow melt		
steep slopes		
peat removal		
deforestation		
building in the floodplain		
rubbish		

Flooding in Mozambique

This case study is all about the causes and effects of flooding in Mozambique in 2000. Mozambique is an LEDC.

What, where, when?

- The flood happened in February 2000.
- 6 different rivers were affected. The waters rose 8 metres in 5 days.
- More than 1 million people lost their homes. Thousands of people drowned.
- The flood survivors had to go to refugee camps – without much food or water and with poor sanitation, so diseases spread quickly.
- Life expectancy in Mozambique before the flood was only about 47 years.
- 90% of the people of Mozambique have to live on less than $1 a day (about 60p).
- Mozambique is an LEDC in Africa, and 83% of the people work in agriculture. The flood destroyed much of the most fertile farmland.
- $30 million was needed to repair the roads, $6 million for railways and $4 million for the electricity supply.

▲ *Thousands of people were trapped at Chibutu.*

Why did the floods happen?

Short-term (immediate) causes:

- 3 days of heavy rain at the beginning of January 2000, then . . .
- 5 weeks of almost continuous rain from the middle of January, then . . .
- Cyclone Eline struck Mozambique on 22 February (cyclones are areas of deep low pressure, so they bring torrential rain and very strong winds).

Long-term causes:

- Grasslands in the upper courses of the rivers are being destroyed. These grasslands are like sponges, so without them more water gets into the rivers.
- In the upstream parts of the rivers that are flowing through South Africa, marshes and floodplains have been drained and used for farmland. They used to be spaces that the river could flood into, so now there's nowhere for the water to go safely.
- Massive urbanisation in South Africa means more water gets into the upper courses of the rivers that end up in Mozambique.

▲ *Hundreds wait to be rescued from Xai Xai.*

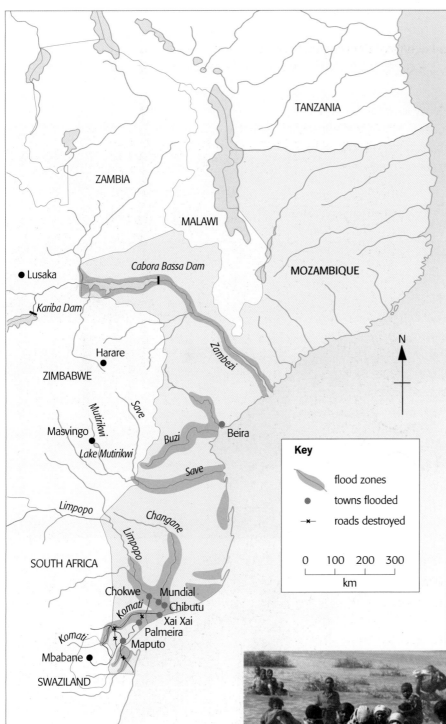

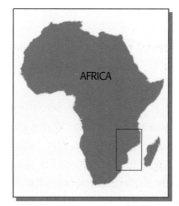

AFRICA

Key

- flood zones
- towns flooded
- ✕ roads destroyed

0   100   200   300
km

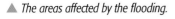

▲ The areas affected by the flooding.

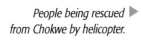

People being rescued ▶
from Chokwe by helicopter.

Activities

1 a What were the short-term effects of the flood?

b What long-term effects would you expect? (Think about economic, social, political, physical, and environmental effects.)

2 Use the information on these pages (and your own research on the Internet) to make a PowerPoint presentation about the Mozambique floods. Remember to include:

- ◆ what happened (lots of detail)
- ◆ why it happened (human and physical causes)
- ◆ some visuals.

3 This is an examination-style question.

Describe the causes of one flood that you have studied. (*4 marks.*)

Managing floods

In this unit you'll learn about the choices we have for managing floods.

There are choices

In England and Wales, the Environment Agency looks after rivers. How does the Environment Agency try to prevent floods? Well, the traditional choices are:

- to build flood defences like dams, embankments, and flood walls
- to straighten and deepen the river and cut off meanders
- to make storage areas for extra water.

These are all called **hard management**. Let's look at them in a bit more detail . . .

Hard management methods

Dams

These can trap and store water, then let it out in a controlled way. They can also generate electricity. But upstream of the dam the land floods to make a reservoir. That's a massive change to the ecosystem. And the dams trap sediment that would normally go downstream. They're very expensive, but very effective.

Embankments

These are raised banks along the river. They effectively make the river deeper so it can hold more water before it floods. They're expensive and don't look natural. But they do protect the land around them.

Flood walls

These are built around settlements and important factories or roads. They're quite expensive and don't look very natural. But they're pretty effective.

Straightening and deepening the river

This is called channelising the river. It makes the water move through that part of the river faster, so it doesn't build up and is less likely to flood. This totally changes the ecosystem in the river and spoils the natural look of the area. And further downstream, where the river isn't channelised, the water builds up and floods there!

Storage areas

The water can be pumped out of the river and stored in temporary lakes. Then it's pumped back in after the water in the river has gone down a bit. Effective, but you do have to have a large bit of spare land that isn't used, so that you can flood it!

And more choices

So, if that's the hard management way, what's the **soft management** way?

Soft engineering

Washlands

These are parts of the floodplain that are allowed to flood. They can't be built on. They're usually used for sports pitches or nature reserves.

Land-use zoning

This is where land has different building controls depending on how far away from the river it is. Land next to the river isn't allowed to be used for building, the next land zone can be but only for low-risk housing, and the last zone is for high-risk buildings like hospitals, old people's homes, and dangerous factories.

Afforestation

This is re-planting trees in the catchment.

Warning systems

Warnings are issued by the Environment Agency so that local people can put sandbags by their homes, take furniture upstairs, or even evacuate the area.

What's the best way?

There's no perfect way to prevent floods. Each has problems – and may fail. To make the best choice, you have to consider:

◆ how often the river floods badly
◆ how much damage it can do
◆ how much each method would cost
◆ how much you can afford to spend.

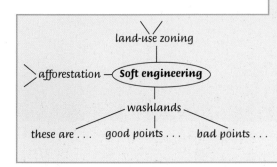

Activities

1 Use the words in the box to complete this paragraph.

dams	structures
control	land-use zoning
afforestation	with
channelisation	

Hard engineering techniques are _____ that are imposed on the river. They try to _____ the river. Examples of hard engineering are_____ and _____. Soft engineering started to be used in the 1990s. Soft engineering methods work _____ the river and use natural processes. Examples include _____ and _____.

2 Draw a table with three columns headed: Hard engineering method, Advantages of using it, Disadvantages of using it. Use the information opposite to help you fill it in.

3 a Make a copy of the mind map on the left on a large sheet of paper. Complete as much as you can.

b Use your mind map to write a short essay starting with 'Soft engineering to prevent floods is . . .'

Controlling flooding in MEDCs and LEDCs

In this unit the two flooding case studies are extended to consider the management of the flood risk.

North Yorkshire

Since the flood £7.5 million has been spent on protecting towns in the catchment like Malton. Here a mixture of hard and soft engineering has been used.

Hard engineering on the River Derwent

◆ Embankments along the river. These are quite old and didn't prevent the flood damage in 1999.

◆ Sluice gates upstream can hold back water and let it out in a controlled way.

◆ The catchment is fairly rural (that means countryside) and there isn't much high-value land use to protect, so expensive hard engineering isn't appropriate for the whole area.

Soft engineering on the River Derwent

◆ Embankments have been built near settlements, with washlands between the embankments and the river. The water can flood here without causing damage.

◆ New building is restricted on the floodplain.

◆ Planting of hedgerows and trees in the catchment.

◆ Reinforcing the river banks with woven willow to stop bank erosion so the river doesn't get silted up.

◆ Early warning systems use data on rainfall to predict floods. Residents are warned and they put out sandbags and move their furniture, cars, and animals.

▲ Sliding flood gate at Stamford Bridge to protect the road and homes.

▲ Flood walls at Stamford Bridge to protect homes and businesses.

Mozambique

Mozambique has to take a different approach.

Activities

1 a You will need two pieces of coloured paper or card – different colours! Cut out 4 cards from one piece and 5 from the other.

 b Write the hard engineering methods for preventing flooding of the River Derwent on to the 4 cards, and write the soft methods on the other 5 cards.

 c You have now made revision cards on a case study of flood prevention in an MEDC. Paper-clip them into your book, or put them in an envelope and glue the envelope into your book.

2 a Why do you think the protection of the River Derwent isn't all hard engineering?

 b What are the disadvantages of hard engineering?

 c What is good about using soft engineering along this river?

3 Make a set of case study notes about flood prevention in Mozambique. Good case study notes have:
 ☺ a clear heading
 ☺ bullet points
 ☺ details like numbers and facts
 ☺ lots of colour
 ☺ a border round them.

The big picture

This chapter is about the coastal landscape – where the land meets the sea. These are the big ideas behind the chapter:

◆ The coast is shaped and changed by waves – and by us humans.

◆ Waves erode, transport and deposit material along the coastline to create a variety of landforms.

◆ Changes in sea level have created landforms – but rises in sea level due to global warming will have quite a different effect.

◆ Managing coastlines isn't easy or cheap. Some coastlines will continue to be protected, some won't.

◆ Coastal management can cause conflict.

Your goals for this chapter

By the end of this chapter you should be able to answer these questions:

◆ What causes waves? Name two different types of waves and say what they do.

◆ How do waves erode the coast? How are these features formed?
cliffs, wave-cut platforms, caves, arches, stacks, stumps, blow-holes

◆ How is material moved along the coast, and how can beaches be protected?

◆ Name four landforms created by coastal deposition.

◆ How are raised beaches, rias and fjords created?

◆ What has global warming got to do with coasts?

◆ Why, and how, do we try to defend the coast? How can we manage the coastline in a sustainable way?

◆ Why is the coast being eroded at Happisburgh? How has it been protected? What's going to happen in the future?

◆ Why is Chesil Beach flooded? Should defences be improved, or should nature take its course?

◆ Why is Lyme Regis being protected? What are the advantages and disadvantages for tourism?

And then . . .

When you finish the chapter, come back here and see if you've met your goals!

Did you know?
At Wick in Scotland, a block weighing 2600 tonnes was ripped from the harbour breakwater during a storm.

Did you know?
◆ The UK's coastline is 12 430 km long.
◆ If you walked at 5 km per hour for seven hours a day, it would take you nearly a year to walk it.

Did you know?
According to legend, a courtier of King Canute (995-1035) said he could even turn back the waves – tired of the flattery, Canute showed he couldn't with a practical demonstration at Thorney Island.

Did you know?
◆ The UK's lifeboat crews had their busiest year ever in 2005 – lifeboats were launched 8273 times.
◆ The busiest areas were South-West England and South-West Wales – and most call-outs were in the summer.

Your chapter starter

Look at the photo on page 86.
What two geographical features can you see in the picture?
How do you think the feature towards the top of the picture was formed?
What was the sea like when the photo was taken?

Take that hankie off your head – you look ridiculous.

All about waves

In this unit you'll learn what causes waves, and begin to find out how waves shape the coastline.

What causes waves?

Waves are caused by the friction of the wind on the surface of the water.

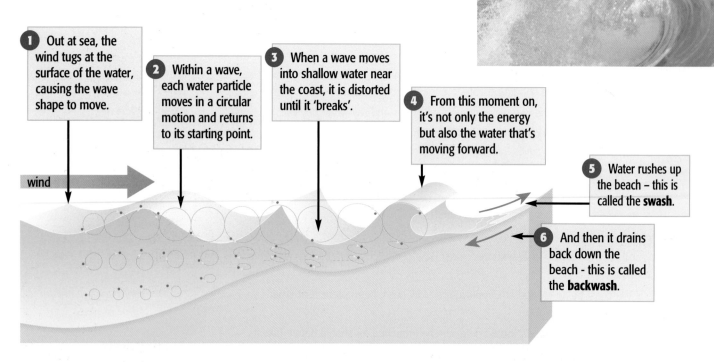

1. Out at sea, the wind tugs at the surface of the water, causing the wave shape to move.

2. Within a wave, each water particle moves in a circular motion and returns to its starting point.

3. When a wave moves into shallow water near the coast, it is distorted until it 'breaks'.

4. From this moment on, it's not only the energy but also the water that's moving forward.

5. Water rushes up the beach – this is called the **swash**.

6. And then it drains back down the beach - this is called the **backwash**.

wind

Why are some waves bigger and stronger?

The height and strength of waves depends on:
- the speed of the wind
- the time the wind blows for
- and the length of water the wind blows over.

The distance (length of water) the wind blows over is called the **fetch**.

Along the south coast of Britain, a south-westerly wind blowing over the Atlantic Ocean will produce large powerful waves, because its fetch is long. But a south-easterly wind from France won't produce large powerful waves because its fetch is quite short.

So, the fetch plays a big part in determining the height and strength of waves. But wind speed is more important. That's why we get big waves during storms.

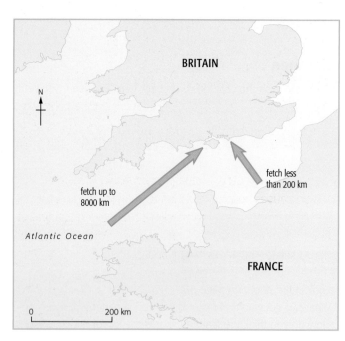

BRITAIN

N

fetch up to 8000 km

fetch less than 200 km

Atlantic Ocean

FRANCE

0   200 km

Different types of waves

Not all waves break in the same way. There are two types of breaking wave:

Constructive waves

These build up the beach.

If the swash is stronger (has more energy) than the backwash, material is carried on to the land and deposited there.

This happens with low waves – they break so that the water runs gently up the beach. They usually occur on gently sloping beaches.

They arrive at a rate of about 6-8 waves per minute.

They are often known as 'spilling' waves.

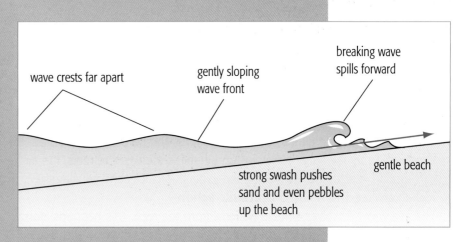

wave crests far apart

gently sloping wave front

breaking wave spills forward

strong swash pushes sand and even pebbles up the beach

gentle beach

Destructive waves

These remove material from the beach.

If the backwash is stronger than the swash, the waves erode the coastline.

This happens with high steep waves – they break so that the water crashes down on to the beach. They usually occur on steeply sloping beaches.

They arrive at a rate of about 13-15 waves per minute.

They are often known as 'plunging' waves.

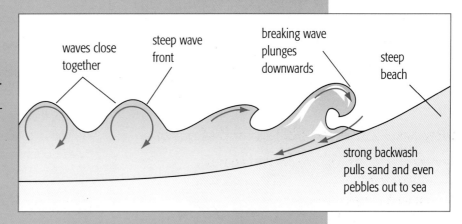

waves close together

steep wave front

breaking wave plunges downwards

steep beach

strong backwash pulls sand and even pebbles out to sea

Waves work non-stop, shaping the coastline. Wave erosion causes some coastlines to retreat. The waves then transport the eroded material, before depositing it in sheltered areas where they lose energy. Wave deposition causes some coastlines to advance.

Activities

1 Define these terms:
   a swash   b backwash
2 Why do you think water 'drains' back along the beach, rather than flowing over the surface?
3 What factors determine the height and strength of waves?
4 Explain how constructive and destructive waves work.
5 What factors other than the strength of waves may determine the rate at which a coastline erodes?

Coastal erosion

In this unit you'll learn how waves erode the coastline, and find out about some of the landforms they create.

How waves erode

This is how waves wear away or erode the coast:
◆ They crash against the rock, non-stop. Over time, this breaks the rock up.
◆ They throw sand, pebbles, and even boulders against the rock. These work like sandpaper, or wrecking balls, and the rock is worn away. This is a very powerful type of erosion, especially during storms. It's called **abrasion**. Another term for abrasion is **corrasion**.
◆ They force water and air into cracks in the rock. The parcels of air can be compressed by the surging water – and then, as the wave retreats, the air can expand explosively, weakening the joints and cracks and causing the rock to shatter. This is called **hydraulic action**.
◆ The sea water dissolves soluble material from the rock. This happens along limestone and chalk coasts when calcium carbonate is dissolved. This is called **solution**, or **corrosion**.
◆ Rocks and boulders already eroded from the coast are knocked together, and slowly worn into smaller and rounder pieces. This is called **attrition**.

The more powerful the waves – the more energy they have – and the softer the rock, the faster erosion will be.

Weathering processes

These contribute to coastal erosion. For example, cliffs can be weakened by groundwater and the action of rain, ice, wind, and sun.

wave-cut notch

wave-cut platform

Cliffs and wave-cut platforms

Where erosion is taking place, cliffs and wave-cut platforms are formed.

This is how it works:
◆ Erosion is concentrated at sea level. At this point, there's often a wave-cut notch where the waves have eaten into the cliff.
◆ The rock above the notch is undercut. When the rock sticks out too far, a section of the cliff breaks off.
◆ Rubble then collects at the foot of the cliff. It protects the cliff from further erosion for a time, but eventually it's broken down by attrition and removed.
◆ As the cliff is worn back, a wave-cut platform develops underwater, a few metres below the waves. Sometimes you can see wave-cut platforms at low tide. As the cliff is worn back further, the wave-cut platform gets wider.
◆ Over a long period of time, erosion drives back the cliff. But as the wave-cut platform becomes wider, it can protect the cliff from the full force of the waves.

Where the coastline is made up of weaker rock, the cliffs are not as dramatic. A good example is the Holderness Coast, north of the Humber estuary in Yorkshire, where the coastline is receding by an average of two metres per year.

fresh slumping of cliff

stack

collapsed arch

cave

wave-cut platform

Caves, natural arches, stacks, stumps – and blow-holes

Many rocks contain joints and faults. These are areas of weakness that waves will open up. These areas can then be enlarged by hydraulic action to form **caves**.

If the cave has been formed on a narrow headland, it can be enlarged until it runs right through the headland, forming a **natural arch**.

The roof of the natural arch will eventually collapse, leaving a **stack**.

The stack will then be worn away until it's a **stump**. And then, in time, the stump will be eroded.

If a cave is eroded upwards by hydraulic action, a **blow-hole** can form. A spray of sea-water is then blasted through the blow-hole each time a wave crashes into the cave.

Activities

1 Describe the different ways in which waves erode a coastline.
2 In what circumstances do you think other weathering processes may make a significant contribution to coastal erosion?
3 Name some other landforms that may also be eroded by abrasion and solution.
4 The photo of the Foreland, Dorset (above), shows coastal erosion features. Find out about another location in the UK where at least some of these features occur. Describe and explain the features of your chosen location, and compare them with those in the photo.

Did you know?

The 162-metre high chalk cliffs at Beachy Head, on England's south coast, are being eroded at the rate of 1 metre a year.

Coastal transport

In this unit you'll learn how waves move material along the coastline.

Longshore drift

Waves carry eroded material away. Some is carried out to sea. But a lot is carried along the coastline. This process is called **longshore drift**. This is how it works:

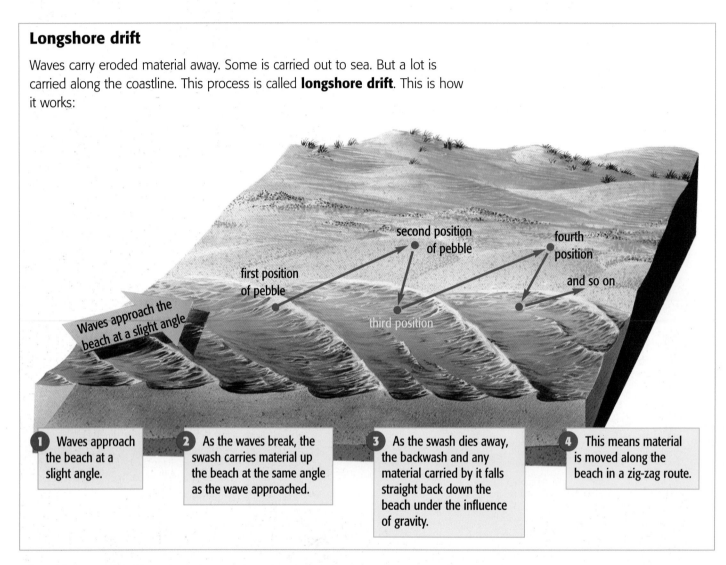

first position of pebble

second position of pebble

third position

fourth position

and so on

Waves approach the beach at a slight angle

1 Waves approach the beach at a slight angle.

2 As the waves break, the swash carries material up the beach at the same angle as the wave approached.

3 As the swash dies away, the backwash and any material carried by it falls straight back down the beach under the influence of gravity.

4 This means material is moved along the beach in a zig-zag route.

Direction and effects

On many coastlines, longshore drift is mainly in one direction. For example, on the south coast of England material moves from west to east, because the strongest and most regular winds are from the south-west.

However, brief changes in wind direction, and therefore wave direction, can cause material to be moved the opposite way.

Longshore drift is the link between erosion and deposition along the coast – eroded material is transported and then deposited further along the coast.

Longshore drift is a continual process and occurs every time a wave breaks at a slight angle to the shore. Beaches can be carried away very quickly. To stop this from happening, the government and many local councils spend large sums of money on sea defences.

> **Did you know?**
> A good way of remembering longshore drift is to think 'along-the-shore'.

Stopping longshore drift

A common method of protecting beaches is the use of wooden breakwaters or **groynes**. These are like fences, running down a beach into the sea. They interrupt the process of longshore drift, and so help to prevent beach material from being transported away.

One problem with groynes is that they cause less material to be transported further along the coast – and this can mean that places further along the coast suffer increased erosion.

A groyne. ▶

▼ *Longshore drift on the Suffolk coast.*

A

B

Activities

1 a On a simple outline of the British Isles, show the direction of longshore drift along the south coast of England.

  b Use annotations (descriptive labels) to explain this direction of drift.

  c Now show on your map the direction you would expect longshore drift to take on the west coast of England and Wales.

  d Explain why you think this drift takes place.

2 What problems may be caused by longshore drift?

3 To what extent do you think it's correct to say that longshore drift is only 'a problem for people, not the coastline'?

4 If longshore drift has to be managed, why do groynes offer only a partial solution?

5 Draw your own simple diagram of longshore drift.

6 Do you think the groyne in photo B is on the beach in photo A. Explain your answer. Hint: think about the direction of the longshore drift.

Coastal deposition

In this unit you'll find out about some of the landforms created by coastal deposition.

Beaches

Beaches are usually found in sheltered bays between two headlands. The headlands protect the area from erosion. Low constructive waves deposit material on the shore. Gradually, a beach is built up.

When we think of a beach, we usually imagine a sandy beach. But some beaches are made of shingle (pebbles). Beach material is usually very well sorted – the bigger particles are nearest to the land, getting finer as you move toward the sea.

The larger the material is, the steeper the beach. So, shingle and pebble beaches are steeper than sand beaches. At the top of the beach there may be a steep ridge where larger material has been thrown during storms.

People love sandy beaches – which means they're a valuable resource for the tourist industry.

beach ridge

Spits

Spits are long, narrow ridges of sand or shingle running out from the coast with one end attached to the land.

They form where the direction of the coast changes – so they are often found across a bay or at the mouth of a river. They grow as material is added by longshore drift. Other conditions also help the formation of spits:
- The sea must be relatively shallow.
- There must be a good supply of sand and other material.
- Waves must approach the coast at an angle, so that longshore drift can work.
- The sea must be fairly calm, with constructive waves.

Many spits develop a hooked or **recurved** end. As the spit grows out into deeper water, the sand or shingle is more easily forced towards the land by the stronger waves.

Because the sea is so powerful, spits can change shape quite quickly. They can be breached and even destroyed by storms - but longshore drift will gradually rebuild them.

▲ *Hurst Castle spit in Hampshire. The recurved end is very clear. Behind the spit are mudflats (these are covered by every high tide) and salt marshes (these are covered only by occasional high tides or floods).*

Bars

Bars are ridges of sand and other material that run roughly parallel to the coast.

They block off river mouths and bays. Water dammed up behind a bar is called a **lagoon**. Lagoons don't last forever – they are eventually filled in by sediment from waves breaking over the bar or from streams flowing into the lagoon.

Off-shore bars and **barrier islands** are not joined to the coast. These bars form some way out to sea, in places where waves break in shallow water.

Slapton Ley in Devon. ▶

Tombolos

Tombolos are ridges of sand and other material that link the mainland to an island a little way out to sea.

Burgh Island tombolo in Devon, and Bigbury on Sea. The island can only be reached at low tide when the tombolo is showing. ▶

Sand dunes

Sand dunes are a distinctive coastal feature – but they are caused by the wind, not the sea. Sand blown up from the beach develops into small hills held together by marram grass, which is tough and long-rooted.

Did you know?
1½ miles have been added to the coast at Pevensey Bay, on England's south coast, since 1066.

Activities

1. Why does the formation of a beach depend upon constructive waves?
2. Why do you think the material on a beach affects its gradient (slope)?
3. Explain how longshore drift may lead to the formation of a spit.
4. Using an atlas, locate three spits on the shoreline of the British Isles. In each case, describe the location of the spit and the direction of longshore drift.
5. Explain why bars may be temporary coastal features.

The effects of changes in sea level

In this unit you'll find out about landforms created by sea-level change – and then we'll look at how global warming might affect our coastline.

Landforms created by changes in sea level

Raised beaches

A raised beach is an old beach now standing above sea level, a few metres inland.

During an ice age, the great weight of the ice forces the land down. When the ice melts, the land 'rebounds' and rises up again. This happens very slowly, over thousands of years. The result can be raised beaches where old beaches are left high above the new level of the sea.

North-west Scotland has some good raised beaches, as shown in this photo. They can be up to 14 metres above the current sea level. The land here is rising by about 3 mm a year.

raised beach

Rias

A ria is the seaward end of a river valley that has been drowned by a rise in sea level.

People have always used rias as ports because they provide sheltered, winding inlets with relatively deep water.

Good British examples of rias are Salcombe, Devon (pictured), and Milford Haven, South Wales.

Fjords

A fjord is a long, narrow inlet caused by the drowning of a glaciated valley.

During the ice age, glaciers eroded the land down to sea level. When the ice melted, the valleys were flooded by the sea. Fjords are deep, with high, steep sides.

The Norwegian coast is famous for its fjords like this one at Naeroyfjord.

Global warming

Global warming means temperatures around the Earth are rising. And this can cause sea levels to rise in two ways:

◆ massive amounts of water are being added to the oceans because the world's ice sheets and glaciers are melting.

◆ water expands slightly in volume when it's warmed.

We're not sure how quickly, or by how much, sea levels will rise. Some scientists think they could rise by 10 cm over the next 100 years. Others think it could be as much as 1 metre, or even 4 metres!

But we know that rising sea levels will have a dramatic effect on coastlines around the world.

Global warming and rising sea levels mean:

◆ there will be more storms at sea.

◆ erosion around the coast will be speeded up, with many beaches, spits, and other features washed away.

◆ homes and land in areas without strong sea defences will be lost.

◆ our existing sea defences won't be strong enough or high enough, so there will be more sea flooding.

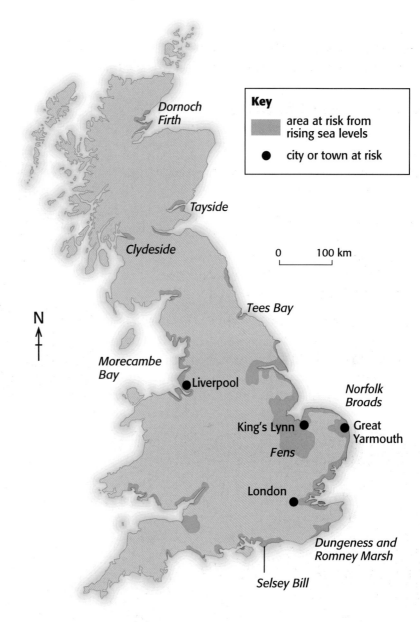

Key
area at risk from rising sea levels
● city or town at risk

0   100 km

▲ *This map shows the areas in Britain most at risk.*

Did you know?
All of the 10 warmest years since records began have occurred since 1990, including every year since 1997.

Management of coastlines

In this unit you'll learn why and how we're defending the coast – and what the latest strategy is.

Why do we try to manage coastlines?

The coast has always been an attractive place for people to settle. From the earliest times we have used the sea for fishing and for transport and trade.

As populations have grown, and as people have made greater use of the coast and the sea, the pressure on the land along the coast has increased. If people were able to build homes and industries, hotels and other leisure amenities just where they wanted there would be chaos. So the coast has been managed for a long time.

Now there's another reason to manage our coasts.

Erosion and flooding by the sea is a growing problem along many stretches of coastline. It threatens people's homes. It threatens the tourist industry. The tourist industry is important because it employs thousands of people in numerous coastal towns and villages. So, people want the coast to be defended.

> **Did you know?**
> About 4300 km of the UK's coastline is protected by sea defences. This costs £325 million a year.

How can we stop coastal erosion?

Coastal erosion can be stopped or reduced in a number of ways:

- **Sea walls** can stop waves reaching valuable land.
- **Rock armour** – a large barrier of rocks – can reduce the impact of waves.
- **Rock barriers** can be built out at sea, to make the waves break earlier, away from the shore.
- **Groynes** can stop sand being carried away by longshore drift.
- **Beach replenishment** builds up a beach by adding more sand or shingle.
- Where cliffs soak up the rain, drainage pipes can remove the water and so reduce the effect of weathering.

Measures like these are called **hard engineering**.

▲ *Rock armour and sea wall at Lowestoft in Suffolk, with groynes in the distance to stop longshore drift.*

Who decides what happens?

In the UK, the government decides on a strategy for coastal defence. Then, along the coast, local councils make decisions based on that strategy. Some of the money for sea defences comes from the government, but the rest comes from local councils.

So, it's easy …

Not really. Coastal defences are expensive. Sea walls cost about £5000 per metre. And coastal defences don't last forever – they wear out and get destroyed.

And now global warming is causing sea levels to rise, and may be causing more storms. This means bigger and stronger waves – so we'll need bigger and stronger defences to cope with them.

And there's a final complication – preventing erosion in one place may make it worse further along the coast. For example, groynes protecting the beach at Highcliffe, in Christchurch Bay on England's south coast, have probably helped to speed up erosion a little further east at Naish Farm.

The latest ideas

Global warming and rising sea levels have led to some new ideas about how to manage Britain's coastline.

The government now plans to stop maintaining coastal defences, unless flooding threatens populated areas.

The previous policy was to hold back the sea. But from now on, only areas of higher population density will be protected. In other areas, the sea defences will be allowed to fail.

The government wants to make this part of a **sustainable** strategy. These are the key ideas:

◆ If land and houses are worth less than the defences will cost, do not defend them.
◆ Think about the effect of defence on other places, and on wildlife.
◆ When planning land use along the coast in the future, always keep erosion in mind.

Where sea defences are allowed to fail, what's known as managed retreat will take place. The sea floods the land behind the breached defences, but builds up its own natural defences such as mudflats, marshes, and beaches. This can only really work where populations are low. It can lead to the loss of farmland, but can benefit wildlife.

▲ *The sea wall at Walton-on-the-Naze, Essex being pounded by waves.*

Activities

1 Why is it important to manage coastlines?
2 Explain some of the problems that may be caused by managing coastlines.
3 What are the advantages and disadvantages of the 'managed retreat' of coastlines?
4 To what extent do you think that the managed retreat of coastlines should be part of the UK government's coastal management strategy?

Did you know?

To improve our sea defences to cope with rising sea levels would cost over £5 billion.

Happisburgh hanging on

In this unit you'll learn how erosion is causing problems for one coastal village.

Broken defences

Happisburgh (pronounced *Haisbro*) is a village on the Norfolk coastline. This stretch of coastline is being eroded very quickly by the North Sea. But despite the loss of land and buildings, shattered sea defences have not been replaced. And there's no plan to renew them.

Why is the coast being eroded?

Erosion is a natural process, but it can be made worse by the actions of people:

◆ Groynes and revetments can protect a stretch of coastline. But they trap sediment that is then not available to protect places further along the coast.

◆ Offshore sediment helps reduce the impact of incoming waves and so slows down erosion. But about 10 million tonnes of sand and gravel are dredged from off the coast of East Anglia every year, allowing incoming waves to erode the soft cliffs.

Global warming will add to the problem. Rising sea levels and more storms will lead to more forceful waves and more rapid erosion.

1 At Happisburgh, the main problem is that the cliffs are soft – sand on top and clay below. To understand this, we need to think about the geology of the coast. The rocks were laid down only 12 000 years ago during the last Ice Age, and this isn't long enough for them to have been consolidated into solid rock. So, the loose sands and clays that form the cliffs at Happisburgh are easily worn away by the sea.

2 Rain soaks into the cliffs and helps to weaken them. (This is one form of weathering.) The more rain they hold, the weaker they get.

3 Meanwhile, the waves erode the cliffs from below. In calm weather erosion will be slower ...

4 ... but when there's a storm, strong waves batter the cliffs, and big chunks of them collapse.

What has been done to protect the coastline?

The coastline has been eroding for 12 000 years. For most of this time no one was affected, so no one cared. It's only recently, when settlements have been threatened, that this natural process has become a problem.

Happisburgh's **sea walls** and **revetments** date from the 1950s. Such defences are expensive and don't last long. Happisburgh's have been damaged by frequent storms. In 2002, a 30-metre stretch of cliff was lost to the sea during a storm, taking several buildings with it. Others are precariously balanced.

▲ *The result of a storm. These wooden barriers (or revetments) were meant to slow down erosion, by making the waves break early. But they have been damaged by previous storms.*

The North Norfolk District Council looks after the defence of Happisburgh. As the defence measures are so expensive – about £5000 per metre of sea wall – the government pays the bill through its Department of Environment, Food and Rural Affairs (DEFRA). DEFRA evaluates whether or not the coast is worth protecting using a cost-benefit analysis.

Happisburgh faces two problems

- First, using their current analysis, DEFRA have decided the coastline isn't worth protecting. This is mainly because most of the village is far enough away from the sea not to be in immediate danger, but also because new defences will cost more than the land and houses are worth.
- Second, no coastal defence scheme gets the go-ahead if people object – and there have been objectors to all schemes to date.

What's the future for Happisburgh?

Without support from the government, the local council has spent £160 000 installing 4000 tonnes of boulders in an attempt to stop the waves. It is at best only a temporary solution, but it's all the council can afford.

The future remains uncertain. The government doesn't think it's right to spend taxpayers' money on **hard defences** for lightly-populated stretches of coastline, like that at Happisburgh. But the local residents, who receive no compensation when their homes are destroyed, want help. The sea defences may not be effective now, but many residents argue they were when they purchased their properties, and that they have a right to expect them to be maintained. Meanwhile, it's predicted that over the next five years the cliffs could retreat 30-75 metres.

Activities

1 Summarise the causes of erosion at Happisburgh.
2 'The actions of people are a major factor in the erosion of this coastline.' Do you agree? Give reasons.
3 Do you think the coastline at Happisburgh is worth protecting? Use a simple cost-benefit analysis, like that shown in this table. Justify your decision.

Positive (benefit)	Negative (cost)

Chesil Beach flood danger

In this unit you'll learn how flooding is a problem along part of Britain's coast – and how people are dealing with it.

How was Chesil Beach formed?

Chesil Beach is an ancient beach, and isn't being formed or eroded by the current work of the sea. Longshore drift, which works from west to east along the south coast of England, has had very little impact. (This is why there are no groynes along it.)

Geographers, instead, think Chesil Beach was formed by the sea driving an offshore bar towards the land as sea level rose. Sea level on this coastline has been rising steadily since the end of the last Ice Age, 10 000 years ago. The sea has eroded and deposited material directly on to Chesil Beach, which is made of material from 35-40 metres below present-day sea level.

▲ Chesil Beach, in Dorset, is a great example of a tombolo. It extends for 18 miles (29 kilometres) from the Isle of Portland to Bridport Harbour.

There's flooding because …

Chesil Beach faces south-west. This means it is exposed to waves that hit it square on. They have a fetch extending right across the Atlantic Ocean before they batter the English coastline. Extreme conditions in the Atlantic, such as those associated with hurricanes, lead to very large waves that can burst over the top of the beach. This happens despite the 13-metre high beach ridge that acts as a dam, protecting the land behind from the sea.

Storms have always hit this coastline. The worst recorded storm was in November 1824. Hurricane-force winds and storm surges devastated much of the coastline of South-West England. Storm waves broke over the top of Chesil Beach, destroying cottages behind and killing sixty people. There have been many floods since, usually between October and February, driven by gale-force winds off the coast. Storm flooding is made worse by percolation, where sea water seeps inland through the beach.

▲ In October 1976, storm waves broke over the top of the beach in several places.

So, what's being done?

Sea defences have been built in certain places to minimise the impact of flooding. As well as those in the photo:

◆ Early defence work included a concrete **sea wall** at Chiswell, to prevent erosion of the cliffs at the southern end of the beach, as well as to reduce flooding.

◆ A flood **drainage channel** takes flood-water away to Portland Harbour.

Conflict and uncertainty

Along with the other measures, the gabions met with protests from environmentalists. They're concerned about the way such defences spoil the landscape and alter natural processes.

But local people are calling for stronger and more effective defences. This conflict will continue – should the defences be improved, or should natural processes be allowed to work unhindered?

There hasn't been a really severe storm for some years, and the flood defences have been able to cope. More and more people are now living along this stretch of coast because it's an attractive area, and because the defences make them feel safe from flooding.

But the flood danger remains for Chiswell and for other villages along the beach. The big storm *will* happen one day. The defences will be breached, and the damage will be severe and costly.

In 1981 a short section of steel **gabions** filled with pebbles was placed on the beach ridge to give extra protection.

The main 300-metre long sea wall near Cove House Inn was built in 1959. It was modified in the 1980s. The effect of the sea walls was to raise the height waves would have to reach to overtop the beach.

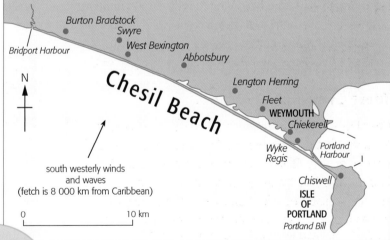

Chesil Beach

Burton Bradstock
Swyre
West Bexington
Abbotsbury
Bridport Harbour
Lengton Herring
Fleet
WEYMOUTH
Chiekerell
Wyke Regis
Portland Harbour
Chiswell
ISLE OF PORTLAND
Portland Bill

N

south westerly winds and waves
(fetch is 8 000 km from Caribbean)

0   10 km

Strengthening the beach ridge is self-defeating. It's just brewing up trouble. Houses are not at risk from annual flooding, but the occasional severe storm. The higher and stronger we make the beach, the more people will move there, and then the more disastrous a flood will be when it eventually breaches the ridge – as it will. The real answer is to ensure that no more people move into the area.

Hang on ... what about the people already there? They want the defences to be maintained and made bigger and stronger, and they should be looked after.

Activities

1 Explain why coastal flooding is a problem at Chesil Beach.

2 a How effective do you think the defences already in place will be in the long term?

  b What do you think should be done?

3 Which do you think is of greater importance – preserving the natural environment in the area or protecting Chiswell and other villages behind the beach? Justify your answer.

4 What is your opinion of the viewpoints on the left?

Protecting Lyme Regis

In this unit you'll learn about a coastal protection scheme that is also impacting tourism.

The Cobb curves out into the sea. It dates from the 13th century, and was built to make a safe harbour for ships.

Lyme Regis has a population of about 3000 people – but this can become 12 000 in the summer. It grew as a trading and fishing port. Smuggling was also part of the town's story. But for 200 years the town has earned its living as a tourist resort.

Lyme Regis is on what's called the Jurassic Coast, which is a World Heritage Site. People think this coastline is one of the natural wonders of the world, on a par with the Grand Canyon and Great Barrier Reef.

In October 2005 the remains of a 190-million year old Ichthyosaur were found in Lyme Regis during coastal protection work. Lyme Regis is famous for its dinosaur fossils.

Why bother?

Lyme Regis has a long history of coastal erosion and landslips. Houses and businesses have been lost. If nothing is done, it's certain that the town and its people will suffer further losses.

Lyme Regis is built on some of the most unstable land in Britain. And it's very exposed to the sea – on one of our most actively eroding stretches of coastline.

The protection scheme

The Lyme Regis Coast Protection Scheme was started by West Dorset District Council in the early 1990s. Most of the money comes from the Department for the Environment, Food and Rural Affairs (DEFRA).

Phase 1 was a new sea wall and promenade east of the mouth of the River Lim. It was finished in 1995.

Phase 2 will protect the foreshore and stabilise the land behind immediately behind it. Work started in 2005, and will cost £17 million.

Further phases are being planned. So the work will go on for many years yet.

The aim of the scheme is to provide long-term protection for homes and businesses in the town, and at the same time to protect the coast and the special natural environment that makes Lyme Regis so attractive to tourists.

West Dorset District Council is trying to make sure there's not too much disruption to the town and tourism during the work.

▼ OS map extract 1 : 25 000.

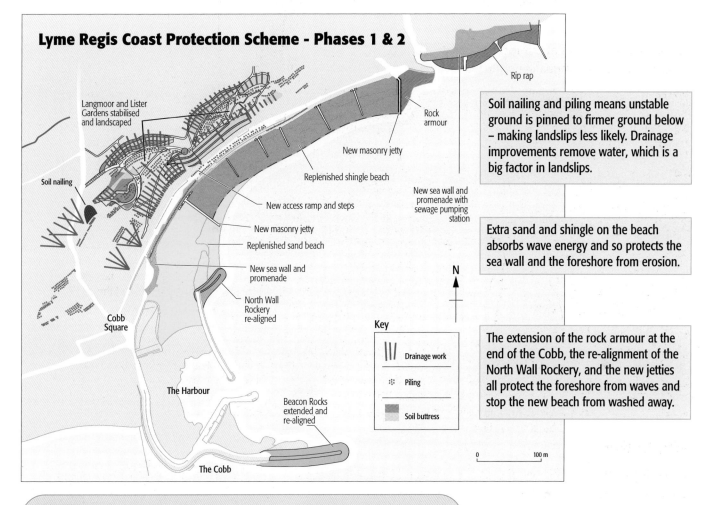

Lyme Regis Coast Protection Scheme – Phases 1 & 2

Langmoor and Lister Gardens stabilised and landscaped

Soil nailing

Cobb Square

The Harbour

The Cobb

Rip rap

Rock armour

New masonry jetty

Replenished shingle beach

New access ramp and steps

New masonry jetty

Replenished sand beach

New sea wall and promenade

North Wall Rockery re-aligned

New sea wall and promenade with sewage pumping station

Beacon Rocks extended and re-aligned

N

Key

Drainage work

Piling

Soil buttress

0   100 m

Soil nailing and piling means unstable ground is pinned to firmer ground below – making landslips less likely. Drainage improvements remove water, which is a big factor in landslips.

Extra sand and shingle on the beach absorbs wave energy and so protects the sea wall and the foreshore from erosion.

The extension of the rock armour at the end of the Cobb, the re-alignment of the North Wall Rockery, and the new jetties all protect the foreshore from waves and stop the new beach from washed away.

Benefits

◆ Long-term protection against destructive coastal erosion and landslips.
◆ More sand and shingle on the beach.
◆ It will be possible to walk along the whole beach even at high tide.
◆ A new promenade along the seafront.
◆ Calmer conditions for boats in the harbour and bay.
◆ Better access to the public gardens, including ramps for people using wheelchairs and prams.
◆ Re-landscaped public gardens with more walks.
◆ Improvements to roads.
◆ A more secure future for the town's people and businesses.

Activities

1 Look at the OS map. List the evidence you can see of:
   a coastal processes
   b coastal defences
   c tourism
2 Give three ways the planned scheme might help to reduce coastal erosion.
3 a Explain how the proposed scheme might bring advantages for tourists and the tourism industry.

   b Is the scheme likely to bring any disadvantages for tourists and the tourism industry, now or in the future?
4 Do you think the scheme is value for money?
5 Do you think the scheme is sustainable (is it going to last for the long term)?

The big picture

This chapter is about weather and climate. These are the big ideas behind the chapter:

◆ Weather and climate are different. Weather is the day-to-day state of the atmosphere, and can change very quickly. Climate is the average weather in a place.

◆ Climate depends on several factors – the effect of latitude is the main one.

◆ Depressions and anticyclones control our weather in the UK.

◆ Droughts have very different causes and impacts in MEDCs like the UK, and LEDCs like Niger.

◆ Tropical storms are extreme weather events and can have devastating effects.

◆ Weather, climate and climate change affect us all.

Your goals for this chapter

By the end of this chapter you should be able to answer these questions:

◆ What's the difference between weather and climate?

◆ How do these factors influence climate?
latitude, distance from the sea, prevailing wind, altitude, ocean currents

◆ What type of climate do we have in the UK?

◆ How do these types of rainfall form?
relief, convectional, frontal

◆ What do these weather terms mean, and how are they measured?
precipitation, temperature, wind direction, wind strength (speed), visibility, cloud type, cloud cover, humidity, air pressure

◆ What type of weather do you get with:
a winter anticyclone? a summer anticyclone? a depression passing over?

◆ What do synoptic charts and satellite images show us, and how are they used?

◆ How do our weather and climate affect what we do?

◆ What causes droughts? What effects do they have, and how do we respond? Think about the UK and Niger.

◆ What causes tropical storms? What were the effects of Hurricanes Katrina and Wilma? How can predicting hurricanes help?

◆ What is climate change, and what effects will it have?

And then . . .

When you finish the chapter, come back here and see if you've met your goals!

Did you know?
Global warming could cause:
◆ Arctic ice to melt and the extinction in the wild of animals like the polar bear
◆ the spread of malaria in Africa and North America.

Did you know?
Global warming could cause the warm North Atlantic Drift to be 'turned off' – that would lead to a much colder Britain.

Did you know?
Scientists think it's unlikely that we can avoid dangerous climate change.

Did you know?
◆ The highest temperature ever recorded is 57.8°C, in Libya, on 13 September 1922.
◆ The lowest is -89.2°C, in Antarctica, on 21 July 1983.

Your chapter starter

Look at the photo on page 106.
What is it?
Where do you think it is?
What do you think might happen to the house?
Have you ever seen anything like it?

I see the Wizard of Oz is on again.

Global climate explained

In this unit you'll learn about the global distribution of climate – and the key factors behind this distribution.

Climate around the world

Climate is the *average* weather in a place. It's a summary of what the weather is usually like, based on measurements taken over a long time, usually 30 years.

Climate varies around the world. But we can divide the world into climate zones – large areas with a similar climate. Some are shown on this map, and by the climate graphs and statistics.

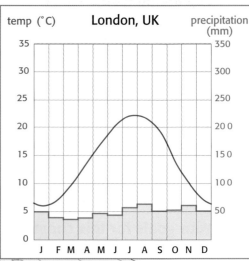

A temperate climate has cool summers, mild winters, and a fairly even distribution of rainfall through the year. Temperate areas lie between 40° and 60°.

The desert climate is hot and dry throughout the year. Rain does fall – but not very often. Desert areas lie between 15° and 30°.

An equatorial climate is hot, wet, and humid all year round. There are no seasons. Equatorial areas lie in a band around the equator.

The savanna climate has two distinct seasons: a warm dry season and a hot wet season. Savanna areas lie between 5° and 15°.

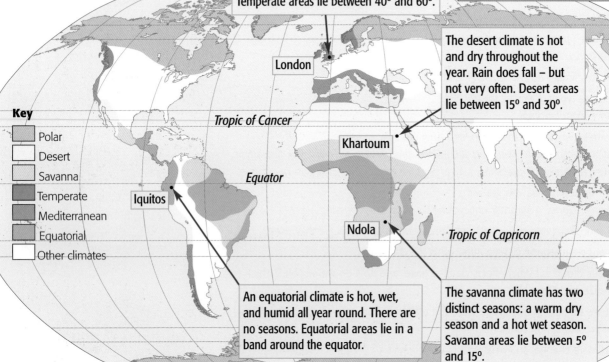

Key
- Polar
- Desert
- Savanna
- Temperate
- Mediterranean
- Equatorial
- Other climates

Tropic of Cancer

London

Khartoum

Equator

Iquitos

Ndola

Tropic of Capricorn

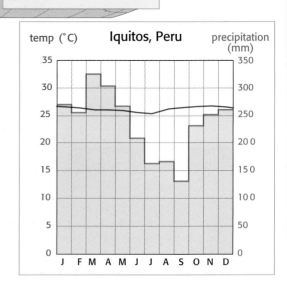

Savanna	J	F	M	A	M	J	J	A	S	O	N	D
Ndola, Zambia												
Temperature (°C)	21	21	21	21	19	17	17	19	23	24	23	21
Rainfall (mm)	290	250	170	46	4	1	0	0	3	32	130	306

Desert	J	F	M	A	M	J	J	A	S	O	N	D
Khartoum, Sudan												
Temperature (°C)	23	25	29	32	35	34	32	32	32	32	28	25
Rainfall (mm)	0	0	0	1	4	5	46	75	25	5	1	0

Explaining global climate

The effect of latitude

Latitude is the main factor in global climate. The further you go from the equator, the cooler it gets.

This is because the Earth's surface is curved – which means the sun's energy isn't distributed evenly. The diagram shows how the energy received at the equator is much more direct and concentrated. This means the Earth gets hottest here.

The poles are colder. You can see from the diagram that the sun's rays hit the pole at a low angle. The heat is spread out – so it's cooler. Ice forms and reflects heat back into space, making conditions even colder.

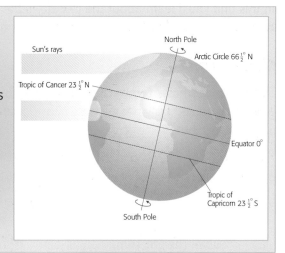

The effect of distance from the sea

The sea is cooler than the land in summer, but warmer in winter. This is because it takes longer to heat up, but is slower to cool down.

Because we're surrounded by sea, the climate of the British Isles is called a **maritime climate**. The sea moderates our climate, making temperatures more even throughout the year. So, our climate isn't as hot in summer or as cold in winter as it could be. Without the seas around us, winter temperatures could fall to -20 °C.

A long way from the sea, the interiors of the large land masses have a **continental climate**, with cold snowy winters and hot dry summers. Siberia and central areas of the USA have this type of climate.

The effect of altitude

Temperatures decrease by 1°C for every 100 metres in altitude (height above sea level). Therefore, mountainous areas are always cooler. Relief rainfall (Unit 6.2) also makes for a wetter environment.

The effect of the prevailing wind

The prevailing wind is the direction the wind blows from most often.

For the British Isles, the prevailing wind is from the south-west. It blows over a warm ocean current (the North Atlantic Drift), so the British Isles is warmer in winter than it could be, given our northerly latitude. And because it blows over the ocean, it also brings moisture – and that means rain.

Our climate would be much colder if the prevailing wind came from the north, from the Arctic (think how we get our coldest weather in winter when the north wind blows).

The effect of ocean currents

Ocean currents are warm or cold, and these affect the climate of coastal areas. For example a warm current called the North Atlantic Drift helps warm the British Isles in winter, by warming the prevailing wind.

Activities

1 Describe the global distribution of these climate zones:
   a equatorial   c desert
   b savanna   d temperate
2 a Draw climate graphs to show the savanna and desert climate data.

   b Compare two of the climate zones with the information shown for the temperate climate (London). Use statistical data from the graphs as part of your comparison.
3 Suggest reasons for the differences you have described in question **2**, using information from here and Unit 7.2.

The climate of the British Isles

In this unit you'll learn about the climate of the British
Isles – and two types of rainfall

Mild and wet

The British Isles has a **temperate**, **maritime climate** – our climate is
generally mild and fairly wet because it's moderated by the sea. In the summer
the sea cools the climate and in winter the sea insulates us, keeping us
warmer than most other places at our latitude.

But the climate does vary across the British Isles. Look at the map and the four
climate graphs.

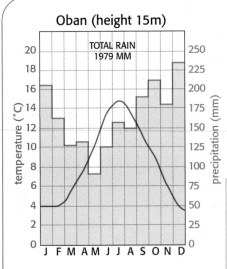
Oban (height 15m)

TOTAL RAIN
1979 MM

Key

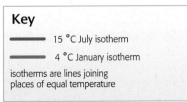

——— 15 °C July isotherm

——— 4 °C January isotherm

isotherms are lines joining
places of equal temperature

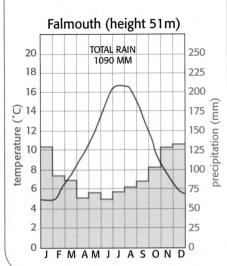
Falmouth (height 51m)

TOTAL RAIN
1090 MM

Why?
Colder temperatures in the
north are due to both the
higher latitude and the
mountainous relief (air cools by
1°C for every 100 metres). So
winter temperatures are quite
harsh. Arctic air from the North
Pole can also blast Scotland,
reducing temperatures further.

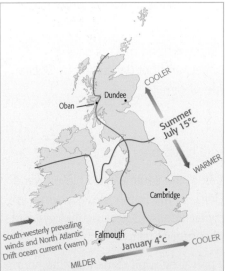

Why?
The North Atlantic Drift is a
very warm ocean current that
starts in the tropical Gulf of
Mexico. The warmth from this
water helps keep the west of
Britain milder during the
winter months – the prevailing
south-westerly winds are
warmed by this water.

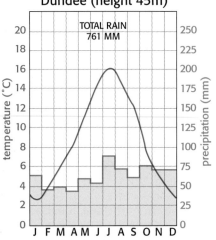
Dundee (height 45m)

TOTAL RAIN
761 MM

Why?
Warm air from Europe helps to lift
summer temperatures. Southerly
continental winds often produce a heat-
wave. And as they're at a lower latitude,
southern areas also get more
concentrated heat energy from the sun.

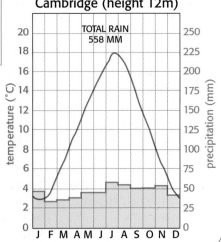
Cambridge (height 12m)

TOTAL RAIN
558 MM

West is wetter!

Three types of rainfall are responsible for all the precipitation received in the British Isles. These are:

1 relief rainfall (sometimes called orographic rainfall)
2 convectional rainfall
3 frontal rainfall (see Unit 6.4).

Remember the precipitation process!
Cooling ➞ **C**ondensation ➞ **C**loud formation ➞ **P**recipitation

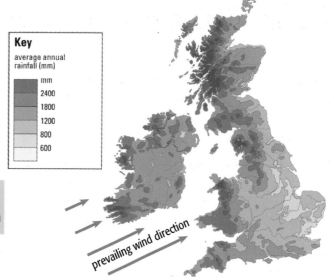

Key
average annual rainfall (mm)

mm
2400
1800
1200
800
600

prevailing wind direction

Relief rainfall

Warm moist air blows in, rises over hills or mountains, cools, condenses into clouds – and we get rain.

Warm moist air arrives from the Atlantic Ocean and rises over the mountains on the western side of Britain – the Cambrians, Pennines, and Grampians. The mountain peaks can receive quite high totals, up to 3000 mm annually. Once the air has passed over the mountains, it begins to descend and gradually warms as it reaches a lower altitude. This produces drier conditions and is known as the **rain shadow**. Our mountains tend to be wetter on the windward, western sides and drier on the leeward, eastern sides.

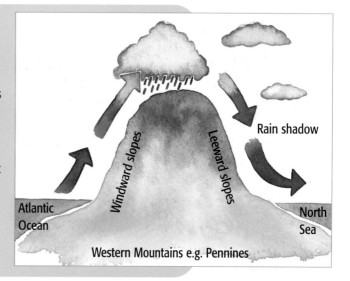

Rain shadow

Windward slopes

Leeward slopes

Atlantic Ocean

North Sea

Western Mountains e.g. Pennines

Convectional rainfall

During the summer, strong heating from the sun causes the ground to heat up rapidly. This can then set up rising pockets of warm air known as **convection currents**. The warm air rises rapidly to a high altitude where it cools and water vapour condenses to form clouds. With time, particularly by late afternoon, thick cumulonimbus clouds can form – and these can produce heavy rainfall, and sometimes thunderstorms. This process helps to explain why Cambridge often has its wettest month in July or August.

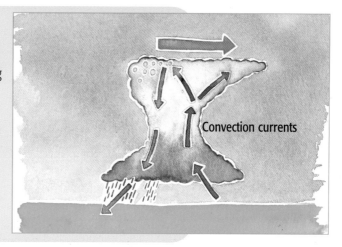

Convection currents

Activities

1 a Draw your own sketch map of the British Isles, and divide it into the four climate areas.

b Using the climate graphs, annotate your map (add explaining labels) with key information about the climate. Remember to include data as part of your answer and remember to use the following terms: maximum temperature, minimum temperature, annual range, and total precipitation.

2 Compare two climate areas of the British Isles. Explain the differences in the climate patterns you identify using the information given.

3 Describe and suggest reasons for the distribution of rainfall across the British Isles (shown by the map above).

6.3 Weather and weather systems

In this unit you'll find out about weather, and the effects of anticyclones.

What is weather?

Weather is the day-to-day condition of the atmosphere.

Over the short term, the atmosphere can change quickly. What's the weather like today? Warm or cool? Wet or dry? Cloudy or clear? Windy or calm?

The changes in the atmosphere can be measured. The results are used to produce quite reliable weather forecasts for the next few days.

Elements of the weather

Precipitation is all forms of moisture from clouds – rain, hail, sleet, and snow. It's measured by a rain gauge, in millimetres (mm).

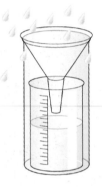

Temperature measures the heat in the air. It's measured by a thermometer, in degrees Celsius (°C).

Wind direction is recorded by identifying the direction the wind is coming from, using a compass or wind vane.

Wind strength (**speed**) is measured with an anemometer, in knots, kilometres or miles per hour. A simple observation scale known as the Beaufort Scale can also be used. The scale goes from 0 to 12: 0 = calm (smoke rises vertically); 6 = strong breeze (difficult to use umbrellas); 12 = hurricane (great damage to property).

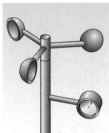

The wind turns the cups which turn a counter.

Visibility is how far we can see. It's measured by a visibility meter, in metres or kilometres.

A beam of light is sent out and a sensor measures how much arrives.

Cloud type. There are five main types of cloud: stratus (layered), cumulus, nimbus (rain bearing), cumulonimbus, cirrus (ice). The cloud above is cirrus.

Cloud cover is how much of the sky is covered by cloud. It's measured in eighths or oktas, just by looking. (See Unit 6.5.)

Humidity is the percentage of water vapour in the air. It's measured with a hygrometer.

Air pressure is the force the atmosphere exerts on the Earth's surface. It is also known as atmospheric pressure. It's measured by a barometer, in millibars (mb). Generally, air pressure is high if it's above 1000 mb, low if it's below this figure. It's the single most important weather element because it controls all the other elements mentioned here.

high pressure

cool air sinking

Cool air sinks. The pressure of the air on the ground increases. The air warms up as it reaches the ground, so no water vapour condenses and no clouds form. The skies stay clear and there's no rain.

warm air rising

low pressure

Warm air rises. The pressure of the air on the ground decreases. The air cools as it rises, moisture condenses to form clouds, and rain follows.

112

The anticyclone

Two large-scale weather systems control our weather in the British Isles:

1   The **anticyclone** – which is associated with high pressure and results in clear calm weather.

2   The **depression** – which is associated with low pressure and results in cloudy, wet, and windy weather (see Unit 6.4).

Air pressure is shown on maps by **isobars**. These are lines of equal pressure. In anticyclones, the isobars are far apart. This means the air pressure doesn't change much over a large distance, so winds are light. In depressions, the isobars are close together, indicating stronger winds.

Anticyclones have high air pressure, light winds, clear skies, and dry conditions. But there are differences between winter and summer.

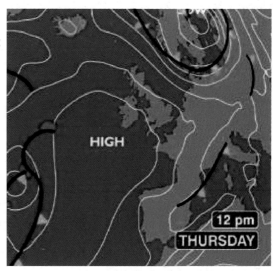

HIGH

12 pm
THURSDAY

Winter anticyclones

In winter, the cloudless skies we often get with anticyclones allow heat to escape. The ground cools quickly at night, cooling the air above it – water vapour condenses and freezes on cold surfaces, giving **frost**. It also condenses on dust and other particles in the air, giving **fog**. This fog can linger into the day, until the heat of the sun evaporates it away. The days are often clear, cold, and bright. Water can freeze into **ice**.

Summer anticyclones

In summer, an anticyclone brings very different weather. The cloudless skies mean the sun is strong and the days are hot. But, because there's no cloud, evenings can be cool. The ground cools at night, so water vapour condenses to form **dew**. No cloud means no rain – which can lead to a **drought**. However, on very hot days, the hot air may rise quickly, cool, and form big black clouds leading to **thunderstorms**.

If a summer anticyclone stays over the British Isles for a few weeks, we talk about a heat-wave. There was a famous one in 1976; more recently, we had one in 2003.

Activities

1 **a** What is atmospheric pressure?
   b Explain how it controls the weather elements.

2 Suggest reasons for the weather associated with a summer anticyclone.

The depression

In this unit you'll learn about the formation of depressions, and how they affect our weather.

How a depression forms

Our weather is wet and windy. The weather system that gives us these conditions is called the **depression**. It's a low pressure weather system that moves across the country from west to east, from the Atlantic Ocean. It brings rain.

Depression systems form over the ocean at the boundary where warm light air from the tropics meets colder heavier air from the poles. The different air types don't mix, and the less dense warm air rises above the cold air to produce a **front**. Moisture condenses to form clouds and **frontal rainfall**.

Remember:
The warm front has warm air behind it.
The cold front has cold air behind it.

The development of a depression occurs in a number of distinct stages, with a lifecycle that usually lasts 5 or 6 days.

Stage 1: Birth
- Cold polar air meets warm tropical air along a polar front.
- The less dense warm air rises over the cold – this starts to lower the air pressure.

Stage 2: Maturity
- Warm air is drawn or 'sucked' into the low pressure centre and the colder air is sucked in behind it.
- The rotation of the Earth causes the system to spiral in an anti-clockwise direction.
- At the warm front, warm air rises over the cold air. Cooling and condensation occurs, resulting in clouds and precipitation along a frontal zone.
- At the cold front, heavy cold air sinks below or undercuts the warm air in the warm sector. Again the warm air is forced to rise resulting in a thick zone of cloud and heavy precipitation.

Stage 3: Old age and death
- The cold front travels faster than the warm front and eventually 'lifts' the warm air off the ground from the warm sector. This is called an occlusion.
- When cold air replaces the warm air the fronts disappear and the depression dies.

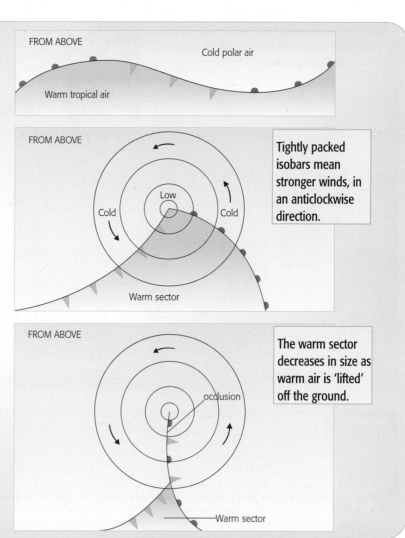

Tightly packed isobars mean stronger winds, in an anticlockwise direction.

The warm sector decreases in size as warm air is 'lifted' off the ground.

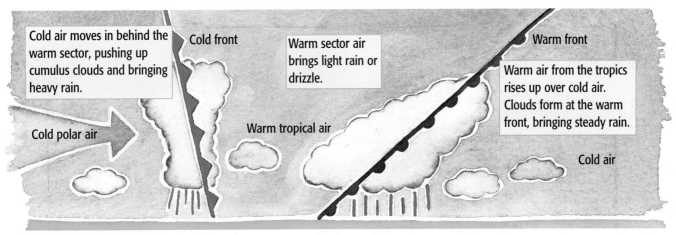

Cold air moves in behind the warm sector, pushing up cumulus clouds and bringing heavy rain.

Cold front

Warm sector air brings light rain or drizzle.

Warm front

Warm air from the tropics rises up over cold air. Clouds form at the warm front, bringing steady rain.

Cold polar air

Warm tropical air

Cold air

▲ *Frontal rainfall in a depression.*

As a depression system moves across the British Isles, there's a definite pattern to the weather. Meteorologists use this pattern to forecast the weather as accurately as possible, but the nature of the weather and its variability makes forecasting very difficult.

Weather associated with the passage of a depression

	Ahead of the warm front	Passage of the warm front	Warm sector	Passage of the cold front	Cold sector
Pressure	starts to fall steadily	continues to fall	steadies	starts to rise	continues to rise
Temperature	quite cold, starts to rise	continues to rise	quite mild	sudden drop	remains cold
Cloud cover	cloud base drops and thickens (cirrus and altostratus)	cloud base is low and thick (nimbostratus)	cloud may thin and break	clouds thicken (sometimes with large cumulonimbus)	clouds thin with some cumulus
Wind speed and direction	speeds increase and direction is SE	veers SW and becomes blustery with strong gusts	remains steady, westerly slightly	speeds increase, sometimes to gale force, sharp veer NW	winds are squally NW
Precipitation	none at first, rain closer to front, sometimes snow on leading edge	continues, and sometimes heavy rainfall	rain runs to drizzle or stops	heavy rain, sometimes with hail, thunder or sleet	showers

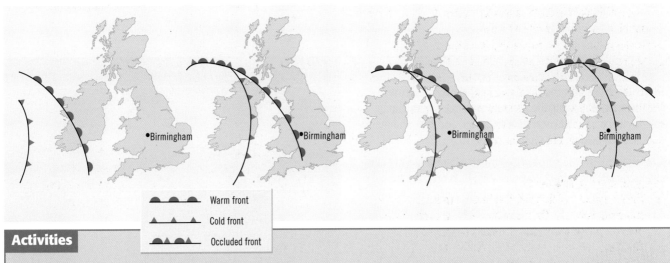

Warm front

Cold front

Occluded front

Activities

1 Using the diagram, produce a TV or radio weather forecast for Birmingham for the next 24 hours. Make reference to each part of the depression.

2 Describe and explain five differences between the weather associated with a depression and the weather associated with a summer anticyclone.

Synoptic charts and satellite images

In this unit you'll learn how to read synoptic charts and satellite images.

What will the weather be like?

Most of our weather comes with the prevailing winds from the south-west, so we look mostly towards the Atlantic Ocean for clues about what will happen next.

Below is an Atlantic synoptic chart, or weather map. It's like many you see on TV. It clearly identifies the position of the weather systems looked at so far in this chapter:

◆ the anticyclone – a region of high atmospheric pressure

◆ the depression – a region of low atmospheric pressure.

The depression

This is a classic depression. It has a leading warm front, a warm sector, and a following cold front. The isobars are tightly packed, indicating strong winds.

It's likely this system will move across the British Isles in the next few days. The fronts will bring cloud and rain. The warm sector will bring slightly drier weather.

The anticyclone and high-pressure ridge

This large area of high pressure indicates an area where the air is sinking. As this air sinks towards the ground it will warm up and evaporate moisture. As few clouds can form, there will be clear skies. Over a cool sea there could be some fog. The isobars are much further apart than in the depression – this indicates calm winds.

In summer this system will provide warm temperatures, and maybe thunderstorms will develop. In winter it will provide cooler temperatures, with frost and fog.

Approaching the British Isles you can see a smaller ridge of high pressure – this should also bring settled weather. The winds blow in a clockwise direction.

An occlusion

The warm and cold fronts have merged here, lifting all the warm air off the ground.

Without a constant supply of warm air the storm will die out after a period of quite heavy rain. The occlusion marks the end of the depression system.

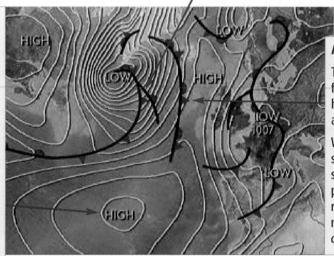

▲ *An Atlantic synoptic (pressure) chart.*

Precipitation

This chart shows how the cloud and rainfall pattern across the Atlantic matches up with the pressure systems. You should be able to match up the frontal bands of cloud and rain, and the clear conditions, with the synoptic chart.

All the rainfall shown is frontal. Notice how the isobars are close together, indicating stronger winds. With high pressure the isobars are much further apart, producing calmer conditions.

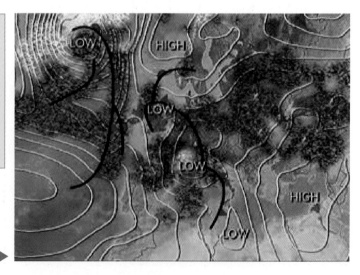

A pressure / precipitation chart. ▶

Satellite images

This is a visual image of the cloud cover associated with weather systems. Satellite images help weather forecasters to see what weather is heading our way. The skill lies in seeing how the atmospheric pressure is linked to the weather system and the amount of cloud and rain.

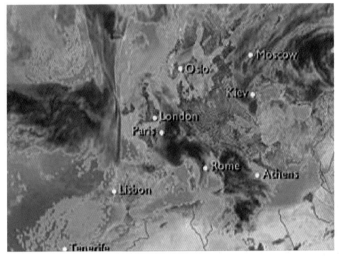

A satellite image of cloud cover.

Weather symbols

If you know a bit about weather symbols, it's possible to interpret synoptic charts in more detail. The symbols describe the weather conditions at a place at a particular time, and can be used to anticipate how the weather conditions may change.

Official weather symbols

Present weather	Wind speed (knots)	Cloud	Fronts
≡ Mist	◯ Calm	◯ Clear sky	●●● Warm
≡ Fog	—◯ 1 - 2	◐ 1/8 covered	▲▲▲ Cold
❩ Drizzle	—◯ 3 - 7	◕ 2/8 covered	▲●▲● Occluded
❩❩ Rain and drizzle	—◯ 8 - 12	◔ 3/8 covered	
• Rain	⟍◯ 13 - 17	◑ 4/8 covered	
✳ Snow	For each additional half feather, add 5 knots	◕ 5/8 covered	
▽ Rain shower		◕ 6/8 covered	
✳▽ Snow shower	⟍◯ 48 - 52	◖ 7/8 covered	
△▽ Hail shower		● 8/8 covered	
Ⓣ Thunderstorm		⊗ Sky obscured	

Wind direction
Arrow showing direction from which wind is blowing i.e. → west

Temperature
Shown in degrees centigrade i.e. 15°

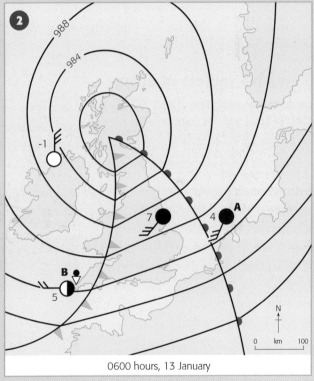

▲ A synoptic chart for 11 August.

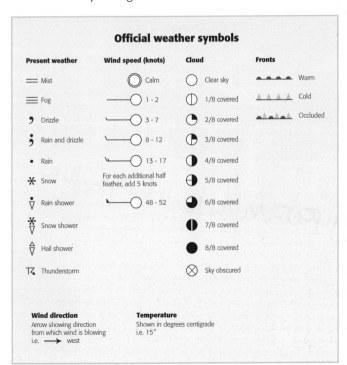

0600 hours, 13 January

▲ A synoptic chart of a depression system.

1 Study synoptic chart 1. Write a brief forecast about the general conditions expected for the British Isles on 11 August.
2 Study synoptic chart 2.
   a Describe the specific weather conditions at places A and B.
   b Suggest how and why the weather conditions for place A may change over the following 24 hours.

Climate and human activity in the UK

In this unit you'll learn how the weather and climate of the UK affects human activity.

Come rain or shine

The UK's weather changes from day to day. But the climate is more predictable. Most of our weather arrives from the Atlantic Ocean as depressions, which bring cloud, rain, and wind. The air is **temperate** (warm) and **maritime** (wet from the ocean), so our weather is mostly warm and wet.

In winter, northerly arctic blasts can cause sharp drops in temperature and can bring snow, especially in Scotland. In summer, heat-waves from North Africa and the Mediterranean can bring sweltering temperatures of around 25-30 °C. If prolonged, southern parts of the UK can experience drought (see Unit 6.7).

The climate affects what we do – the crops we grow, the holidays we take, the sports we play.

Alternative sources of energy

Our wet and windy climate could provide us with alternative, renewable sources of energy. Fossil fuels (coal, oil, and gas) won't last forever, and carbon dioxide emissions from burning fossil fuels are contributing to global warming, so the government is looking for alternatives.

Hydro-electric power (hep) uses the power of running water to generate electricity. The western side of the UK is much wetter and more mountainous than the east. So this is where the hep stations are located. Most are in Scotland. The Dinorwig station in Wales is inside a huge mountain chamber. However, set up costs are high and finding the right location is difficult.

We're the windiest country in Europe – so there's plenty of potential for **wind power**. Most of our windfarms are on the western side of the country – because the high land is exposed to the prevailing wind. The first offshore windfarm – North Hoyle, off the coast of North Wales – started generating electricity in 2003 (see Unit 12.6). At least 30 more offshore windfarms are planned or being built already. Wind power is clean and non-polluting. But a thousand turbines will generate only 1% of our energy needs.

Remember:
- weather is the short-term state of the atmosphere – it can change from day to day
- climate is the average weather over a longer period of time.

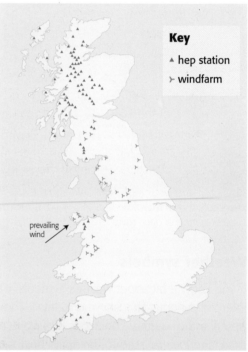

Key
- ▲ hep station
- ⊁ windfarm

prevailing wind

▲ A windfarm in Cumbria.

LAMBRIGG WINDFARM

Farming

There's a direct link between type of agriculture and climate. Eastern England has a drier, warmer, sunnier climate, with an average of five or six hours of sunshine per day in the summer – so arable crops such as wheat and barley ripen well. The western side of the UK has a wetter climate – this produces good pasture for cattle, so pastoral farming dominates.

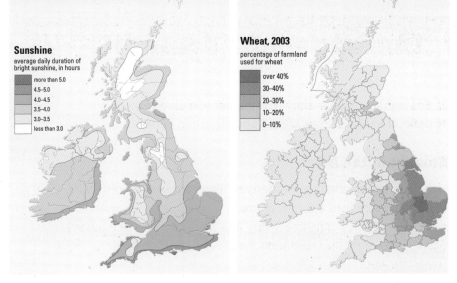

Sunshine
average daily duration of bright sunshine, in hours

- more than 5.0
- 4.5–5.0
- 4.0–4.5
- 3.5–4.0
- 3.0–3.5
- less than 3.0

Wheat, 2003
percentage of farmland used for wheat

- over 40%
- 30–40%
- 20–30%
- 10–20%
- 0–10%

Flooding

Flooding can hit almost any part of the UK. But the western side of the UK often suffers more than other areas because it gets a lot of heavy rain, especially in the autumn and winter months. Carlisle in Cumbria was closed off by flood waters in the winter of 2004. A flash flood caused havoc in Boscastle in Devon in August 2004. The threat of flooding affects how we use land, for example where we build new homes and roads.

▲ *Game off.*

Tourism

The UK is the world's sixth most popular tourist destination, but many visitors enjoy our landscape and historical attractions whilst shouting 'shame about the weather!'. The tourist industry earns the country over £30 billion a year and provides many jobs in hotels, restaurants, souvenir shops, and attractions – although many of these jobs are for the summer only. There are many seaside resorts, especially along the warmer, sunnier south coast. The wetter parts of the country, such as the Lake District and Highlands of Scotland, rely on their stunning landscape to attract walkers, climbers, and mountain bikers.

▲ *Summer work.*

Sport and leisure

We play different sports at different times of the year. Traditionally it's been football in winter, cricket in summer. There are more outdoor events in the summer. We take most of our holidays in the summer, because that's when the weather's better.

Activities

1 Compare and explain the patterns shown by the two maps above.
2 Think of three further examples of how climate has a direct impact on human activity in the UK. Explain clearly the link between activity and climate.
3 Using the information on these pages and your own ideas, construct a mind map which illustrates the links you have thought of. You could even show how some activities are interrelated.

The impact of drought

In this unit you'll learn about the impact of and response to drought in the UK (an MEDC) and Niger (an LEDC).

Drought in the UK

In the UK an official drought is declared when at least 15 consecutive days go by without more than 0.2 mm of rain.

The South-East is the driest part of the UK, and it experiences drought more often than other regions.

A **drought** is defined as a long period of abnormally dry weather.

The causes of drought in the UK

There are two main physical causes:

◆ Long periods of high atmospheric pressure (anticyclones). Clouds don't form so it doesn't rain. If anticyclones last for several weeks, they can lead to drought.
◆ Long periods of high temperatures. This means more evapotranspiration than precipitation – in other words, water is lost back into the atmosphere.

Human factors also play a part:

◆ Land use. A lot of water is used in homes, industry, and agriculture (watering crops).
◆ High population density. People use a lot of water. The South-East is densely populated, and its population is going to increase.
◆ Changes in the way we live, and increasing wealth. Power showers, dishwashers, washing machines, cleaning cars (especially at car washes or with hose-pipes), lawn sprinklers and so on mean each person uses more water today then ever before.

Impact and response

Drought in the UK mainly causes inconvenience. Immediate impacts include:

◆ restrictions or even bans on the use of hosepipes and garden sprinklers
◆ campaigns to get people to reduce their consumption of water
◆ lower crop yields, and therefore lower earnings for farmers.

There are also longer term impacts:

◆ Water companies are investing millions of pounds in repairing and improving water pipes. It's estimated that over 3 billion litres of water are lost every day through broken or leaking pipes – this represents one-fifth of our total water supply.
◆ Our wetter areas also have fewer people and therefore less demand for water – so there are plans to pipe water from reservoirs in the north and west of the country, such as Kielder Water in Northumberland, to the South-East.

Save water
Cleaning your teeth with the tap off uses 1 litre of water – leave the tap running and you use 6 litres a minute.
• have a shower instead of a bath
• fit a low-flush loo
• use a bowl for washing up – not a dishwasher
• only fill kettles with the water you need
• fix dripping taps

How many litres to ...

fill a kettle:	1
flush a toilet:	9
have a shower:	30-50
fill a bath:	80
use a dishwasher:	25-60
do laundry:	70-120

Drought in Niger

In the Sahel, a drought is declared when there's below average rainfall for 2 years. The Sahel has actually suffered drought for most of the last 30 years.

The causes of drought in Niger

Niger's climate has a wet and a dry season. But the wet season is unreliable. And when the rains fail, drought follows.

Impact and response

Drought and mismanagement (poor use) of the land causes **desertification**.

Desertification is the spread of desert-like conditions. It takes place when climatic and human processes combine to reduce the ability of the land to support vegetation.

The Sahel ecosystem can cope with one or two drought years. But if the drought lasts longer, the ecosystem breaks down because of the lack of water.

Human factors are part of the process:

◆ Overcultivation. Too many crops exhaust the soil so that it can no longer support vegetation. Too many animals results in overgrazing. Without grass and bushes to protect it, the soil is easily eroded.
◆ The collection of firewood. Firewood is used in cooking. As the population has grown, more has been collected. The land is stripped of its trees and bushes, so again the soil is easily eroded.

Land that was once fertile enough for farming starts to suffer soil erosion and eventually turns to desert. In the Sahel, prolonged drought and human activity have resulted in widespread desertification.

Drought and desertification lead to crop failure and livestock deaths. Hunger and famine follow.

This happened in Niger in 2004. The rains failed, prolonging the drought and making the land unable to support crops. Things were made worse by a plague of locusts that ate the remaining crops.

Niger is one of the poorest countries in the world, and many people were already short of food stocks. A massive international aid effort sent emergency food supplies to 3.5 million people.

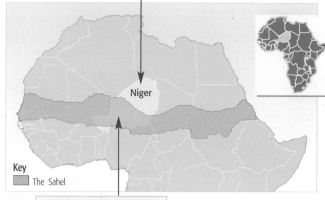

Northern Niger is in the Sahara Desert. This area is virtually rainless.

Niger

Key
■ The Sahel

Southern Niger is in the Sahel, a region that runs across Africa to the south of the Sahara Desert. This area has moderate but unreliable rainfall.

Did you know?
Famine is where a high proportion of the general population could die from hunger-related disease.

Activities

1 Design a contrast chart to show the differences between the impact of drought in an MEDC compared to an LEDC country. Try to explain the differences you identify.
2 a What is desertification?
  b What are the main causes of desertification in the Sahel?
3 Research what measures could be taken to reduce the impact of desertification in the Sahel.

Tropical storms

In this unit you'll find out what causes tropical storms – and about their effects.

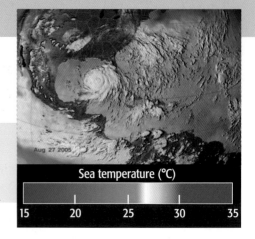

Tropical storms are intense, destructive low pressure weather systems. They develop between 5° and 15° latitude either side of the equator. They have very strong sustained winds of over 75 mph and torrential rain – 250 mm can fall in one day. This one's heading for the USA.

Aug 27 2005

Sea temperature (°C)

15	20	25	30	35

Why do they happen?

Several environmental conditions are required for hurricanes to develop:

◆ Sea temperatures of at least 27 °C to a depth of 60 metres (look at the colours on the satellite image and its key). This warmth is the energy source of the hurricane. It is transferred to the storm's latent heat through evaporation. When the water vapour condenses into clouds, the latent heat is released, adding to the storm's power. When a hurricane reaches land, this source of energy is cut off and the storm weakens. The necessary high sea temperatures exist between summer and early autumn.

◆ Low latitudes. This means the trade winds can spiral into the storm due to the Earth's rotation. This spiralling effect is known as the Coriolis force.

◆ Low atmospheric shear. In order for the storms to remain intact, wind speeds have to be near constant between ground level and 12 km in height, otherwise the hurricane can be literally pulled apart.

Most hurricanes start their journey as a convectional thunderstorm off the coast of West Africa, near Cape Verde. Over the tropical waters the latent heat available allows them to grow and strengthen as they head towards the Caribbean, the Gulf of Mexico and the USA.

The continual process of warm air rising steadily lowers the air pressure. Trade winds blowing towards the eye of the storm therefore increase in strength as they are 'sucked in'. As long as the sea remains warm and the atmospheric shear stays low, the hurricane will become more and more powerful. The exception is the **eye of the storm**, where conditions are clear and calm. Rising air is thrown away or diverges from this central core, meaning that it remains cloud free.

These pages focus on Atlantic hurricanes, which are more widely reported in the news. Hurricanes form over the tropical Atlantic Ocean. For tracking purposes, each one is given a name, which alternates between male and female. The two satellite images on these pages are of Hurricane Katrina in August 2005.

Key

9   average number of tropical storms per year

   sea temperature over 27 °C

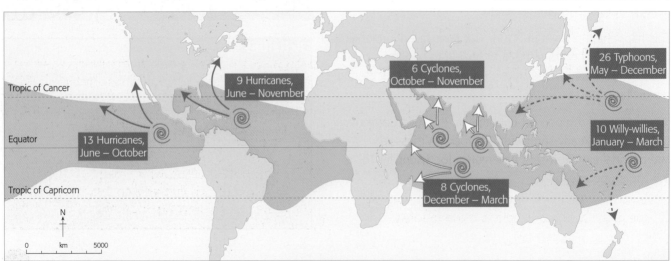

Primary effects

◆ The strong winds can cause the destruction of homes, businesses, transport, power, and communication lines. The severity of destruction depends on the strength of the wind and the strength of the buildings.

◆ Most deaths from hurricanes – up to 90% – are caused by drowning, either due to the torrential rains or the storm surge. The surge occurs as the strong winds push great volumes of sea-water on to the coastline.

◆ Associated primary effects also include localised tornadoes, widespread flooding as rivers burst their banks, and landslides as hill-slope soils become saturated. Hundreds of lives were lost in Mexico in 2005 when a weak hurricane drenched some areas, causing many landslides.

Prediction can save lives

Rich MEDC nations, such as the USA, can invest in technology. This means they can usually predict the general area where the hurricane will strike. However, predicting its exact strength and location of landfall remains difficult.

◆ In Miami, Florida, there's the National Hurricane Centre. Here meteorologists process information from a number of sources, providing predictions and warnings to US states and surrounding countries.

◆ Advances in satellite technology have helped prediction. Both visible and infra-red images reveal information about the intensity and size of approaching hurricanes.

◆ 'Hurricane hunters' are trained pilots who fly into the storm to collect data about air pressure and wind speed and direction.

◆ Improved prediction allows authorities to give out evacuation warnings, using the media. If necessary, the police will force people to move to safety.

Flow of dry air diverging from the upper atmosphere keeps the **eye** calm and free of clouds.

Direction of movement.

Warm air rises through convection, producing thick cloud.

Bands of torrential rain.

Water at more than 27 °C provides energy.

Anticlockwise surface flow creates spirals of clouds due to the rotation of the Earth.

Typical hurricane size/speed
Whole hurricane – 240-320 km across
Eye – 16-48 km across
Height – may exceed 13 km
Speed – 16-24 km/h

How hurricanes are measured: The Saffir-Simpson Scale

Scale	Damage	Wind speed	Storm surge
1	minimal	74-95 mph	1-2 metres
2	moderate	96-110 mph	2-3 metres
3	extensive	111-130 mph	3-4 metres
4	extreme	131-155 mph	4-6 metres
5	catastrophic	>155 mph	> 6 metres

Activities

1 Look at the satellite image above. Draw a simple sketch of a hurricane cross-section, with labels to describe its main features.

2 a How do you think LEDCs are able to predict and warn their people about approaching storms?

  b To what extent is interdependency between nations important with hurricane prediction?

The hurricane season of 2005

In this unit you'll learn about the effects of two particular hurricanes.

The busiest and costliest hurricane season on record

We're not sure why 2005 saw some of the most intense tropical storms ever. Some scientists think the effects of global warming are beginning to be felt and that warmer seas will fuel stronger storms. If hurricanes are going to be more frequent and more powerful, the Caribbean islands and Gulf Coast areas of Mexico and the USA face a tough future.

The devastating hurricanes of 2005: Dennis, Emily, Katrina, Rita, Stan, and Wilma.

Katrina, August 2005

Much of the US coastline from Louisiana to Alabama was devastated by Hurricane Katrina. It arrived as a category 4 storm with winds of over 140 mph and storm surges of over 6 metres.

New Orleans is built on low-lying land, mostly below sea level. It's surrounded by water. Engineers have protected the city from storm surges of up to category 3 strength (3-4 metres) by a system of levees, or concrete sea walls. But, when Katrina hit, the surges were too powerful and the levees broke. Large parts of the city were flooded.

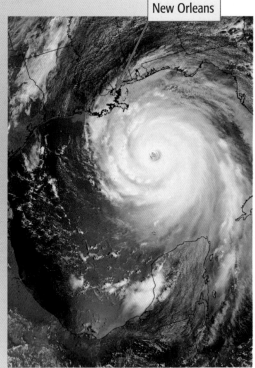
New Orleans

- The National Hurricane Centre predicted accurately where Katrina would make landfall and how strong it would be.
- The mayor of New Orleans ordered people to evacuate. 80% of the city's population escaped to safety, but 20% remained.
- It was mainly the poorer people with no transport of their own who stayed.
- Over 10 000 people sought refuge in the Superdome football stadium. But conditions deteriorated rapidly – there wasn't enough food and water, and the toilet facilities couldn't cope. The atmosphere was described as very tense and unsafe.
- Almost 1200 people drowned in flood-waters as over two-thirds of the city became submerged.
- 1 million people were made homeless, temporarily displaced across the rest of the USA.
- There was looting – not all of it for survival essentials such as food and clean water.
- Katrina also had a global impact. Many offshore oil facilities were damaged, and supplies of oil for fuel were reduced. The price of petrol in the USA and the UK rose considerably as a result.

Katrina was one of the most damaging hurricanes to hit an MEDC.

The US Federal Emergency Management Administration (FEMA) was criticised for a slow response to the unfolding devastation. Eventually, evacuation of survivors was completed by air and coach. 30 000 National Guardsmen were sent in to maintain law and order. The government released $50 billion initially for the rescue and recovery programme. The UK government sent 1 million army ready-meals to help. New Orleans will take years to recover.

◀ *Catherine McZeal and Louis Jones head for the Superdome and safety, days after Katrina flooded New Orleans.*

Key
- Hurricane Katrina
- Hurricane Wilma

Wilma, October 2005

The tourism hotspot of Cancun in Mexico and the southern parts of Florida in the USA were hit by Wilma, another category 4 storm.

- Wilma caused 30 deaths – fewer than Katrina, mainly because the storm surges were not as strong, but also because more people heeded the warning to evacuate or to 'hunker down' in a secure building.
- Hotels and thousands of poorly built homes were destroyed around Cancun.
- Over 10 000 British tourists were stranded, without access to clean water and electricity.
- Storm-damaged shops were looted.
- A military command centre was set up to stop the looting and help the tourists.
- One popular resort called Maya Riviera suffered damage of $1.5 billion. Mexico's $11 billion tourism industry was severely dented.

After regaining strength crossing the Gulf of Mexico, Florida was next in Wilma's path. It made landfall here as a category 3 storm. One resident described its arrival as like 'a freight train driven by the devil'.

- The storm brought down trees and power lines, peeled roofs off houses, and broke water pipes.
- 6 million people were left without electricity.
- Florida was declared a major disaster area. The US government again released money for repairs and reconstruction.

Activities

1 Assess why so many people choose to live along hurricane-prone coastlines, knowing the risks these storms present.
2 Why is it important that national authorities ensure the safety of tourists in the event of a hurricane strike? What would happen if they were not looked after?
3 Produce an information chart highlighting the key facts, causes, effects of, and responses to hurricanes Katrina and Wilma. Try to sort the information into:
   - economic, social, and environmental effects
   - individual, regional, national, and international responses.

Climate change

In this unit you'll learn about the issue of climate change

The big issue

Is global climate changing? If so, how quickly? What effects will it have?

A small rise in global temperature of just a degree or two could have a big impact. Already the Arctic ice seems to be melting. People and animals living there are already being affected. Some scientists predict more droughts, more floods, and more extreme weather events such as hurricanes.

What is climate change?

Over very long periods of time the Earth's climate has naturally changed. But now scientists think the natural cycles of change have been overtaken by rapid global warming. **Global warming** is the rise in temperature of the Earth's atmosphere.

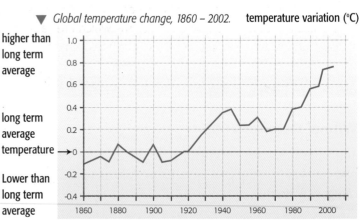

▼ *Global temperature change, 1860 – 2002.* **temperature variation (°C)**

What's causing it?

The scientific principle behind global warming is the **greenhouse effect**. This is an essential process – without it the Earth would be too cold for life.

But human activity is putting more of the greenhouse gases such as carbon dioxide (CO_2) and methane into the atmosphere. These activities include:

◆ burning coal and petrol (fossil fuels) for industry and transport – particularly car and air transport
◆ cutting down of rainforests and other forests
◆ farming – animal waste produces methane.

Most scientists agree that increasing greenhouse gases will cause a rise in the Earth's temperature. But it's difficult to assess how quickly this will happen and how it will impact the planet.

▼ The natural greenhouse effect and how it alters with increased CO_2.

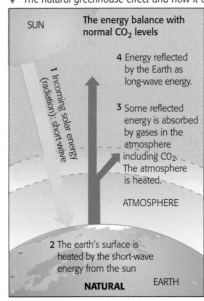

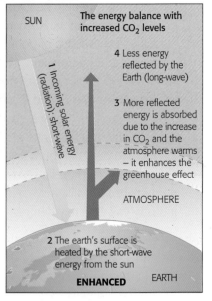

▼ *The big emitters.*

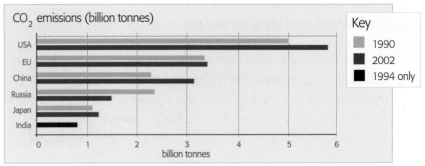

So what could happen?

If the Earth gets hotter, there could be big changes:

◆ Water expands when it's heated, so sea levels would rise.
◆ Sea levels would also rise due to the melting of the ice caps and glaciers.
◆ Cities on coasts would flood.
◆ Places that now get lots of rain and snow might get hotter and drier.
◆ Lakes and rivers could dry up.
◆ There would be more droughts, making it harder to grow crops.
◆ Less water would be available for drinking, showers, and sanitation.
◆ Some plants and animals might become extinct because of the heat.
◆ Hurricanes, tornadoes and other storms which are caused by changes in heat and water evaporation may get more common.

Did you know?
The concentration of CO_2 in the atmosphere has increased by more than 30% since 1800.

Did you know?
Computer models predict that if nothing is done the world will be warmer by 1.4-5.8 °C by 2100.

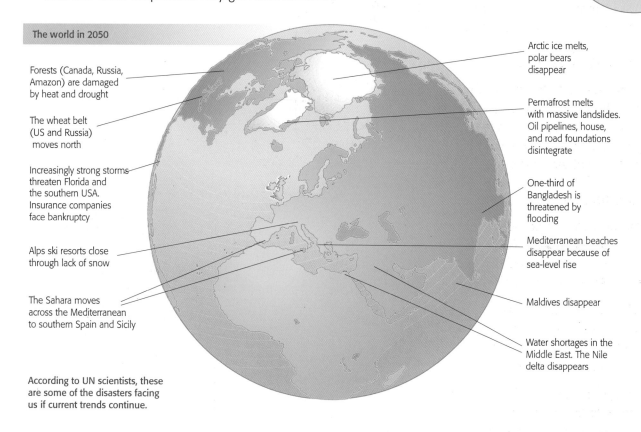

The world in 2050

Forests (Canada, Russia, Amazon) are damaged by heat and drought

The wheat belt (US and Russia) moves north

Increasingly strong storms threaten Florida and the southern USA. Insurance companies face bankruptcy

Alps ski resorts close through lack of snow

The Sahara moves across the Mediterranean to southern Spain and Sicily

Arctic ice melts, polar bears disappear

Permafrost melts with massive landslides. Oil pipelines, house, and road foundations disintegrate

One-third of Bangladesh is threatened by flooding

Mediterranean beaches disappear because of sea-level rise

Maldives disappear

Water shortages in the Middle East. The Nile delta disappears

According to UN scientists, these are some of the disasters facing us if current trends continue.

What are we doing about it?

◆ An international agreement called the Kyoto Protocol commits MEDCs to reducing greenhouse gas emissions to 5% below 1990 levels. This was agreed in 1997 and came into effect in 2005. The USA, the largest producer of greenhouse gases, has pulled out.
◆ People are trying to develop alternative sources of energy such as wind power, solar power, and hydroelectricity.
◆ Countries are investing in technology that will help us use less fuel – this means more efficient car engines, more efficient heating systems, and so on.
◆ Countries are trying to cut the use of cars by investing in public transport.
◆ We're trying to slow the rate of deforestation in regions such as the Amazon rainforest – sustainable practices are being encouraged.

Activities

1 Explain the process of global warming.
2 Is there sufficient evidence to state that climate is changing?
3 Produce a diagram or table to show the impact of global warming on both MEDCs and LEDCs.
4 What can individual people do to reduce greenhouse gases?

Ecosystems

The big picture

This chapter is about ecosystems – living things and their non-living environment. These are the big ideas behind the chapter:

◆ The world can be divided into eight big ecosystems, or biomes.

◆ Climate is the main factor affecting the distribution of ecosystems.

◆ The vegetation in different ecosystems has adapted to the climate and soil.

◆ We humans use different ecosystems in different ways, and have caused a lot of damage.

◆ We are learning to use and manage ecosystems in a sustainable way.

Your goals for this chapter

By the end of this chapter you should be able to answer these questions:

◆ How do ecosystems work?

◆ What affects the distribution of ecosystems?

◆ What do these terms mean?
ecosystem, producer, consumer, decomposer, food chain, food web , biome, deforestation, desertification, afforestation, sustainable management

◆ Where can you find tropical rainforests, savannna grasslands and coniferous forests, and what types of climate and soils do they have?

◆ How have the plants adapted to the climate and soils in tropical rainforests, savanna grasslands and coniferous forests?

◆ Why have people cleared the Amazon rainforest?

◆ What examples can you give of sustainable management strategies in the Amazon rainforest?

◆ What has caused desertification in the Sahel?

◆ Can you give four examples of sustainable land management in the Sahel?

◆ How is the coniferous forest used in Norway?

◆ What methods are used in sustainable forests?

And then . . .

When you finish the chapter, come back here and see if you've met your goals!

Did you know?
The dodo, a metre-high flightless bird, was discovered on the island of Mauritius in 1598 – killed mainly by animals introduced to the island by people, it was extinct by 1693.

Did you know?
◆ 103 species are known to have become extinct in the last 200 years.
◆ Today, over 1100 mammals, 1200 birds, and 800 fish are threatened with extinction.

Did you know?
Since 1950, nearly half the world's original forest cover has been lost.

Did you know?
Rainforest trees are called hardwoods. The valuable species are mahogany, rosewood, and teak.

Your chapter starter

Look at the photo on page 128.
What are the bears doing?
What's the fish doing?
Do you have any idea what type of fish it is?
Where do you think this is?

It was THIS big! Honest!

Introducing ecosystems

In this unit you will learn what an ecosystem is, how the things in it are linked to each other – and how we humans fit in.

What's an ecosystem?

An ecosystem is a unit made up of two parts:

◆ living things (plants, animals, bacteria)
◆ and their non-living surroundings or **environment** – air, water, soil, and the climate.

In any ecosystem, the living things interact with the environment and each other. For example, caterpillars in a wood breathe the air, feed on leaves, and get eaten by birds. If it gets too cold, they die.

How big is an ecosystem?

An ecosystem is any size you choose to study. It could be a pond, a field, a wood, the tropical rainforest, or even the whole Earth.

How does an ecosystem work?

An ecosystem is a bit like a canteen where living things eat. Every ecosystem works in the same way:

◆ The plants use sunlight, water, and nutrients from the soil to produce their own food. (So they are called **producers**.)
◆ The animals feed on the plants, or each other. (So they're called **consumers**.)
◆ Fungi and bacteria feed on dead and waste material, and make things break down or rot. (So they're called **decomposers**.) They recycle nutrients that the plants can use again.
◆ Without plants, all other living things would die.

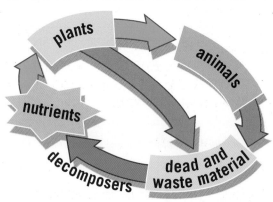

▲ How living things are linked in an ecosystem.

Food chains and food webs

Below is a **food chain**. It shows what eats what. The arrow means *eaten by*.

plant ➤ caterpillar ➤ wood mouse ➤ fox

Food chains always start with plants. You can draw them for any ecosystem.

Often several consumers eat the same food. For example, in an oak wood, both caterpillars and aphids (a type of fly) feed on oak leaves.

So food chains link to form a **food web**. The diagram on the right shows just part of the food web for an oak wood.

The complete food web for a wood (or any ecosystem) can be large and complex.

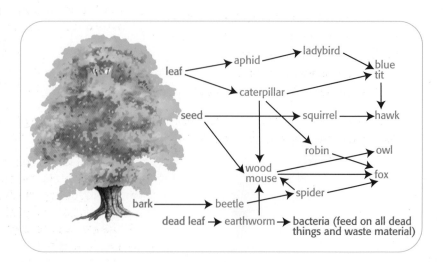

How we humans fit in

Unlike most animals, we've spread all over the world.

- We have moved into every ecosystem (although some climates don't suit us too well).
- Our numbers have grown quickly. Now there are over 6.4 billion of us.
- We consume a lot. Over 40% of the plants now growing on the Earth will be consumed by us and our livestock (our cows, sheep …).
- We use a lot of land. Not just to live on, but to grow food, and provide water and fuels, and dump waste, and so on. Experts say we each 'use' 2 hectares of land (about 1.5 football pitches) in our lifetime. This is called our **ecological footprint**.

There are problems with this

- The more land we use up, the less there is for the Earth's other 6 million species.
- As we've spread through ecosystems, we've tended to take them over – and drive many other species to extinction.
- In places, we've treated the soil so badly that we've ruined it.
- We burn a lot of fossil fuels, and now we think this is causing global warming. That will affect every ecosystem on the Earth.

We can change

We need food, fuel, water, and houses.

But we're learning that we must get them in a **sustainable** way. This means in a way that doesn't harm us, or other species, and isn't wasteful.

Later units in this chapter look at three big ecosystems in detail:

- the tropical rainforests
- the savanna grasslands
- the coniferous (or boreal) forests.

You will learn how we've used them and damaged them – and how some damage is being repaired.

Did you know?
Rhinos are killed for their horns. The horn fetches high prices as a traditional medicine in the Far East

Did you know?
On average, 130 species of plants and animals become extinct each day.

▲ *The endangered black rhinoceros.*

Activities

1 Write your own simple definitions for these terms
   a ecosystem
   b food chain
   c food web
   d ecological footprint

2 Write out and complete this paragraph by filling in the gaps.

   Every _____ works in the same way. The _____ use sunlight, water, and nutrients from the soil to produce their own food. They're called _____. The animals feed on the plants, or each other. They're called _____. Fungi and bacteria feed on dead and waste material, and make things break down or rot. They're called _____. Without plants, all other living things would _____.

3 Look at the food web opposite, and write out two food chains.

4 Explain why you think we study ecosystems in geography.

5 Think about the information in this unit. Will it affect how you think about the world around you? Explain your answer.

6 The greatest pest ever known. Is this a fair description of humans? Justify your answer.

The global distribution of ecosystems

In this unit you'll find out about the location of the world's main ecosystems, and learn why they're so different.

The 8 big ones

The world can be divided up into eight big ecosystems, or **biomes**. Each one has its own type of vegetation. Individual biomes are mainly determined by climate. This is because climate affects the growth conditions for vegetation. It does this in a number of ways:

◆ precipitation – particularly the total amount and how it's distributed through the year

◆ temperature – especially the seasonal pattern and the length of the growing season

◆ the number of sunshine hours – which determines the amount of light for photosynthesis

◆ rates of evaporation, transpiration, and humidity.

Other factors such as geology (rock type), soils, relief, and the drainage of water are also important.

The map on the right shows the distribution of the world's biomes.

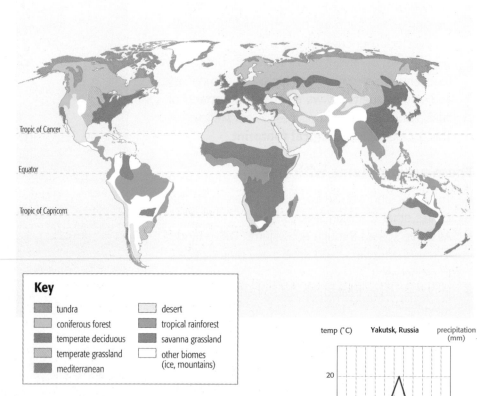

Key

- tundra
- coniferous forest
- temperate deciduous
- temperate grassland
- mediterranean
- desert
- tropical rainforest
- savanna grassland
- other biomes (ice, mountains)

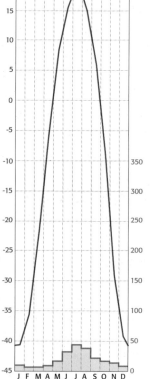

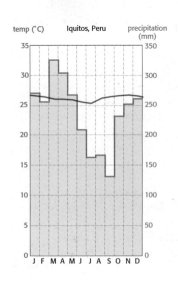

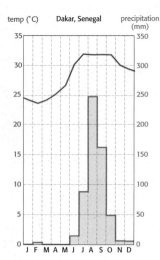

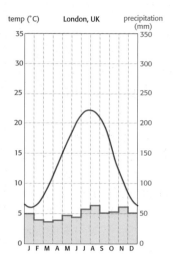

Explaining the global distribution

Temperature

Temperatures around the world vary according to latitude. This is because the Earth has a curved surface and is tilted (at an angle of 23.5°), which means places near the equator are much warmer than places near the poles.

Look at the diagram on the right. At the equator, the sun's heat is concentrated over a small area as the energy falls directly on to the Earth's surface. It is called the overhead sun.

At higher latitudes, the curvature of the Earth means the sun's energy is spread over a wider area. As a result, temperatures are much cooler.

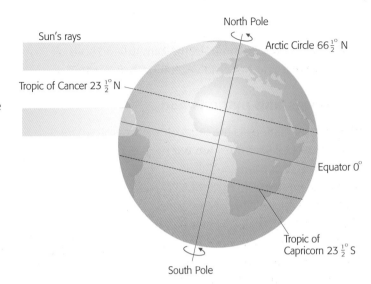

Precipitation

Explaining the variation in precipitation around the world is harder. The amount of rain or snow that falls is mainly controlled by **atmospheric pressure**. Air pressure can be either high or low. The general rule is that:

◆ high pressure brings dry and settled conditions
◆ low pressure brings cloudy and wet conditions.

At the equator, the strong sun heats the ground very intensely and causes warm moist air to rise. As it cools, giant cumulonimbus clouds form by **convection** to produce heavy rain. As the air is rising, the air pressure is **low**. However, the warm air is also rising because two prevailing trade winds collide at the equator in a region known as the **Inter-Tropical Convergence Zone (ITCZ)**.

So the ITCZ is a band of wet-weather conditions linked to low air pressure. It runs right round the globe. In January, the ITCZ is more or less over the equatorial regions – where the rainforests are located (see right).

At 30° north and south, air falls back towards the ground. As it reaches the ground it warms up. It creates a zone of **high** atmospheric pressure. These are therefore dry regions – the world's hot deserts are found at these latitudes.

Between the equator and the hot deserts lie the savanna grasslands. They have two seasons each year – a wet rainy season and a drought season. These seasons are caused by the annual northward movement of the ITCZ in the summer. So, for example, the savanna in northern Africa has a rainy season in the northern hemisphere summer.

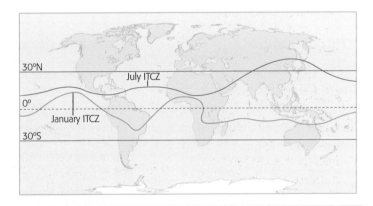

Activities

1 a Each of the climate graphs opposite shows the typical climate features for one of the biomes shown on the map. Using an atlas, find the location of each climate graph station.

b Using the map, match each climate graph with its global ecosystem or biome.

c Use the climate graphs to describe the general climate features of the four biomes you have now identified.

2 Define the following terms:
precipitation   atmospheric pressure
latitude   Inter-Tropical Convergence Zone

3 Design a fully annotated cross-section diagram to show the movement of air between the equator and 30° latitude to explain why the equator is hot and wet and the deserts warm and dry. You must include:
◆ a latitude line
◆ rising air at the equator
◆ sinking air at 30° latitude
◆ the location of the tropical rainforests, hot deserts, and savanna grasslands

4 In your own words, explain why the savanna biome experiences both a wet and a dry season each year.

Tropical rainforests

In this unit you'll learn about the climate and soils of the rainforest and how the vegetation has adapted.

Tree frogs and pythons and ...

The tropical rainforests are found in the tropics, where it's hot and wet all year. They are our most ecologically bio-diverse ecosystem.

- They are home to 50% of all life-forms on the planet.
- They produce 40% of the world's oxygen.
- The vegetation is luxurious and dense, and trees can grow to over 50 metres in height.

The tropical rainforests now cover less than 6% of the Earth's surface. 200 years ago they covered twice as much.

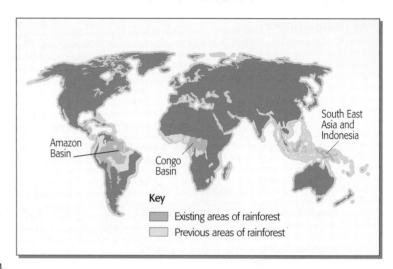

Amazon Basin

Congo Basin

South East Asia and Indonesia

Key

◼ Existing areas of rainforest
◻ Previous areas of rainforest

Climate control

Daily rhythm

There are no real seasons in the rainforest. Each day is similar to the next. But there is a daily pattern to the weather:

8.00 a.m. – dry with intense heat from the sun
12.00 noon – high temperatures, up to 33 °C, and the formation of cumulus clouds
6.00 p.m. – thick cumulonimbus clouds, thunderstorms, and torrential downpours of rain.

Temperature

The average daily temperature is usually about 28 °C. Only occasionally does it go above 35 °C. It never goes below 20 °C. The temperature range may be as little as 2 °C.

Precipitation

Typically, 2000 mm of rain falls per year – but it can be more. The atmosphere is sticky – it's hot and humid.

Soils and the nutrient cycle

The lush appearance of the rainforest is very deceptive. It suggests deep fertile soils. But in fact the fertile part of the soil is at the surface and is relatively thin. Much of the deep soils are iron-rich **laterites**, and these are not good for vegetation growth. So, the rainforest ecosystem is very fragile.

80% of the nutrients available in the forest come from the vegetation itself. Plant matter falls to the ground throughout the year and decomposes quickly in the hot and wet climate. The nutrients are freed up, ready to be recycled back into the forest. This naturally sustainable cycle is shown in this diagram.

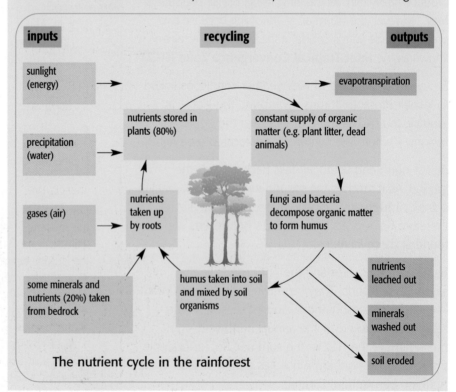

| inputs | recycling | outputs |

sunlight (energy)

evapotranspiration

nutrients stored in plants (80%)

constant supply of organic matter (e.g. plant litter, dead animals)

precipitation (water)

nutrients taken up by roots

fungi and bacteria decompose organic matter to form humus

gases (air)

nutrients leached out

some minerals and nutrients (20%) taken from bedrock

humus taken into soil and mixed by soil organisms

minerals washed out

soil eroded

The nutrient cycle in the rainforest

Explaining the rainforest structure

The way the rainforest is divided into four distinct layers is all due to the availability of light, which all plants need for the process of photosynthesis.

The **emergent trees** and those in the **canopy** receive most of the light and therefore grow tall.

Below the canopy, competition for sunlight is fierce. Trees in the **under-canopy** are shorter, as they are in the shade, but they are waiting for their chance to take advantage of the next light space to become available.

Only 1% of sunlight reaches the forest floor, so growth in the shrub layer is more limited.

Special plants

This is how the vegetation has adapted to the climate:

- Trees are branchless and the trunks are tall and thin – this helps them to reach the light from the sun more easily. (**A**)
- Trees are evergreen – this helps them take advantage of the continuous growing season. They can shed their leaves at any time of year.
- Leaves often have **drip tips** – this helps them to shed the heavy rain. They can also be waxy – this helps shed the rain, and also helps protect them from hungry insects. (**B**)
- Some trees have large **buttress roots** – these support them in the shallow soil. Others spread their roots over the surface – this helps them capture as many of the available nutrients as possible. (**C**)
- **Lianas** are woody climbing vines which drape the rainforest. They climb high into the canopy to reach the sunlight, dropping their roots down to the ground. (**A**)
- **Epiphytes** are plants that grow in the branches of trees – they use the tree for support, not for food. (**D**)

The canopy is the thickest layer, and is where most animals and insects live.

Activities

1 Look back at Unit 7.2, and explain why the rainforest ecosystem receives a lot of rainfall. Use your knowledge to explain why the temperatures remain constantly high.
2 Explain some of the connections between the adaptations of vegetation and the rainforest climate and soils.
3 Compare and contrast the tropical rainforest with one other global natural ecosystem you have studied.

Human impact in the tropical rainforest

In this unit you'll learn how people are clearing the Amazon rainforest – and how they're trying to preserve it.

Chainsaws and fires

For millions of years the rainforests were undisturbed. Small tribes of people lived there, but they were too few in number to alter the ecosystem.

But **deforestation** – the felling of trees – is now taking place very quickly. The world's rainforests may be all gone by 2030. It's claimed that in the Amazon 2.5 hectares of forest are cleared each minute. That's the equivalent of five football pitches. Let's look at the reasons for this intense human activity.

Did you know?
- Quinine, a drug to help malaria sufferers, was developed from rainforest plants.
- Scientists think useful new drugs could be developed from other rainforest plants.

Economic exploitation

Mining
The Amazon rainforest has developed above a rich base of mineral resources. The most abundant of these is iron ore (haematite). It's exported to countries for steel making. Other metal ores include gold, platinum, copper, lead, and bauxite for aluminium. Vast areas have been cleared to gain access to these reserves. The Carajas Project near to Manaus (see the photo) is the largest open-cast mine of its type.

Logging
There's great demand for tropical hardwoods such as mahogany and rosewood. Consumers in MEDCs find these deep red woods attractive, and pay high prices for furniture and interior fittings made from them. But random logging means that for every tree cut down, at least 30 more may be destroyed in the process. Five million hectares of forest are lost in the Amazon each year as a result.

Cattle ranching
Large areas have been cleared for cattle. Since 1950, two-thirds of the Amazon's lowland forest has been turned into pasture for grazing and the production of beef. Zeebu cattle are reared, as they are best adapted to the humid conditions. But the quality of the grass soon declines as the nutrients are lost from the soil. Many ranches have simply increased in size because of this.

Peasant farming
Since the 1970s, the Brazilian government, concerned about overcrowded cities in the south of the country, has encouraged landless citizens to move to the rainforest, giving them land to clear for subsistence farming. This hasn't been very successful due to the infertile soils – without the forest canopy, there's nothing to replenish the soil with nutrients.

Do rainforests naturally regenerate?

They will, if only small areas are cleared and then left alone. But large-scale deforestation breaks the natural nutrient cycle that has evolved, described in Unit 7.3. As the land is cleared, the soil becomes vulnerable to erosion and the nutrients get washed away by the rains. New tree shoots are unable to establish themselves and the landscape becomes barren. The ecosystem dies (see the photo on the right). Tribal communities lose their way of life. And the global oxygen and carbon dioxide balance changes, contributing to global warming.

Sustainable management

The exploitation of the Amazon's natural resources can help Brazil boost its GDP and improve the quality of life of its population. Activities like logging and mining need to continue. But if they happen in an uncontrolled way, irreversible damage could be done to the rainforest. So, sustainable forest management is required. This means meeting the needs of the present without harming the environment, and so allowing future generations the opportunity to meet their needs.

The state of Acre on the western tip of the rainforest is one area where sustainable approaches are proving successful. These long-term policies are underpinned by three aims:

- to protect the forest canopy and bio-diversity, preventing soil erosion
- to maintain the operation of the nutrient cycle
- to ensure the natural regeneration of the forest.

Activities

1 Describe and add to the range of human activities responsible for the rapid deforestation of the Amazon rainforest.

2 Prioritise three of the sustainable approaches shown in the spider diagram. Why have you selected these as the most important strategies?

3 Find out what 'slash and burn' farming is. In your opinion, is this sustainable practice? Justify your thinking.

4 What problems might be caused by sustainable management strategies? What would you advise the Brazilian government to do about these problems?

Agro-forestry
This is the practice of growing trees in combination with agricultural crops. This means farmers can take advantage of the protective canopy and the supply of nutrients from decomposing plant matter.

Forest Reserves
These are areas of forest that are completely protected from all activities, in a similar way to U.S. Wilderness Areas. They are often close to areas known as extractive reserves, which are dedicated to sustainable products, such as plants for medicines and latex from rubber tapping.

Tree measuring
The felling of a tree should only occur once it has reached a specific height. This ensures that younger trees have a chance of survival.

Sustainable management strategies

Afforestation
This is the planting of new trees once mature trees have been felled. This ensures the canopy is maintained.

Selective logging
Individual trees are felled only when they have matured. This helps preserve the existing canopy, and helps the slower growing hardwoods such as mahogany.

Education
A key component of any successful forest management strategy is to enable those who use the forest to become the stewards of the forest, protecting its future.

Savanna grasslands

Key
savanna grasslands

In this unit you'll learn about the climate and soils of the savanna and how the vegetation has adapted.

The long grass

In tropical parts of the world where the climate alternates between a long wet season and a long dry season, grasses tend to dominate the landscape. There's just a scattering of trees.

The savanna grasslands are generally found between 5° and 15° latitude, both north and south of the equator. This belt of grassland is squeezed between the tropical rainforests and the deserts. Savanna grassland is found in Venezuela and north-eastern parts of Brazil in South America, northern Australia, and across Africa between the equator and the Sahara Desert.

The diagram shows a transect across the savanna.

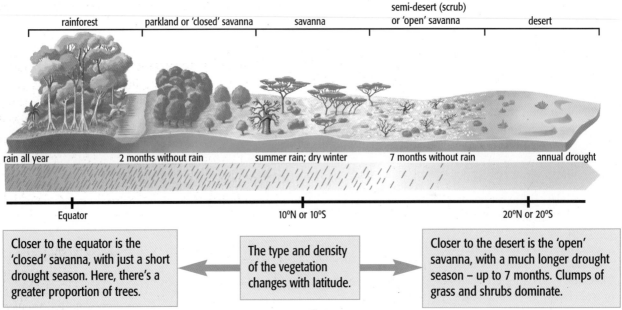

| rainforest | parkland or 'closed' savanna | savanna | semi-desert (scrub) or 'open' savanna | desert |

rain all year | 2 months without rain | summer rain; dry winter | 7 months without rain | annual drought

Equator | 10°N or 10°S | 20°N or 20°S

Closer to the equator is the 'closed' savanna, with just a short drought season. Here, there's a greater proportion of trees.

The type and density of the vegetation changes with latitude.

Closer to the desert is the 'open' savanna, with a much longer drought season – up to 7 months. Clumps of grass and shrubs dominate.

Climate control

The savanna climate has alternating wet and dry seasons.

Wet season
In the northern hemisphere, the rainy season is between May and October. 90% of the annual rainfall can fall during this period, often in heavy downpours. August can receive as much as 240 mm. Temperatures are around 25°C.

Dry season
In the northern hemisphere, the dry season is from November to April. There's little if any rain during this time. Temperatures can be over 30°C. This creates a harsh environment for plants and animals.

Wind direction
Moderately strong trade winds blow across the savanna grasslands. In the northern hemisphere they blow from a north-easterly direction. They meet the south-easterly trades at the ITCZ. The movements of the ITCZ determine the Savanna rainfall.

Soil conditions

Savanna soils tend to be very **porous**. This means water drains easily and quickly through them.

The nutrients available to plants are mainly found in a thin layer on the surface, where vegetation has decomposed from the previous year.

Special plants

Savanna plants have developed special ways of surviving the long dry season. They have **xerophytic** features – which make them drought-resistant. Different species have developed ways of both storing and preserving their moisture supplies – which is vital when there's no rain and temperatures are high. Let's look at how three savanna species have adapted:

> **Did you know?**
> The word savanna comes from Spanish and literally means grassland.

> **Did you know?**
> A 'xerophyte' is a plant that can grow in arid (dry) conditions.

Elephant grass

Activities

1. Describe the environmental problems that savanna vegetation has to adapt to.
2. Draw a mind map to explain how savanna vegetation adapts to the wet and dry seasons. Make reference to specific named species. Make links to the problems you identified in question 1.

As its name suggests, this type of grass grows very tall – anything from 3 to 5 metres in height. The individual blades of grass curve away from the strong sunlight to preserve moisture. At the end of the wet season the grass turns yellow and dies back, putting nutrients back into the soil. The seeds lie dormant on the surface ready to grow immediately when the next rains arrive, as here.

Acacia tree

With its flat top or crown, the acacia is a very recognisable savanna tree. It can grow up to 20 metres in height. It has a very long tap-root – up to 35 metres – reaching down to the underground water supplies. It has small waxy leaves and thorns to help reduce the loss of water through **transpiration**.

Baobab tree

This giant of a tree can grow up to 25 metres tall and an incredible 10 metres wide. It is sometimes called the 'upside-down tree' because the trunk can be wider than the crown. Water is stored in the trunk during the drought, protected by a very thick bark. Like the acacia tree, small waxy leaves and thorns reduce the loss of water through transpiration.

Human impact in the savanna grasslands

In this unit you'll learn how people are affecting the savanna grasslands – and how they're trying to preserve them.

The Sahel

- ◆ The savanna covers almost half of Africa - about 5 million square miles.
- ◆ The Sahel is a strip to the south of the Sahara Desert.
- ◆ It's under intense pressure from human activities. Some geographers say that most of the natural savanna vegetation has been all but destroyed.
- ◆ In places the quality of the land is declining so much that it's turning to desert. This process of land degradation is called **desertification**.
- ◆ The countries of the Sahel are all LEDCs, with rapidly growing populations.

Tropic of Cancer

Equator

Tropic of Capricorn

Key

☐ The Sahel

∴∴ Areas with a high risk of desertification

Human activity

Fire
Some fires are started by lightning strikes, but many are started deliberately – the ash makes the soil more fertile. The problem is that they can get out of control.

Hunting
People hunt for food – especially species such as zebra and wildebeest.

Agriculture
More and more land is being used for growing crops and grazing cattle and goats.

Deforestation
Population growth has resulted in increased demand for wood – it's used for cooking and heating. So trees are cut down.

Tourism
Tourists come to see the wildlife – especially animals like lions, cheetahs, giraffes, and rhinos.

Desertification

Desertification takes place when human and climatic processes combine to reduce the ability of the land to support vegetation.

Land that was once fertile enough for farming starts to suffer soil erosion and eventually turns to desert. In the Sahel, prolonged drought and human activity has resulted in millions of hectares of land being lost to the desert each year. This can contribute to major human disasters such as the 2005 famine in Niger. The rains failed, making the land unable to support crops. Nearly 4 million people were affected by starvation. A massive international aid effort sent emergency food supplies to the country.

Did you know?
The word 'Sahel' literally means 'shore of the sea of sand'.

The causes of desertification

Overcultivation

Population growth has put pressure on the farmland to produce more and more food. This more intensive use of the land exhausts it of nutrients – which means crops can no longer grow and soil is lost through wind and water erosion.

Overgrazing

Permanent and nomadic pastoral farmers are having to let their livestock graze on marginal land closer to the desert. Once the protective vegetation cover is eaten away, the soil becomes vulnerable to erosion.

Deforestation

Across the Sahel, 80% of domestic energy comes from burning firewood. Increased population means increased demand for wood, and so the land is cleared of trees. Again, the soil becomes vulnerable to erosion.

Climate change

The climate of the Sahel has become much drier over the last forty years. Less rainfall means poorer grazing and lower crop production. Underground water reserves have been used up. Population pressure makes the problem worse.

These causes combine to create a 'spiral into desertification' (see right).

Sustainable land management

There are examples in the Sahel of land management practices that benefit people and the savanna. These include:

◆ Tethering cattle and goats to limit the area they can graze. This has the added advantage of creating manure in one place that can then be spread as a fertiliser. Fodder (animal food) is taken to the animals.

◆ Farmers diversifying into a more varied range of crops and trees. This helps bind the soil together and prevents erosion. And the vegetation matter will then put a continual supply of nutrients back into the soil.

◆ Harvesting fuel-wood from branches – rather than taking the whole tree – is more sustainable as the branches will grow back. This prevents deforestation.

◆ Building stone walls on levelled pieces of land to trap soil and water when the rains arrive. This prevents erosion and can help increase crop production.

◆ Controlled burning of grasses to prevent the spread of devastating wildfires.

Measures like these can stop, and even reverse, the process of desertification.

▲ The advancing desert.

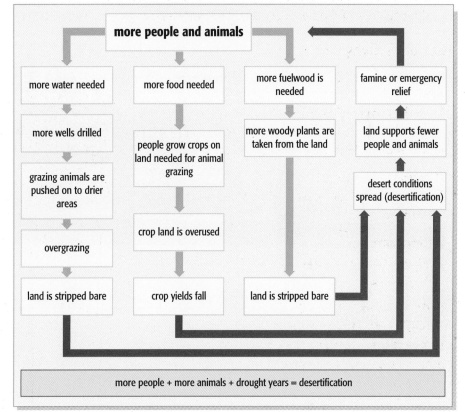

Activities

1 a Write a definition of the term 'desertification'.
 b State where it occurs in Africa.
2 Explain in your own words what is meant by the 'spiral into desertification'.
3 To what extent can desertification be called a problem of human creation?
4 Write down at least two ideas that would help stop the destruction of the savanna grasslands.

Coniferous forests

In this unit you'll learn about the climate and soils of the coniferous forests and how the vegetation has adapted.

Evergreen forests of the north

The coniferous forest is the world's largest forest biome. It's found between 50°N and 60°N. The trees have needles rather than leaves, and are usually evergreen as they keep their needles all year round. Instead of producing flowers or blossom as deciduous trees do, coniferous trees produce cones.

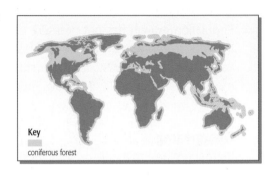

Key
coniferous forest

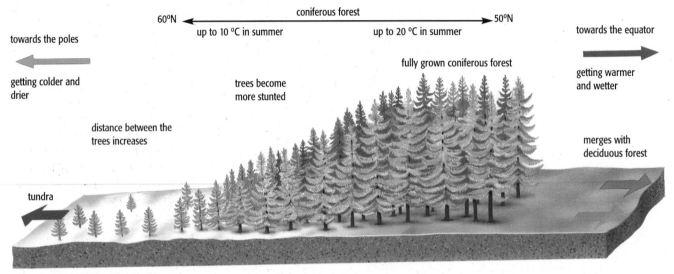

coniferous forest

60°N — up to 10 °C in summer — up to 20 °C in summer — 50°N

towards the poles

getting colder and drier

trees become more stunted

fully grown coniferous forest

towards the equator

getting warmer and wetter

distance between the trees increases

merges with deciduous forest

tundra

▲ *Changing vegetation with latitude.*

Climate control

Temperature

Long severe winters – temperatures can fall as low as -40 °C and are below 0 °C for at least six months of the year.

Short summers – temperatures can reach a maximum of 20 °C, but only four months of the year are totally free of frost.

This means coniferous forests have only a very short **growing season** (when temperatures are above 6 °C).

Precipitation

Annual precipitation is 300-900 mm. Much of this is heavy snowfall in the winter months.

Wind direction

A strong northerly wind from the Arctic adds to the already harsh conditions.

Soil conditions

Soils are usually thin, so the trees don't have deep roots. The most common soil type is called **podzol**, named after the Russian word for 'ash-grey' in colour. These are acidic soils, with few nutrients.

Did you know?

- Coniferous forests are also known as **boreal forests** or **taiga**.
- Taiga is the Russian word for the cold north wind that blows for much of the year.

How the trees have adapted

It's all about survival in the harsh climate.

The trees grow very close together, and this helps keep the trees warmer in winter.

The conical shape of the tree is very distinctive – and important. The sloping drooping branches are flexible and don't break under the weight of heavy snow. The conical shape also helps the tree to shed snow.

Thick bark protects the tree from the extreme cold.

Seeds are formed in a protective cone. This protects them from the winter cold. When summer comes the cone bursts open to release the seeds.

Needles remain on the tree all year round. As soon as temperatures are warm enough for growth, these needles start the process of photosynthesis immediately, without the lag time of waiting for new leaves to form.

The narrow surface of each individual needle helps prevent moisture loss through transpiration. This is vital in winter when roots can't get water because the ground is frozen. Furthermore, each needle has a hard waxy coating which provides a waterproof cuticle. This also reduces water loss through transpiration.

The dark colour of the needles helps the tree absorb heat from the sun more easily.

Activities

1 Provide a short, accurate description of the global distribution of coniferous forests.
2 Draw a sketch of a coniferous tree. Annotate your sketch with at least five of the adaptations which ensure the tree survives in the harsh climate and soil conditions. To fully annotate your diagram, don't forget to explain how the adaptations enable the trees to survive. Use the information from this unit to add detail to your notes.

Did you know?

Tree species
Coniferous trees are called **soft woods**. They grow to about 40 metres in height. The most common species are spruce, fir, and pine.

In this unit you'll learn how people are using the coniferous forests – and how they're trying to preserve them.

A change of attitude

Norway, Sweden, and Finland have a lot of coniferous forest. Until quite recently, the forests were seen as providing an endless supply of wood. Deforestation occurred without any real control and there wasn't much replanting of trees (**afforestation**). People thought the trees would simply grow back naturally.

But over the last twenty years, all the Scandinavian countries have realised there would be a shortage of trees in the future if things were allowed to continue.

So now they're controlling the forest industries and trying to protect the forests. The forests are no longer seen as an inexhaustible natural resource.

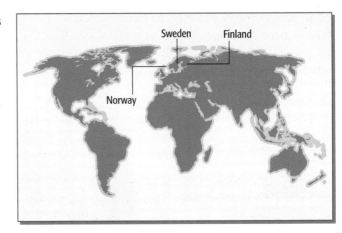

Did you know?
In Norway 37% of the landscape is covered by coniferous forest.

Did you know?
Norway, Sweden, and Finland together are often known as 'Scandinavia'.

Forestry in Norway

Timber

Norway has 225 saw-mills harvesting timber for domestic use and export, including to the UK. About half the timber felled in Norway is used in house-building and for doors, window frames, and furniture.

Leisure and recreation

Skiing in winter – both downhill and cross-country. Walking, camping, and other outdoor activities in summer.

Bio-energy

Although it provides only a very small proportion of Norway's energy needs, waste materials from the timber and pulp industries can be burnt as a source of fuel. The need for bio-fuel may increase in the future as we try to find alternatives to fossil fuels (coal, oil, and gas).

Pulp and paper

Wood fibres or pulp are used in the production of paper and card. Norway has 17 large pulp production centres, providing over 7 million tonnes of paper a year (see on the right).

Why preserve the forests?

The forests play a vital role in stabilising climate by absorbing carbon dioxide from the atmosphere. Increasing the amount of forested land should help limit the rate of global warming.

The forests help maintain **biodiversity** – they provide habitats for a range of animals, insects, and other plants.

Sustainable management

In order to get maximum economic benefit from the forests and to ensure their future protection, Norway and the other Scandinavian countries have adopted a **sustainable approach** to forest management. This means:

◆ meeting the needs of people now without compromising the ability of future generations to meet their own needs;
◆ limiting the harm done to the environment.

Sustainable Forest Status

All timber and pulp products must come from sustainable forests. Privately owned forests have to be certified to show that the principles and standards of sustainable management are being met and adhered to. These are some of the methods:

◆ The complete protection of environmentally sensitive areas or sites of special interest.
◆ Ensuring that replanting takes place – afforestation after deforestation (see the photo on the right).
◆ Allowing natural regeneration to take place.
◆ Ensuring that older trees aren't felled – this protects wildlife habitats. Complete clear cutting has been stopped.
◆ Education and training programmes are provided to forest owners to promote sustainable practices. These programmes have already reached over 100 000 foresters.
◆ Using all parts of felled trees to minimise wastage.

Sustainable forest management is proving successful. The area of coniferous forest in Norway has doubled over the last 100 years. Eco-friendly, sustainable forest management practices are widely used. Suppliers have to show that they have used sustainable practices. They can only do this through the certified forest system. Consumers increasingly expect products to have been made in an eco-friendly way. Labels often tell you if a product has been supplied from a sustainable forest.

Did you know?
This book is printed on paper produced from sustainable forests.

Using all of the tree

The smallest wood at the top of the tree is used to make chip-board.

The thinner part of the trunk is used for paper products.

The thicker trunk is sawn for timber.

The bark is used as bio-fuel or chippings for gardens.

Activities

1 Why are the coniferous forests important to both Norway and the world?
2 Write a short definition of the term 'sustainable forest management'.
3 Prioritise the top three methods of sustainable forest management in Norway, which you think are vital to secure the future of the coniferous forests.
4 Think of one more additional approach that could be taken to ensure forest protection.

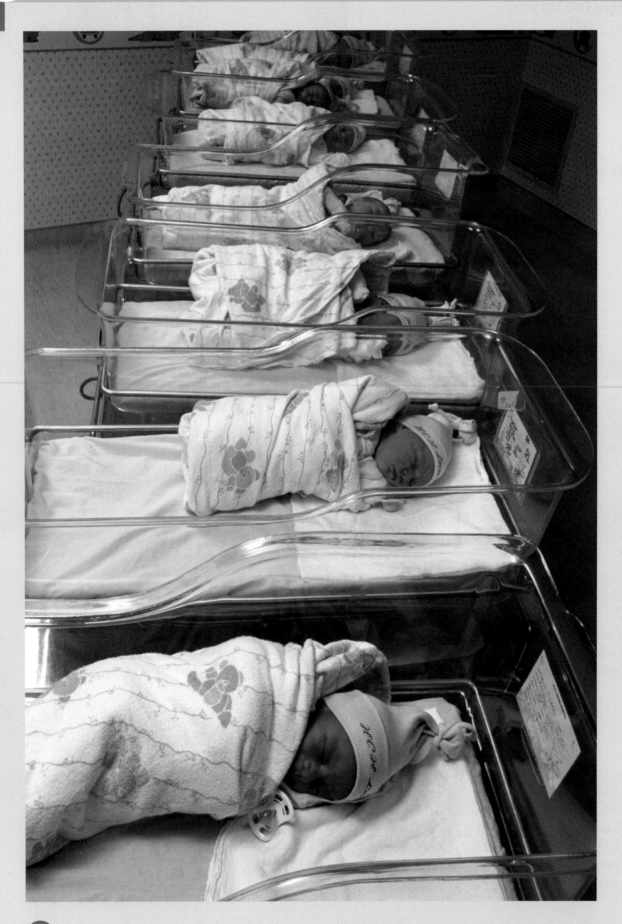

The big picture

This chapter is about people – all of us. These are the big ideas behind the chapter:

◆ There's a lot of people in the world – 6.5 billion and rising – but we're not evenly spread out.

◆ Population is increasing fastest in LEDCs.

◆ Migration is the movement of people from one place to another. It affects population sizes and structures – but most of all it affects people themselves.

◆ Population change can cause problems – too many people, especially young ones in LEDCs, too many older people in MEDCs.

◆ Immigration might help to sort out some of the problems in the UK, population control and family planning can help in LEDCs.

Your goals for this chapter

By the end of this chapter you should be able to answer these questions:

◆ What factors affect population density? How many can you name?

◆ What does the demographic transition model show us (and can you draw it)?

◆ Where is population growing fastest, and slowest?

◆ What do population pyramids show, and why are they useful?

◆ List four types of migration, four push factors and four pull factors.

◆ How does migration affect the UK? (Think about international and internal migration.)

◆ Give an example of international refugees. Why are they refugees? What's happened to them? What's being done to help?

◆ What's the problem of population change in an MEDC like the UK? How will we cope?

◆ What are the problems of population change in an LEDC like India? What are they doing about it?

◆ What do these terms mean?
population density, birth rate, death rate, natural increase, population growth rate, fertility rate, infant mortality, life expectancy, refugee, economic migrant

And then . . .

When you finish the chapter, come back here and see if you've met your goals!

Did you know?
◆ The world's population hit 6.5 billion in the spring of 2006.
◆ It's increasing by 201 331 people every day.

Did you know?
◆ The UK's population reached 60 million in 2005.
◆ It's expected to peak at 67 million in 2050 and then start falling.

Did you know?
The UK's birth rate has fallen to an all-time low.

Did you know?
The average age of the UK population was 34 years in 1971 – it rose to 38 in 2002 and will be 43 by 2031.

Your chapter starter

Look at the photo on page 146.
Where do you think these babies are?
What will their lives be like?
How many children will they have?
How long might they live?

Which one's ours?

Where in the world is everyone?

In this unit you will learn why the world's population is unevenly distributed.

A lot here, a few there

The first humans left Africa about 70 000 years ago. Since then, people have spread all over the world. We're capable of living almost anywhere!

But the world's population certainly isn't evenly distributed. Some places are **densely** populated – they have lots of people. Other places are **sparsely** populated. Look at this map:

Population density explained

The **population density** of an area or place is the average number of people per square kilometre. It is calculated like this:

Population density = population ÷ area (km²)

You will come across population density figures for all sorts of areas: continents, countries, regions, and even parts of cities.

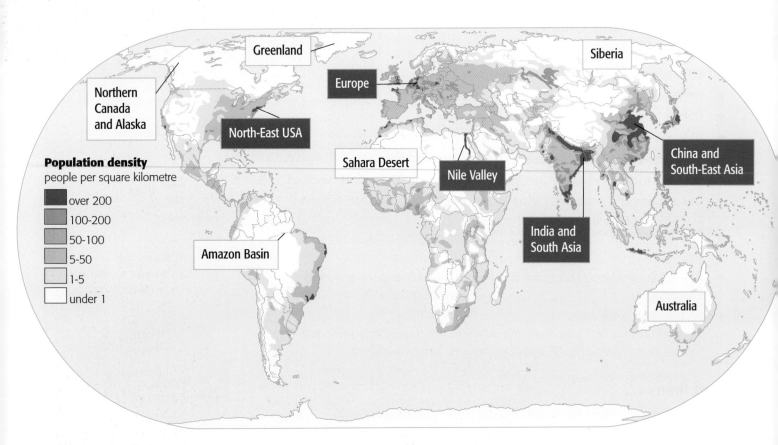

Population density
people per square kilometre

- over 200
- 100-200
- 50-100
- 5-50
- 1-5
- under 1

Greenland
Northern Canada and Alaska
North-East USA
Amazon Basin
Europe
Siberia
Sahara Desert
Nile Valley
India and South Asia
China and South-East Asia
Australia

Why aren't we spread more evenly?

The more densely populated areas are generally easier for people to live in. These factors combine to make an area easier or harder for people to live in:
- **physical** factors, like relief, climate, and water supply.
- **human** factors, like industry and transport.

So flat lowlands, areas with a moderate or temperate climate, and areas with a reliable water supply are usually densely populated. The extreme environments – the polar regions, the high mountains, the deserts, and the rainforests – are usually sparsely populated.

Transport and trade mean that dense populations can be found at major ports, or where transport networks like roads and rail lines come together.

Did you know?
- Monaco has a population of 32 409 and an area of just 1.95 sq. km – giving it a population density of 16 620 people per sq. km.
- It is one of the most crowded places in the world.

Western Europe is an area of high population density. It has a temperate climate, with reliable rainfall. The land is low and fairly flat. Transport networks have been easy to develop. Resources like coal encouraged industries, making it even more attractive. Scandinavia has a much lower population density. It has a rugged landscape, a cold climate, and some dense coniferous forests.

In North Africa, the Nile Valley is much more densely populated than the **Sahara Desert**. In the Nile Valley there's a reliable water supply, so the land can be irrigated, and crops can be grown in fertile soils. Contrast this attractive environment with that of the Sahara Desert. People have found living in the Sahara much harder. The climate is hot, with very little rainfall, so water for drinking and farming is in short supply.

You will often see population density figures for countries. But remember that there can be great variations in density within a country. Take the UK, for example. The population density for the country as a whole is 247 people per square kilometre. But within the UK the density varies widely – from over 500 people per square kilometre in the cities to under ten people per square kilometre in northern Scotland.

A Countries with highest population densities, 2005	People per sq. km
Bangladesh	1002
Taiwan	636
South Korea	492
Netherlands	395
Lebanon	368
Belgium	340
Japan	337
India	329
Rwanda	320
El Salvador	319

B Countries with lowest population densities, 2005	People per sq. km
Australia	2
Mongolia	2
Namibia	2
Botswana	3
Canada	3
Mauritania	3
Central African Rep.	6
Chad	6
Kazakhstan	6
Bolivia	8

C Ten other countries, for comparison, 2005	People per sq. km
UK	247
Germany	231
France	111
Spain	81
USA	31
Afghanistan	46
China	136
Brazil	21
Nigeria	141
Iraq	60

Activities

1 Using the map:
   a Describe the distribution of the most densely populated parts of the world.
   b Explain why population density is low in any two named locations.
2 Explain why population density is low in any two of the countries in table B.
3 Explain why population density varies so much within the United Kingdom.
4 Which sparsely populated environments do you think will be least likely to gain population in the future? Why is this?
5 'Low population density is because of physical factors, high density is due to human factors.' To what extent do you agree with this statement?

In this unit you'll find out how quickly and how evenly the world's population is increasing.

The population explosion

In the next two seconds, ten babies will be born around the world.

Of course, some people will have died. But overall, it adds up to 200 000 extra people every day. That's just over 70 million a year.

The graph below and the tables on the next page tell the story.

Birth rate: the number of births in a country in a year, per 1000 people.

Death rate: the number of deaths in a country in a year, per 1000 people.

Natural increase: the birth rate minus the death rate, often given as a percentage. Don't confuse this with 'population growth rate'.

Did you know?
96 100 000 000 people have lived on the Earth.

Did you know?
- At a growth rate of 1%, the population of a country will double in 70 years.
- At 2%, it will double in 36 years.
- At 3%, 24 years.
- At 4%, 18 years.

Did you know?
- About 6% of all the people ever born are alive today.
- That's actually a fairly large percentage, when you think about it!

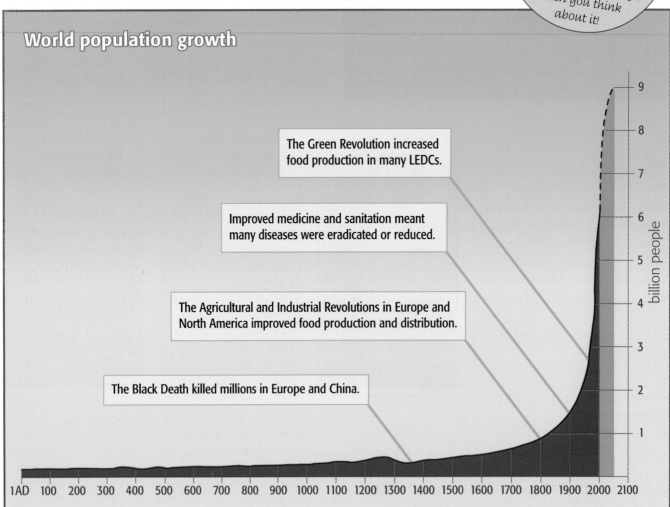

World population growth

The Green Revolution increased food production in many LEDCs.

Improved medicine and sanitation meant many diseases were eradicated or reduced.

The Agricultural and Industrial Revolutions in Europe and North America improved food production and distribution.

The Black Death killed millions in Europe and China.

billion people

1AD 100 200 300 400 500 600 700 800 900 1000 1100 1200 1300 1400 1500 1600 1700 1800 1900 2000 2100

World population increase

	total population (billions)	natural increase (%)	annual increase (millions)
1950	2.56	1.47	37.8
1955	2.78	1.89	52.9
1960	3.04	1.33	40.8
1965	3.35	2.08	70.2
1970	3.71	2.07	77.6
1975	4.09	1.75	72.2
1980	4.46	1.70	76.3
1985	4.85	1.70	83.0
1990	5.28	1.56	83.2
1995	5.69	1.36	77.7
2000	6.08	1.26	77.3
2005	6.46	1.14	73.8
2010 (est.)	6.82	1.03	70.8
2015 (est.)	7.17	0.97	69.6
2020 (est.)	7.52	0.88	66.4

The number of countries with a population over 50 million

1950	8
2000	22
2050	33

When did/will we reach the next billion?

year (estimate/projected)	amount	years in-between
1804	1 billion	-
1927	2 billion	123
1960	3 billion	33
1974	4 billion	14
1987	5 billion	13
1999	6 billion	12
2013	7 billion	14
2028	8 billion	15
2054	9 billion	26

Population increase for selected countries, 2005

	birth rate (per 1000)	death rate (per 1000)	natural increase
Afghanistan	47.02	20.75	2.68%
Nigeria	40.65	17.18	2.35%
Angola	44.64	25.90	1.87%
India	22.32	8.28	1.40%
Brazil	16.83	6.15	1.07%
China	13.14	6.94	0.62%
USA	14.14	8.25	0.59%
UK	10.78	10.18	0.06%
Germany	8.33	10.55	−0.22%
Bulgaria	9.66	14.26	−0.46%

Is population increase spread evenly?

No – there are big differences from country to country.

- India has a natural increase of 1.4% and, because it has such a large population, this adds about 15 million people a year.
- Afghanistan has a natural increase of 2.68%, one of the fastest in the world in 2005 – but because it has a smaller population than India, this adds just 800 000 people.
- The UK's natural increase is 0.06%, and this adds about 36 000 people a year.
- A few countries have a falling population. We'll look at these differences in Unit 8.8.

Overall, the rate of world population increase is slowing down a bit. But people are still worried that we won't have the resources to support everyone.

Activities

1 Use this writing frame to make notes about world population increase.

> Birth rate is …
> Death rate is …
> Natural increase is …
> The world's population is currently increasing by …
> Overall, the rate of increase is …

2 a When was the world's population increasing most quickly in percentage terms?
  b When was it increasing quickest in terms of millions added each year?
3 When would you say the world's population explosion began?
4 Look at the table of population increase for selected countries.
  a Both Afghanistan and Angola have a high death rate – but their natural increase is still high. Why?
  b What's happening to the population in Germany and Bulgaria?
  c Why do you think Brazil and China have lower death rates than the UK and Germany?
5 Do you think the 'population explosion' was due mainly to high birth rates or decreasing death rates?
6 To what extent do you think it's correct to say that the population explosion is a problem caused by population change in LEDCs?

The demographic transition model

In this unit you'll find out **why** the world's population is increasing.

Many countries have had a similar pattern of population increase over time. Geographers have devised a model to show and explain this.

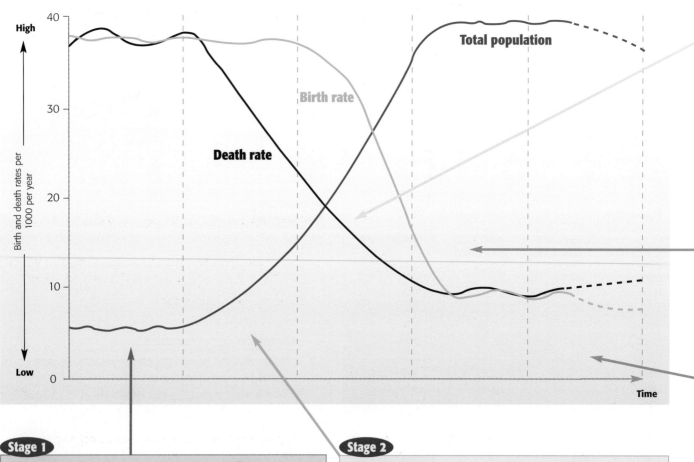

Stage 1

High stationary

The death rate is high due to diseases, famines, a lack of clean water, and a lack of medical care.	But the birth rate is also high due to a lack of birth control, a low age of marriage for women, and the fact that children work so they can add to the family income.

So the natural increase is low – the population doesn't increase much.

The UK was in Stage 1 before 1760.

Few places are in this stage today – perhaps a few remote tribes in the tropical rainforests.

Stage 2

Early expanding

The death rate is starting to fall due to improved medicine, cleaner water, more and better food, and improved sanitation.	But the birth rate is still high, for the same reasons as before.

So the natural increase is high – the population increases quickly.

The UK was in Stage 2 between 1760 and about 1900, during the Industrial Revolution.

Today some LEDCs are in this stage – for example, Bangladesh and Nigeria.

Stage 3

Late expanding

The death rate is still falling, for the same reasons as before.

But now the birth rate is starting to fall because there are fewer farmers needing children to work the family land, birth control is available, infant deaths are falling, and women are staying in education and marrying later.

So there's still some natural increase, but it's lower than it was – population increase is slowing down.

The UK was in Stage 3 between 1900 and about 1950.

Today many LEDCs are in this stage – for example, India, Brazil, and Mexico.

Stage 4

Low stationary

The death rate remains low.

And the birth rate is low – through birth control, people are now having the number of children they want.

So there's little or no natural increase – the population doesn't increase much.

The UK has been in Stage 4 since about 1950. Many other MEDCs are currently in this stage, such as the USA, France, and Japan.

Few LEDCs have reached this stage.

Stage 5

Declining

The death rate could go up because a greater proportion of the population is elderly.

The birth rate remains low and could get lower – lifestyle changes mean people have children later in life, and have fewer of them.

If more people die than are being born, there's negative natural increase – so the population falls.

This stage wasn't on the model when it was first devised – it has been added to show recent developments in population change.

The UK could enter Stage 5 soon. Other MEDCs are already there – Germany, Sweden, and Italy.

The demographic transition model works quite well for countries that have gone from a rural, poorly educated society to an urban, industrial, well educated one. So it fits what has happened in the UK, the rest of Europe, and other MEDCs. But LEDCs might not follow the same transition.

Activities

1 a Which stage of the demographic transition model has a high birth rate and a high death rate?
  b Which stages are MEDCs in?
  c Which stages are LEDCs in?
  d In which two stages will population increase? Why?

2 Could there be a 'stage 6' of the demographic transition model at some time in the future? If so, what might it look like?

3 Why might some LEDCs not follow the stages of the model.

Population contrasts

In this unit you'll learn how population increase varies between MEDCs and LEDCs, and how to use population pyramids.

Where's the increase?

Population increase isn't happening everywhere at the same rate.

◆ Six countries account for about half the world's current increase in population.

◆ India, on its own, accounts for about 20% and China about 10%.

◆ Over 90% of the world's increase is in the LEDCs.

◆ In many MEDCs, population increase is slowing down – and in some, in Europe, populations are declining.

Did you know?

● It's predicted that by 2050 India and China together will contain 3 billion people – that will be about 30% of the total world population, and more than the total world population in 1950.

Daily increase in population

1 India		41 435
2 China		20 758
3 Indonesia		9 613
4 Pakistan		9 033
5 Nigeria		8 361
6 Bangladesh		8 264
World		**201 331**

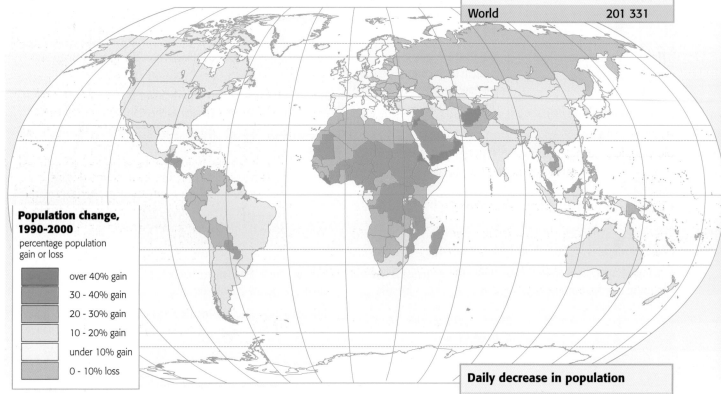

Population change, 1990-2000

percentage population gain or loss

	over 40% gain
	30 - 40% gain
	20 - 30% gain
	10 - 20% gain
	under 10% gain
	0 - 10% loss

Daily decrease in population

1 Russia	1 454
2 Ukraine	819
3 South Africa	377
4 Bulgaria	182
5 Romania	73
6 Hungary	71

So, in many LEDCs, rapid population increase is the problem. But in the MEDCs, people are starting to get worried about ageing populations and population decline. We'll look at these problems more closely in Unit 8.8.

The last 50 years

The world's population has increased from 2.5 billion to 6.5 billion. Much of this increase has been in China, India, and other countries in Asia, Africa, and South America. This is because they have had high birth rates and a dramatic fall in death rates – especially infant mortality – due to improvements in health and the availability of food.

Population pyramids

These are a type of graph that shows the age structure of a country's population. They show the percentage or number of males and females in each age group – the number aged 0-4 years, 5-9 years, 10-14 years and so on.

The trick is to know how to 'read' the pyramid.
◆ First, look at the overall shape, to see what that tells you. For example, if the pyramid is wide at the bottom, it means there are lots of young people in the population – we say the country has a young population.
◆ Then look for details, like bars that are longer or shorter than those above and below them. For example, shorter bars could indicate high death rates in those age groups, perhaps through war or famine.

Why are they useful?

They tell us how the population might develop, and this can help us plan for the future needs of that population. If the country has a very young population, it will need more schools and more teachers. If the country's population is ageing, it will need more old people's homes and more money for pensions. Population pyramids also help us to compare the populations of countries.

Population pyramids and the DTM

The stages of the demographic transition model (Unit 8.3) produce different-shaped population pyramids. So, by recognising the shapes, and understanding what they show, you can tell which stage of the model the country is at.

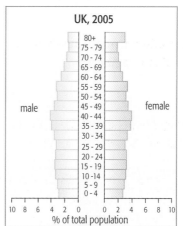
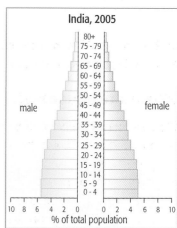

UK, 2005 — India, 2005

Activities

1 Explain the causes of population increase in LEDCs.
2 Why do you think birth rates remain high in many LEDCs, despite a decrease in death rates?
3 Why do many MEDCs have an ageing population?
4 Compare and contrast the population pyramids for India and the UK.
5 Look back to the demographic transition model in Unit 8.3. How do the population pyramids for India and the UK help to explain their positions on the model?
6 A fifth stage to the demographic transition model is where a country has a continued decline in birth rate, together with a further increase in life expectancy. Draw an outline population pyramid to show this stage. Which countries do you think might reach stage 5?

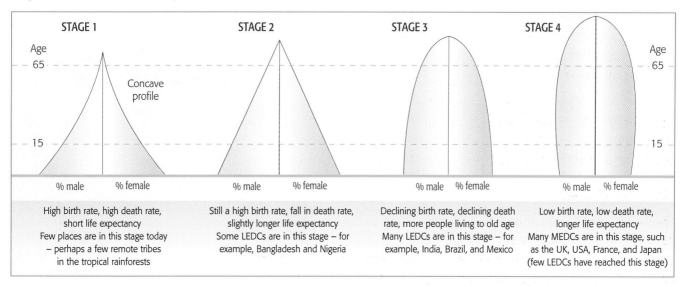

STAGE 1 — High birth rate, high death rate, short life expectancy. Few places are in this stage today – perhaps a few remote tribes in the tropical rainforests

STAGE 2 — Still a high birth rate, fall in death rate, slightly longer life expectancy. Some LEDCs are in this stage – for example, Bangladesh and Nigeria

STAGE 3 — Declining birth rate, declining death rate, more people living to old age. Many LEDCs are in this stage – for example, India, Brazil, and Mexico

STAGE 4 — Low birth rate, low death rate, longer life expectancy. Many MEDCs are in this stage, such as the UK, USA, France, and Japan (few LEDCs have reached this stage)

Migration

In this unit you'll learn what migration is, what causes it, and about population change due to migration.

What is migration?

Simple - **migration** is the movement of people from one place to another.

It has always gone on – people have always moved around. As geographers, we get interested when a migration involves a lot of people. We do two things:

1 We identify the reasons for the migration, and say what type of migration it is.
2 We analyse the effect of the migration – on the place sending people, on the place receiving people, and on the people themselves.

Four types of migration

Voluntary migration

This is when people move of their own free will – they're usually trying to find a better standard of living. For example, many people from Eastern European countries, like the Poles on the right, are moving to Western European countries for jobs and higher wages. They are called **economic migrants**.

Forced migration

This is when people have no choice – they either move, or face extreme hardship or even death. This often happens when there's a natural disaster or war. These migrants are called **refugees**. For example, by the end of 2005, 200 000 people had fled Sudan for Chad after two years of civil war (there's more about this in Unit 8.7). The picture on the right shows Afghan refugees fleeing to Pakistan during the recent war.

Permanent migration

This is when people move forever, to find a new place to live. An example from history would be the millions of people who left Ireland during the 19th century, largely due to famine, and settled in the USA.

Temporary migration

This is when people don't move forever – they always intend to go home at some point in the future. For example, each summer many workers come to the UK from Eastern Europe to pick fruit and vegetables and, when the season's over, they go home (see Unit 8.9).

The United Nations says there should be a new term: **environmental refugee**. It calculates that drought, flooding, deforestation, and falling soil fertility now cause more refugees than wars. It says there will be up to 50 million environmental refugees in the world by 2010.

Migration between countries

This is **international migration**. It takes place because of **push and pull factors**. It's important because it can affect the population size and structure of the countries involved.

How does migration affect population size?

People leave one country, and go to another – this obviously affects the number of people living in each country. In many cases, a country loses some and gains some – the balance is called **net migration**. So, migration plays an important part in the **population growth rate**.

> **Population growth rate explained**
>
> The **population growth rate** is the number of people added to a population each year due to natural increase and net migration. It is given as a percentage, and is calculated like this:
>
> Population growth rate (%) = the number of extra people ÷ the total number of people before x 100

How does migration affect population structure?

This is a bit harder to understand. You need to think about who's migrating.

In some migrations – like those forced by war or starvation – whole families leave. But in other migrations – such as when people go looking for work – it's often a certain group that leaves. This might be the young men, or young couples. So a country loses people from just a few age groups in its population pyramid. The country these people go to receives extra young people – and in time, it also gets their children.

Migration inside a country

This is called **internal migration**. It's important because it affects the distribution of the country's population.

A good example is the migration of people from the country to the towns and cities. This is called **rural-urban migration**.

It happened in the UK and many other MEDCs during the Industrial Revolution in the 19th century.

Today it's happening on a massive scale in the LEDCs. Again, it takes place because of push and pull factors:

- People are pushed to leave the rural areas. They are trying to escape the population pressure and environmental deterioration that are making it more and more difficult to survive there.
- The urban areas act like magnets. They are pulling people from rural areas and small towns. The cities offer more hope of jobs, education, and better living standards.

Push and pull factors for migration between countries

Push factors encourage people to leave their own country:

- not enough jobs
- low wages
- poor educational opportunities
- war with another country
- civil war
- drought and famine

Pull factors attract people to a new country:

- hope of finding a job, or a better job
- higher wages
- better health care
- chance of a better education
- better all-round standard of living
- family or friends may have already moved
- safety

Other factors

Barriers to international migration are important:

- cost of travel can be high
- there are legal restrictions *
- cultural differences – language, way of life

Most people prefer their own country:

- existing job and work contacts
- family and friends are near
- familiar surroundings and culture
- living costs may be lower

Migrants may return home:

- with capital to start a business
- with new skills and qualifications
- if they have difficulty in settling overseas
- when they retire
- if they are forced to return for legal reasons

* Most countries have restrictions on migration. They are willing to take those who have been well educated and have valuable work skills, and are in good health. Family members are often allowed to follow. Migrants with a criminal record aren't wanted.

Activities

1 What effects is economic migration likely to have on the countries from which people have migrated?
2 How might push and pull factors be different for internal and international migration?
3 'Push factors are more important for international migration, while pull factors are more important for internal migration.' To what extent do you agree?

Migration and the UK

In this unit you'll learn how migration is affecting the UK.

International migration

Just over half the UK's population growth in the last ten years has been due to immigration. It now accounts for about 80% of the country's population growth.

1973-1982 net migration **out** 430 000
1983-1992 net migration **in** 240 000
1993-2002 net migration **in** 1 million

Looking ahead, the UK's population is expected to increase from 60 million to 67 million in the twenty-five years from 2006 to 2031. This means a population growth rate of about 0.4% per year. But the rate of natural increase is only 0.06%. It's immigration that will make up the difference.

Of the 7 million growth, about 4 million – 57% – is expected to come from immigration. A further 1.8 million is expected to be the children of the immigrants. If it was left to natural increase, the population would go up by just 1.2 million.

50% of immigrants settle in South-East England, mostly in London. But immigration is now affecting almost every area of the country. The North-East and North-West would have had population declines without the current rate of immigration.

Did you know?
- In 2004, a record 582 000 people migrated to the UK.
- Of course, others left – 360 000 emigrated.
- That meant an extra 222 000 people living here.

There's a big reason why migrants head to the UK: jobs. The people coming are mainly **economic migrants**.

Where the migrants come from

The graph on the bottom right shows the most common countries of origin. A new trend in migration to the UK has been the arrival of workers from the EU's new eastern countries.

The UK is the favourite destination for workers from these countries. This is because the government has introduced generous employment rules for workers from the EU to plug what it says are labour shortages in a strong economy.

About 130 000 new EU workers came to the UK in the first year after EU enlargement in May 2004.

What about illegal immigrants?

The government's official guess is that in 2005 there were between 310 000 and 570 000 illegal immigrants. No one can tell if that's accurate.

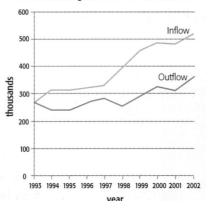

International migration into and out of the UK

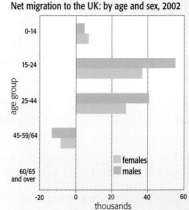

Net migration to the UK: by age and sex, 2002

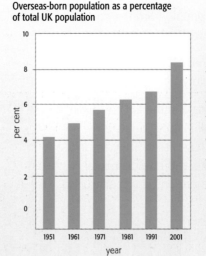

Overseas-born population as a percentage of total UK population

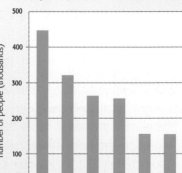

Most common countries of origin, 2001
(excluding Irish Republic)

Internal migration

There's a lot of internal migration in the UK. People are moving to and from every part of the country, but there are two clear trends:

◆ There's a general movement of people from the North to the South – people are moving away from the old industrial areas of the North to southern England, especially the South-East.
◆ At the same time, there's a movement of people out of the cities, especially the inner cities.

Around one in ten people moved within the UK in the year before the 2001 Census. Many were workers who moved south to find jobs. The northern regions of England, the Midlands, Wales, Scotland, and Northern Ireland all had a loss of full-time workers. The South-East had the largest net gain. London, the South-West, and the Eastern regions of England also had a net gain of full-time workers.

London's a special case

More people leave London for other parts of the UK than move there. But London's population is increasing because it's where most international migrants head for.

We're leaving the cities

People are moving from the big cities and conurbations to smaller towns and villages, often quite nearby. This is called **counter-urbanisation**. They're usually looking for bigger houses in quieter, less-polluted places.

Why does all this matter?

Knowing about internal migration matters because we need to know how the distribution of our population is changing – so that we can build houses, schools, hospitals, sports centres, and so on in the right places. For example, there are 850 000 empty homes in the UK, but the government says we need to build 4 million new homes across the UK, mostly in the South and South-East.

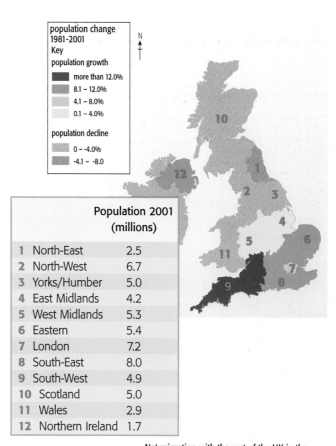

population change 1981-2001 Key	
population growth	
	more than 12.0%
	8.1 – 12.0%
	4.1 – 8.0%
	0.1 – 4.0%
population decline	
	0 – -4.0%
	-4.1 – -8.0

Population 2001 (millions)	
1 North-East	2.5
2 North-West	6.7
3 Yorks/Humber	5.0
4 East Midlands	4.2
5 West Midlands	5.3
6 Eastern	5.4
7 London	7.2
8 South-East	8.0
9 South-West	4.9
10 Scotland	5.0
11 Wales	2.9
12 Northern Ireland	1.7

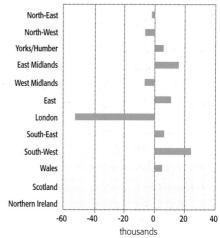

Net migration with the rest of the UK in the year to April 2001: by region

Activities

1 Describe how international migration patterns to and from the UK have changed since 1973.
2 What effect has international migration had on the total population of the UK?
3 What impact has the expansion of the European Union had on migration into the UK?
4 What do you think might be some of the consequences of large-scale migration from other countries?
5 Why do you think that government estimates of the number of illegal immigrants are likely to be inaccurate?
6 Describe and explain the pattern of internal migration within the UK.
7 Why is London 'a special case?'
8 Do you think it's right for the government to propose the building of 4 million new homes, when there are so many empty? Justify your answer.

Darfur refugee emergency

In this unit you'll find out about an example of international refugees.

Aisha's story, from a refugee camp in Chad

I'm 27. My three children have diarrhoea. We live in one hut with my sisters, Neimad and Mona. My husband is dead. Neimad's husband was taken away. We haven't seen him for months.

We had to leave our village when the Janjaweed attacked us. The village had 7000 goats, 1000 donkeys, 2000 camels, 3000 horses and many thousands of chickens. They took the men away, and then we heard shots. The women stayed.

The Janjaweed said: "Why do you stay? We killed your men." Later I went to where the shots came from and found my husband's body.

This is a real story – though the names have been changed.

Aisha is just one victim of the Darfur refugee crisis. By early 2006, there had been three years of civil war in Sudan's western region of Darfur. The UN said events in Darfur could have 'a devastating impact' on Chad and Sudan – two of the poorest countries in the world – as well as on the refugees.

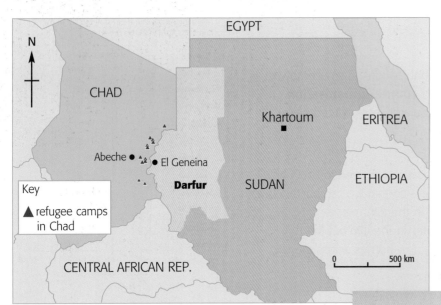

Key
▲ refugee camps in Chad

EGYPT
CHAD
Khartoum
ERITREA
Abeche ● Abeche ▲ ● El Geneina
Darfur SUDAN
ETHIOPIA
CENTRAL AFRICAN REP.
0   500 km

The two sides

Sudan's government, and the Arab militias that support it, especially the Janjaweed. They're accused of war crimes against Darfur's black African population.

Black African Darfuris. There are two main rebel groups – the Sudan Liberation Army (SLA), the biggest, and the Justice and Equality Movement (Jem). The SLA was formed in 2002 to defend black African farmers against the Arab militias.

Details of the crisis

- ◆ 180 000 Darfuris have been killed.
- ◆ 200 000 have fled to next-door Chad, and live in refugee camps.
- ◆ Up to 1.8 million live in camps within Darfur.
- ◆ News reports say militias have killed, raped, and forced hundreds of thousands from their homes.
- ◆ Hundreds of villages have been burnt (see right).

What's the fighting about?

The black African Darfuris say that Sudan's government favours the ruling Arab elite in the north of the country. Both groups are Muslims, but the Darfuris say that as non-Arabs they suffer discrimination.

There has been tension in Darfur for many years over land and grazing rights. In 2003, rebels started attacking government targets. The government struck back. It admits supporting 'self-defence' militias, but says it doesn't support the Janjaweed.

Refugees from Darfur say that following air raids by government aircraft, the Janjaweed ride into villages on horses and camels, slaughtering men, raping women, and stealing or burning whatever they can find.

Refugees in Chad

Refugees fled to Chad, seeking safety. They arrived in a remote, desert region where water is in short supply. They made rough shelters, often just yards from the border – still within reach of raiding militias. In 2004, The United Nations High Commission for Refugees (UNHCR) moved most of the refugees to camps a safe distance from the border.

The UNHCR and other aid agencies built the camps to provide everything from family shelters to wells, toilets, clinics, and schools. Twelve camps were built by the summer of 2005. Emergency airlifts flew thousands of tonnes of tents, blankets, plastic sheeting, soap and other relief items.

Many refugees remain camped along a 600-km stretch of the border and are still vulnerable to attacks from Sudan.

No one knows if or when the refugees will be able to go home.

▲ *Fleeing to Chad.*

▲ *Safe at last?*

What's being done in Darfur?

Lots of aid agencies are working in Darfur, but they can't get access to wide areas. They say the government blocks their movements by demanding visas. Aid workers have warned that many thousands are at risk of starvation and disease in the camps, with 1 million children threatened by malnutrition.

Peace talks keep failing. The lives of thousands of people are being ruined.

Did you know?
An all-star charity concert Voices for Darfur was held to raise money for the refugees.

Activities

1 Describe the background to the conflict in Darfur.
2 Why do you think the conflict has gone on for so long without being resolved?
3 Why did the UNHCR move the refugees who had fled into Chad?
4 Why do you think the government of Chad relied upon the UNHCR for emergency relief and aid?
5 What do you think might be some of the effects on Chad of such a large number of refugees?
6 Find out about another example of international refugees. Compare and contrast this example with the situation in Darfur and Chad.

161

The problems of population change

In this unit you'll learn about the different problems caused by population change in LEDCs and MEDCs.

Population growth in LEDCs

◆ Over 90% of the world's population increase is in LEDCs.
◆ They have falling death rates and high birth rates – which means their natural increase is high.
◆ Most are at Stages 2 and 3 of the Demographic Transition Model (see Unit 8.3).
◆ They have population pyramids that are wide at the base.

Death rates are falling due to better sanitation and health care. Birth rates are high for a number of reasons:
◆ lack of **family planning** education or contraceptives
◆ in rural areas children are needed to work on farms; in urban areas they're needed to work to earn money for their families
◆ **fertility rates** are high – women have a large number of children as there's a high level of **infant mortality**
◆ culture or religion often mean it's unacceptable to use contraception.

The problem

Many LEDCs are being held back by rapid population growth – it's slowing down their development. They're struggling to earn enough money from farming and industry to provide for more and more people. The growing population puts too much pressure on resources.
◆ Some LEDCs find it difficult just feeding everyone – but they're getting more and more mouths to feed. *The result*: millions of people go hungry.
◆ LEDCs can't afford better schools and more teachers. *The result*: millions of people aren't getting the education and skills that would help them and their countries to prosper.
◆ LEDCs can't afford the best health care, with more hospitals, doctors, and nurses. *The result*: millions of people are suffering from illnesses and diseases that could be cured or prevented.

So, having a young, rapidly growing population makes it hard for any LEDC to improve the living standards of its people.

Fertility rate: the number of children, on average, a woman will have in her lifetime. If it's about two, the population will replace itself each generation. If it's more than two, the population will increase, if it's less than two, it will fall.

Infant mortality: the number of babies dying before they reach the age of one, per 1000 births.

Did you know?
Andorra has the longest life expectancy in the world – 83.5 years. Botswana has the shortest – 30.8 years.

Indicators of population change

	Population growth rate	Fertility rate	Life expectancy (years)	GDP per capita (US $ ppp)*
China	0.58%	1.69	72.0	5 600
India	1.40%	2.85	64.0	3 100
Bangladesh	2.09%	3.15	61.7	2 000
Sudan	2.60%	4.97	58.1	1 900
Chad	2.95%	6.38	48.2	1 600
Brazil	1.06%	1.97	71.4	8 100
UK	0.28%	1.66	78.3	29 600
France	0.37%	1.85	79.4	28 700
Germany	0.00%	1.38	78.5	28 700
Italy	0.07%	1.27	79.5	27 700
Bulgaria	−0.89%	1.37	71.8	8 200
Japan	0.05%	1.38	81.0	29 400
World	1.14%	2.62	64.1	8 800

* ppp = purchasing power parity

Population change in MEDCs

- Population growth in most MEDCs is slow – and some MEDCs even have a falling population.
- MEDCs have low birth rates and low death rates – which means their natural increase is low.
- They're in Stages 4 and 5 of the Demographic Transition Model (see Unit 8.3).
- They have population pyramids that are narrow at the base.

Birth rates are low. In some countries it has fallen below the rate needed to replace the people who die. Women are choosing to have children later in life, and they're having fewer of them. So there are fewer young people in the population.

Life expectancy, on the other hand, is increasing. People are living longer due to improvements in health care, diet, and lifestyle. So, there are more and more elderly people in the population.

> **Life expectancy:** how long people can expect to live, on average.

The problem

Fewer young people entering the population and more people living longer adds up to an **ageing population**. This means the proportion of older people in the population is going up.

This is a problem because it means there are fewer and fewer workers to pay for more and more old people. We say there will be a greater number of **elderly dependents**. We need to make sure the older people have:

- pensions to give them money to spend on food and housing and so on
- the right health care and hospital facilities, with doctors and nurses trained to deal with the illnesses that affect older people
- old people's homes and trained carers.

All these things cost a lot of money.

Fewer and fewer workers could also cause a problem for MEDC economies – there could be a shortage of labour. There could then be economic decline, and this would lead to falling living standards.

Activities

1. Why have birth rates remained high in many LEDCs, despite a fall in death rates?
2. What solutions do you think are most likely to reduce birth rates in LEDCs?
3. **a** Draw a scattergraph to show the relationship between life expectancy and GDP per capita for the countries shown in the table.
   b What does 'per capita' mean?
   c Describe and explain the pattern shown on your graph.
   d To what extent do you think that GDP per capita is a good indicator of development? Explain your answer with reference to information on your graph.
4. **a** Draw another scattergraph, this time to show the relationship between fertility rate and life expectancy (choose the scales for the axes carefully!).
   b Describe and explain the pattern shown on this graph.
5. Compare your two graphs. Explain the similarities and any differences between them.
6. Explain why ageing populations are a problem for many MEDCs.
7. Suggest ways in which MEDCs may attempt to solve some of these problems, and possible consequences if they do not.

How the UK is coping

In this unit you'll learn how the UK is coping with population change – and how individuals are coping.

Ageing UK

◆ For the first time ever, the UK has more people aged over 60 than under 16.
◆ There are five times more people aged over 85 than there were in 1951.

The age structure of the UK's population has been getting older – and this is going to continue. This gives us two problems:

1 an increasing number of **elderly dependents**
2 an economy that could run short of workers.

How are we coping with these problems?

Save more, work longer

People working now pay for the pensions of people who have retired. (A pension is the money we get to live on when we're no longer working). At the moment, there are four workers to support a pensioner, but the increasing number of pensioners means this will fall to two workers.

So the government thinks each of us will have to save more towards pensions. We might also have to work longer – instead of retiring at 60 or 65, we might have to work into our 70s.

The country will also need more old people's homes, and more trained carers for elderly people. Higher taxes might be needed to pay for this.

Immigration

The number of people working in the UK is at a record high of 28.5 million, but there are half a million job vacancies. There's a shortfall of 150 000 hotel and catering workers, 25 000 lorry drivers, and 4000 dentists. The construction industry will need 200 000 new workers over the next few years.

These labour and skills shortages in the economy are being filled by immigrants.

So immigration is beneficial:

◆ The UK gets highly motivated, well-educated workers who are keen to do well – they will play a vital part if our economy is to continue to be successful.
◆ The migrants get more money and a higher standard of living than they would at home.
◆ Migrants to the UK have always contributed a lot in other ways as well – think food and music, for a start.

Did you know?
◆ In the UK life expectancy for women is 80.8 years.
◆ It's 75.8 years for men.

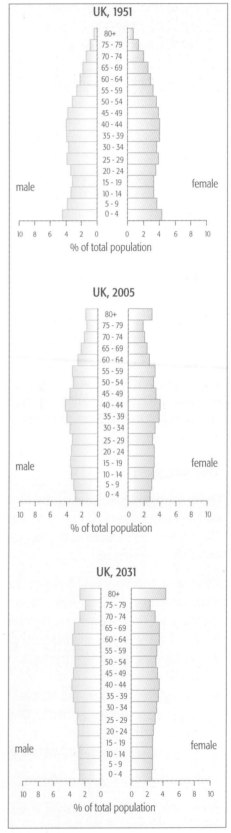

UK, 1951

UK, 2005

UK, 2031

Lucky to have them

Farmer Alan Dawes relies on workers from Eastern Europe to pick and pack fruit and flowers at his farm.

His old source of workers has gone. "Young mums have got jobs and students are going abroad" he said. "We're now employing Eastern European graduates. We're lucky to have them. There wouldn't be a fruit industry without them."

The workers like the UK because the pay is better than at home and they can improve their English. One worker from Poland said "I'm here to earn more money and get more experience. I've had good times here."

But . . .

New migrants are often treated with hostility. Some people think the migrants will take their jobs and swamp their way of life.

Many migrants find it hard to fit in. Some find it hard to learn English. Others can't get used to our customs. Many are exploited, working long hours for low pay in jobs that other people don't want to do. They end up in poor housing. They are attacked in some newspapers, and sometimes in the street. They face discrimination. They feel unwelcome.

Hidden army

Britain has a hidden army of foreign cleaners that most of us rarely see. While we sleep, they clean. Britain's economic strength pulls in people from around the world willing to mop our floors and clean our loos.

London alone now has an estimated 250 000 immigrant cleaners. The industry relies on cheap foreign labour. Much of the new immigration to Britain is to low-paid jobs from areas with no historic ties to Britain.

But according to cleaners it's an industry 'run on fear' as migrants find themselves exploited. Thomas, from Ghana, said he worked 75 hours a week on minimum wage to make money to send home to his family.

These are real opinions – though the names have been changed.

I was born in Somalia and came to the UK in 1990. I work in Essex as a civil engineer. Britain has welcomed many immigrant communities. This diversity has contributed to the economy. Look who your doctors, nurses, shopkeepers, bus drivers and street cleaners are. **Abdi**

I was born in Kenya and was brought up in Leicester. I consider myself British, not an immigrant. I pay taxes. Do I feel accepted as British? Sadly, no. Britain is paranoid about immigration, but without it we'd have no-one to earn money to contribute towards the NHS or schooling. More immigration is needed. **Judy**

We have water shortages, house shortages, traffic congestion, crowded schools and hospitals. There must be a limit to the number of people who can live on our small island. **John**

I was born in Serbia, and came to the UK in 2000 on a work permit. I'm applying for citizenship. I feel at home here. I think people who are against immigration don't understand that the diversity is one of the best things in this country. **Savo**

Activities

1 **a** Explain why the average age of people living in the UK is increasing.
   b Outline the problems that this trend may cause.
2 Explain why the UK is relying more and more on foreign workers.
3 Give your opinion of the comments made by each of the people shown on this page. Justify your opinions.
4 Draw a graph or graphs to show the information in this table. Explain the trends shown in your graph(s).

UK population – millions in each age group

	under 19	20-64	65+
1991	14.8	33.8	9.1
2005	14.7	36.2	9.5
2031	13.3	36.3	14.7
2050	12.5	35.0	16.4

How India is coping

In this unit you'll learn how india has tried to use family-planning to tackle population growth.

Some LEDCs are relying on economic development to bring higher living standards – which will in turn bring lower birth rates. These LEDCs would move into Stage 4 of the Demographic Transition Model (Unit 8.3).

But many LEDCs see **population control** as important. **Family planning** campaigns have worked better in some LEDCs than others, but overall the average number of children born per woman has been going down.

▲ *India's youthful population is typical of many LEDCs.*

India in the early 1950s

India's population was growing very quickly. The birth rate was over 45. The fertility rate (how many children a woman has in her lifetime) was 6.

India's government thought this would hold the country back. So 'population control' was seen as a way of helping the country to develop.

The government set two targets: to get the birth rate down to 21 and the fertility rate down to 2.1 (this is replacement fertility) by the year 2000.

Sterilisation and contraception

In 1952, the government started offering contraceptive advice and sterilisation. So India became the first country in the world with a population policy.

But the population continued to grow quickly. In the 1970s, the government declared a population 'state of emergency'. The government began forced sterilisations in the poorest areas. Medical workers who performed most operations were rewarded.

In 1976-77 a record 8.26 million sterilisations were performed, mostly on men. Many people were angry, and the government was brought down. The programme was changed to female sterilisations.

A policy to encourage just two children per family led to abortions and the killing of children, especially girls.

These policies were criticised because of the way they treated the poor, and women.

Did you know?
China's one-child policy is the best-known population policy in the world. It was introduced in the 1970s when China was afraid it couldn't continue to feed its rapidly growing population.

Did you know?
Kenya was the first African country to begin a national family-planning campaign. The average number of children per woman has fallen from around 8 in the 1980s to 3.3 in 2005.

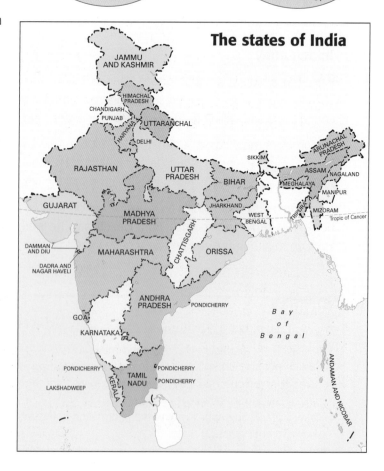
The states of India

India today

The population control policies did have an effect on India's rate of population increase. By 2005, the birth rate was down to 22.3, and the fertility rate was down to 2.8.

But the population has still trebled since 1952, from 0.36 billion to 1.1 billion at the start of 2006. This has been due to a big fall in infant mortality and a doubling of life expectancy, from 31 to 64.

The population is now growing by about 15 million per year. So India still faces population problems.

New population policies

Population control is now seen in the context of improving social and economic conditions, especially for women. In India, women have been the least powerful decision makers. Better health and welfare, including education, is now seen as a key part of controlling population growth – rather than relying on just contraception.

To reduce the rate of population growth, the Indian government has set targets to be met by 2010.

Small families are encouraged. Cash payments are on offer for the birth of girls (the first two children), for women who have their first child after the age of 19, and for couples getting sterilised after two children.

There are still controversial policies. In 2005, the Maharashtra state government announced a plan to cut off irrigation supplies to farmers who have more than two children.

But the Indian prime minister said forcing people to limit the size of their families was not the way to control population growth. He said people should be able to choose the number of children they have.

In some states in the south of the country, the fertility rate has fallen to low levels – in Kerala it's now 1.8. This is like many European countries (it's 1.6 in Germany, for example). But in the northern states of Uttar Pradesh, Bihar and Rajasthan the rates of population increase are still high. If the Indian government is to have any chance of meeting its population targets, it's in these states that the average fertility rate of 4.5 will need to fall.

Nearly one in five of the world's people live in India.

India is set to overtake China as the world's most populous country by 2050. By this time, 40% of the world's people will live in these two countries.

Family planning techniques and their advantages being explained. ▼

Targets for 2010

◆ All women, especially young women, should know about and be able to get contraception. It's predicted this would lower the fertility rate to 2.1.
◆ All births should be delivered by trained workers.
◆ All children should be immunised against common diseases such as polio, tetanus and measles.
◆ The infant mortality rate should be reduced to 30 per 1000 (in 2005 it was 56).
◆ The number of people affected by AIDs needs to be stabilised or reduced.
◆ All births, marriages and deaths should be registered.
◆ The law stating that women cannot marry before 18 should be properly enforced.
◆ All children should be entitled to primary education.

Activities

1 Explain why India's early attempts at population control were only partly successful.
2 Why do you think that population policies in China and India are important to the population of the whole world?
3 What is happening to the population in Kerala? Why is this?
4 Do you think the Indian government's new policies are likely to be more successful in controlling population growth? Explain your answer.

The big picture

This chapter is about settlements – the places where people live. These are the big ideas behind the chapter:

◆ All settlements, however big or small, have a site and at least one function.

◆ Settlements are ranked in order of size and importance (the biggest and most important at the top).

◆ More and more people in MEDCs and LEDCs are living in towns and cities.

◆ Land use changes across cities, and there are different models of land use in MEDC and LEDC cities.

◆ Cities in MEDCs and LEDCs have problems of deprivation – but these problems can be tackled.

◆ Other problems include traffic (everywhere seems to have this problem!) and urban sprawl.

Your goals for this chapter

By the end of this chapter you should be able to answer these questions:

◆ What factors were important for the original sites of settlements? How many can you name?

◆ What is a settlement function?

◆ What is a settlement hierarchy, and what does a diagram of it look like?

◆ Why is urbanisation happening later and faster in LEDCs than MEDCs? And where are the world's fastest growing cities?

◆ How does land use change across an MEDC and an LEDC city? Draw two models of land use in each.

◆ Why do urban zones develop?

◆ Give examples of problems in MEDC and LEDC cities. Then give some examples of how these problems can be tackled.

◆ Why is traffic such a big problem? What can we do about it?

◆ Urban sprawl – what's causing it, and what are the problems? Can we stop it?

◆ What do these terms mean?
sphere of influence, urbanisation, CBD, urban model, urban zones, redevelopment, renewal, shanty town, favela, rural-urban fringe, counter-urbanisation, green belt

And then . . .

When you finish the chapter, come back here and see if you've met your goals!

Did you know?
Footprints found in the Mexican city of Puebla have been dated at over 40 000 years old.

Did you know?
The city of Bravos in Romania is becoming increasingly popular with the local bear population. They can be seen on the outskirts of the city at night looking for dinner in dustbins.

Did you know?
Urban areas generally have fewer married people, and lower birth rates, than rural areas.

Did you know?
One billion people in cities live in absolute filth, without clean water or toilets, gas or electricity.

Your chapter starter

Look at the photo on page 168.
Where do you think this is? Why?
Why has this place been built here?
Is this place likely to have any problems? What might they be?

Out moose!

Site

In this unit you'll find out about the things people looked for when choosing a place to settle.

What is 'site'?

A settlement's **site** is the land it is built on: a hill or a plain, bog or dry land, or a location that has **resources**.

Drained marshland

A

B

C

D

E

F

Looking for a place to stay

The photographs opposite show locations that people have found useful.

- Water is always needed. So a site with a good water supply is a **wet point**.
- If a region is wet and low-lying, a slightly higher location is a **dry point**.
- If you live in lawless times, you'll be looking for a site that's easy to **defend** – perhaps on the top of a hill, or within a river meander.
- You might want **shelter** from the burning sun in hot areas like the Sahel.
- Or you might locate on the sunny side (or **aspect**) of a deep valley.
- Some settlements are located near passes (or **gaps**) through hills.
- Settlements often locate near river crossings, or where main transport routes such as rivers and roads meet, so they can **trade**.
- Many settlements are sited close to **resources** such as good farmland.

As times changed, the sites people preferred to settle on changed.

If the site is a really good one, the settlement will grow and adapt.

You can see from the second map here that London was a **route centre** by Tudor times. There's a bit of chicken-and-egg here – did London become important because it was a route centre, or did routes radiate to and from London because London was important?

Good sites were more important in the past, but are less so now. This is because we now have better technology. A settlement will grow almost anywhere, if there's a strong enough **economic** reason (if there's money in it!).

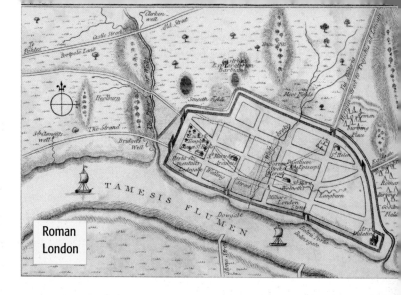

Roman London

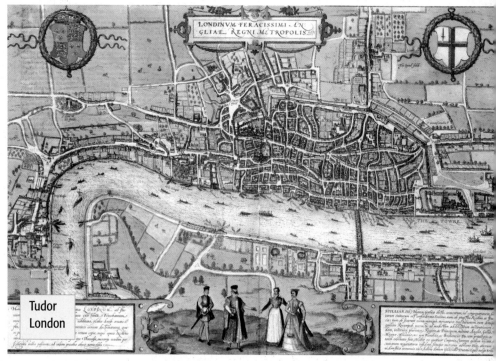

Tudor London

Victorian London

Activities

1 Describe the site of your school.
2 For each of the sites listed A to F opposite, decide which of the site factors above apply, e.g. shelter, defence, etc. Some may have one, two, or more site advantages.
3 a Why do you think London's site was first chosen?
  b How do you think London changed and adapted to become a site with many advantages?

Settlement functions

In this unit you'll learn about the things that happen in settlements, and the role settlements play in our lives.

What is a 'function'?

A **function** is a job or process. An **urban function** is an operation that happens in a town or city. It could:

◆ sell expensive or rare goods
◆ sell expensive or rare services
◆ provide jobs – in industry or in services
◆ administer the area surrounding it
◆ have great museums and galleries
◆ be home to a football club
◆ have lots to do – movies to watch, parks to play in, places to eat
◆ have many schools
◆ have one – or more – universities
◆ be a place of pilgrimage for one or more religions
◆ have specialist hospitals
◆ be a transport hub (**route centre**)
◆ and have housing areas for all the workers who help to provide these functions.

All settlements perform one or more useful functions that give a good reason for their survival. Most settlements have several functions:

◆ A **hamlet** is a little group with only houses.
◆ A **village** has houses, and at least one other function – maybe a church, a village hall, a pub, and possibly a shop. It may be a meeting place for people and the goods and services they need, and not be very different from a thousand other villages. Some villages and towns have specialised functions. For example, the Welsh village of Hay-on-Wye has 39 bookshops, but a population of only 1450. Once a year it has a festival (pictured on the right), which draws around 8000 people.
◆ Lots of towns are **market towns**. Their markets may have been running for hundreds of years, and now they may have lots of supermarkets – but the open-air market still runs once a week, or more often.

Land use in urban areas (that's towns and cities) is mostly the result of the **primary functions** of the town or city – residential, industrial, retail, administrative, commercial and recreational.

Jerusalem is a holy place for me.

... and me!

... and me!

Glastonbury it ain't!

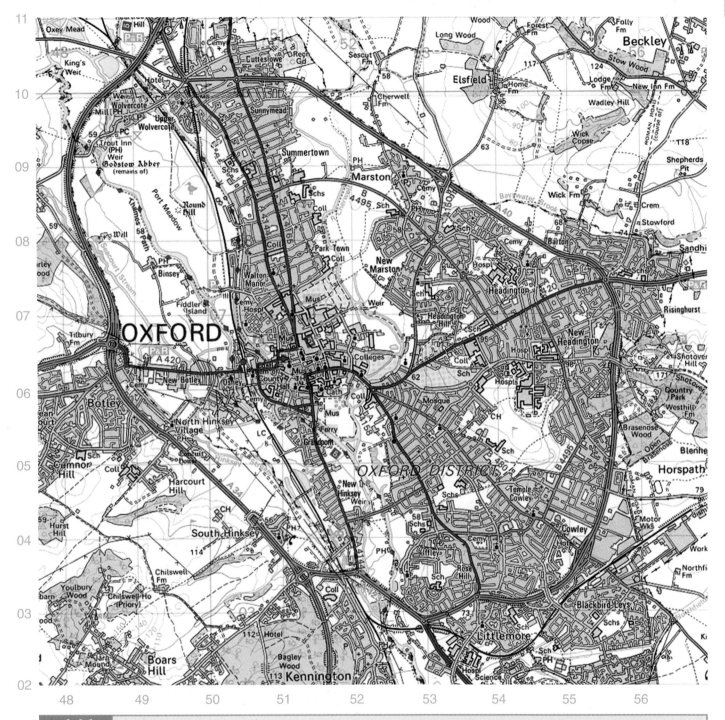

Activities

1 a What is an urban function?

b What do you think is the main function of Oxford? (Look at the OS map above.)

c What is the main function of the place where you live?

d Is there a market town near you? A route centre? An industrial town? A tourist centre? Give named examples.

2 When a settlement becomes a town or city, it has many functions, not just one. Using the OS map above, what is the evidence that Oxford is a university town? Give grid references in your answer.

3 Look for evidence for other functions of Oxford:
◆ a cultural centre
◆ a county town
◆ an industrial centre
◆ a historic town
◆ a recreational centre
◆ a route centre
◆ a tourist town
◆ a residential settlement
Provide a grid reference every time.

Settlement hierarchies

In this unit you will learn how settlements are ranked in order of size and importance.

How the hierarchy works

For this unit, you need to know the word **hierarchy** – a simpler word is **ranking**. On the right is a diagram of a **settlement hierarchy** – a ranking of settlements, with the biggest settlement at the top. Settlements at the top not only have larger populations, they also have more – and more varied – functions, and a bigger **sphere of influence** than settlements lower down the hierarchy.

There are two questions arising from this diagram:
◆ What are the definitions of each of these settlement types?
◆ Why is the settlement hierarchy shaped like a pyramid?

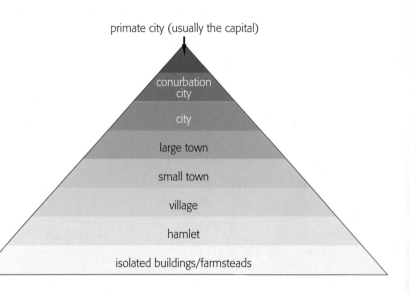

primate city (usually the capital)

conurbation city

city

large town

small town

village

hamlet

isolated buildings/farmsteads

Definitions of settlement types

An **isolated building** (or isolated dwelling) is just a building on its own. There are definitions of hamlet and village in Unit 9.2. However, the real problems come in working out the difference between a **village** and **town**, and town and **city**.

Different countries have different ideas about this. The table on the right shows six examples of how big a settlement has to be in those particular countries in order to be called a town. And the size difference between **towns** and **cities** is just as variable, depending on the country you're in.

country	minimum population size to be a town	urban population as a % of country's total population
Sweden	200	83%
South Africa	400	57%
Israel	2000	90%
Belgium	5000	97%
UK	10 000	90%
Japan	30 000	78%

Why is the hierarchy shaped like a pyramid?

The width of each level of the pyramid is a rough indication of the number of settlements in each class. In the UK, London is the primate city. Then there are seven conurbations, fourteen large cities and seventeen small cities. (And 1.7 million postcodes!)

Even if there are difficulties over population sizes, it's still possible to rank settlements. There are four measurements:
◆ population size
◆ number and variety of functions
◆ the distance between a settlement and the nearest settlement of similar size
◆ the size of the **sphere of influence**.

Did you know?
There are 24 000 towns in the UK.

Did you know?
◆ London is the UK's largest city, with a population of 7.2 million.
◆ Birmingham is the second largest, with a population 1.0 million

What's a sphere of influence?

The sphere of influence is the area surrounding a settlement that is affected by that settlement. The people who live within the sphere of influence depend on the settlement for services such as education, employment, retailing, and finance. The settlement is, in turn, 'served' by the labour supply from the sphere of influence.

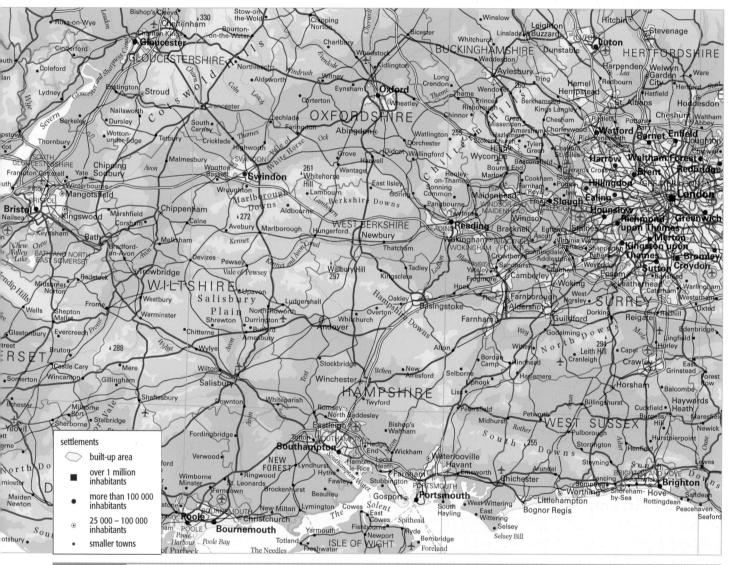

settlements

⬡ built-up area

■ over 1 million inhabitants

● more than 100 000 inhabitants

⊙ 25 000 – 100 000 inhabitants

• smaller towns

Activities

1 What is a hierarchy?

2 Give two reasons why a pyramid shape is a good symbol to show the idea of a settlement hierarchy.

3 London is the primate city in the UK. Name a UK conurbation, city, town, village, and hamlet.

4 What connection would you expect there to be between the minimum population size to be a town and the urban population as a percentage of a country's total population? Now look at the table opposite. Does this show the connection you expected? Explain why/why not.

5 What is a sphere of influence?

6 Using the map and key above, arrange these places between Bristol and London into a hierarchy with 5 levels: Bristol, Marshfield, Chippenham, Calne, Avebury, Swindon, Marlborough, Hungerford, Newbury, Thatcham, Reading, London.

7 Which settlement shown on the map above do you think has the largest sphere of influence?

8 Look at these pairs of settlements on the map. For each, say which you think has the largest sphere of influence:
   a Bristol, Chippenham,   b Oxford, Abingdon
   c Swindon, Reading,   d Salisbury, Abingdon

Urbanisation

In this unit you will learn how more and more people are living in urban areas.

What is urbanisation?

Urbanisation means a rise in the percentage of people living in urban areas (towns and cities), in comparison with rural areas.

	urban population as a % of total population				
	1950	1975	1990	2000	2030
World	38	38	43	47	60
MEDCs	55	70	73	76	84
LEDCs	18	27	33	40	56

Urbanisation in MEDCs

European and North American MEDCs, like the UK, urbanised during the late 18th and the 19th centuries.

As a country industrialises, the number of people living in urban areas tends to increase. Industrialisation in the 19th century attracted millions of workers to the new factories and the houses built by the factory owners. Today, 90% of the UK population lives in towns or cities.

A recipe for urbanising a 19th-century MEDC

You will need:
- ✔ efficient farming
- ✔ better industrial machinery
- ✔ lots of coal
- ✔ state-of-the-art transport.

Time needed:
About 25 years.

Directions:
1 Combine agricultural machinery with crop rotation and/or fertilisers. You should then have more than enough food for everybody, and you will free up a labour supply.
2 Using new steam-engine technology, coal and industrial machinery, build factories.
3 Build small back-to-back houses for workers.
4 Advertise for large numbers of workers (from step 1). You can then employ them and their children.
5 Use high-tech transport (firstly canals, then railways), to bring raw materials to factories, and to send finished goods to shops nationwide and empire-wide.

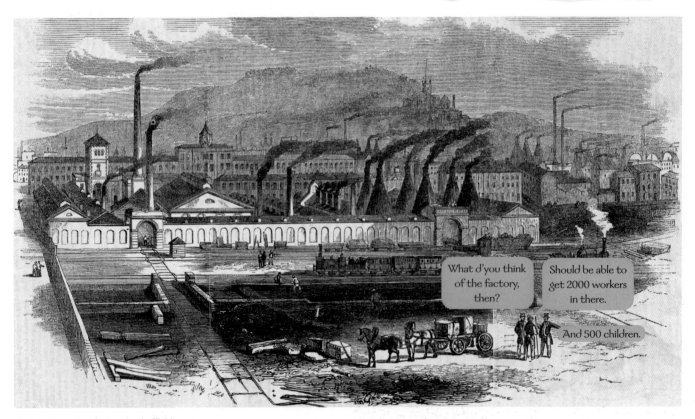

▲ *A 19th–century factory in Sheffield.*

Urbanisation in LEDCs

Is urbanisation in LEDCs following the same pattern as in MEDCs? Yes and no.

Yes

◆ In both MEDCs and LEDCs, people have been pushed from rural areas through the use of machinery.

◆ And, just as in MEDCs, people in LEDCs are pulled towards cities, for jobs.

No

◆ The other pushes from rural to urban areas in LEDCs are different. They include landlessness, drought, famine and civil war.

◆ There are different pulls, too – the chance of an education, of piped water, electricity, and much more entertainment.

◆ The settlement hierarchy is usually different in LEDCs. There's often one very big city, up to ten times bigger than the second city.

◆ Urbanisation is happening a lot later in LEDCs – only since the 1950s. And it's happening a lot faster than it did in MEDCs. You can see the evidence of this if you look at the location of the world's mega-cities – cities with over 10 million inhabitants (see the table on the right).

While LEDC cities continue to grow, many MEDC cities are losing population (more about this in Unit 9.11).

◀ Mumbai, India: a mega-city.

The world's mega-cities (population in millions in brackets)

1975	2000	2015 (projected)
Tokyo (19.8)	Tokyo (26.4)	Tokyo (26.4)
New York (15.9)	Mexico City (18.1)	Mumbai (26.1)
Shanghai (11.4)	Mumbai (18.1)	Lagos (23.2)
Mexico City (11.2)	São Paulo (17.8)	Dhaka (21.1)
São Paulo (10)	Shanghai (17)	São Paulo (20.4)
	New York (16.6)	Karachi (19.2)
	Lagos (13.4)	Mexico City (19.2)
	Los Angeles (13.1)	New York (17.4)
	Kolkata (12.9)	Jakarta (17.3)
	Buenos Aires (12.6)	Kolkata (17.3)
	Dhaka (12.3)	Delhi (16.8)
	Karachi (11.8)	Metro Manila (14.8)
	Delhi (11.7)	Shanghai (14.6)
	Jakarta (11)	Los Angeles (14.1)
	Osaka (11)	Buenos Aires (14.1)
	Metro Manila (10.9)	Cairo (13.8)
	Beijing (10.8)	Istanbul (12.5)
	Rio de Janeiro (10.6)	Beijing (12.3)
	Cairo (10.6)	Rio de Janeiro (11.9)
		Osaka (11.0)
		Tianjin (10.7)
		Hyderabad (10.5)
		Bangkok (10.1)

Activities

1 What is urbanisation?

2 Draw a graph of the data shown in the table 'urban population as a % of total population'. Make it a cumulative line graph (your teacher will show you how).

3 Which type of countries urbanised first – MEDCs or LEDCs? Why do you think this was?

4 What is the connection between industry and urbanisation?

5 Why is it that agricultural change and industrialisation are often referred to as a 'chicken and egg' cause of urbanisation? Explain your answer.

6 a On a world map, mark the location of all the mega-cities in 1975 from the table.

   b Now, using a different colour, mark on all the mega-cities in 2000.

   c Describe the changes shown on your map, in terms of number and location.

   d Is the trend you identified in answer **c** likely to continue until 2015? Explain your reasoning.

You are entering the twilight zone

In this unit you will learn how land use changes across a city – and how to recognise the different land use zones.

Inside the city

Travel through a typical MEDC city and you'll see how the **land use** changes.

What's land use, then?

It's what they *use* the land for. Buildings don't just spring up anywhere. Have you noticed that many cities seem to follow the same pattern of land use? Big shops seem to cluster in the middle, houses mostly get bigger and smarter as you move away from the centre, and garden centres and supermarkets are located at the edge. Let's go through the city, from the centre to the edge, and you'll see for yourself.

1 The Central Business District (CBD)

Here's the CBD. Lots to see and do: shops, cinema, clubs, bars, banks and offices.

Yeah, and to cram it all in, they have to build upwards.

The roads, canals, and railway lines all meet at the CBD.

2 The inner city – aka the twilight zone

But some people are doing up the old houses because it's near the city centre.

Look how fast it's changed! Old terraced houses, corner shops. Lots of the factories have closed.

The streets make a grid pattern, and the houses are small. They were built for factory workers. Little or no green space.

3 The inner suburbs

The pavements are wider.

And the houses are bigger. There are parks.

The streets are curvier, and there's more open space – but the houses are still quite close together.

4 The outer suburbs

Trees, big houses, but a long way to work.

I wouldn't mind in *that* car.

Houses often in small groups. Parks, maybe woods, perhaps a golf course.

5 The rural-urban fringe

Great view here! They're building new houses and a shopping centre, though.

Can we take the bus back?

Almost in the countryside, but only 40 minutes by train from the city centre.

A man called Ed Burgess noticed this pattern in Chicago, and drew an **urban model** of it. This model is shown on the right.

An urban model is a simplified diagram of the way land is used in a city. Of course, real cities are much more complicated, but models help you to understand what's going on, why things are where they are, and where things might change.

The kind of journey shown on the opposite page is called a **transect**. Looking at transects helps geographers to understand how and why a city changes from the centre to the edge.

Burgess urban model

Key
1 Central Business District (CBD)
2 inner city
3 inner suburbs
4 outer suburbs
5 rural-urban fringe

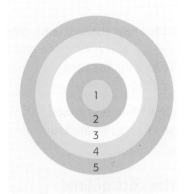

Activities

1 Draw a sketch of the photo above of Cardiff. Label the land use zones. (The CBD is labelled to help you.)

2 a Read the five sentences below. Which sentence matches which land use zone? Explain your answers.

   A Mrs Ponsonby can't decide which of her four bathrooms to use.

   B Izzy and her friends are off to town for a shopping spree.

   C They're knocking down the old houses and building posh flats.

   D Mr Brown is parking his car in his new garage. It only just fits.

   E Protesters are sitting in trees to stop the bulldozers clearing the site for a new football stadium.

   b Now try to write five sentences of your own to match with each zone.

3 For a town or city that you know, write an account of your journey from the town or city centre to the rural-urban fringe.

4 The words 'twilight zone' usually describe an inner city area as it begins to change from being an industrial zone. How could people 'brighten up', or improve, the twilight zone?

9.6 Urban zoning: why does it happen?

In this unit you will learn why urban zones develop.

Two key factors

Unit 9.5 showed how an urban area is made up of different districts – called **zones**. There are two basic causes:
- the cost of land
- accessibility.

The cost of land

The graph shows how much rent is paid, per square metre per year, at different distances from the centre of the CBD.

Think of getting the best land as a 'sale'. Different 'bidders' at the sale know where the locations they're interested in are to be found – and they know how much they can pay:

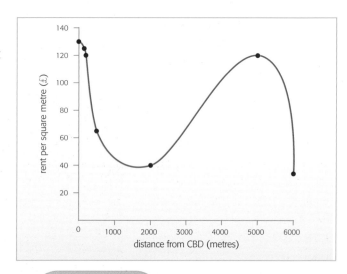

Everybody wants to locate at the heart of the city – but not everybody can afford it. We at Megacoffee can.

Rookems Solicitors want to be as central as possible, but we can't pay the huge rents that other businesses pay.

Obviously, we want to be close to the banks and our customers, but the only land that Loorolls Manufacturing can afford is 500 metres from the centre.

Yes, the house is big but the land is a third of the cost of city centre land – and it's only ten minutes by bus!

The zones develop as a settlement grows. Look at this map of the growth of Bedford.

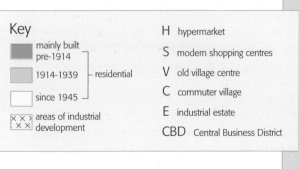

Key
- mainly built pre-1914
- 1914-1939 — residential
- since 1945
- ××× areas of industrial development

H hypermarket
S modern shopping centres
V old village centre
C commuter village
E industrial estate
CBD Central Business District

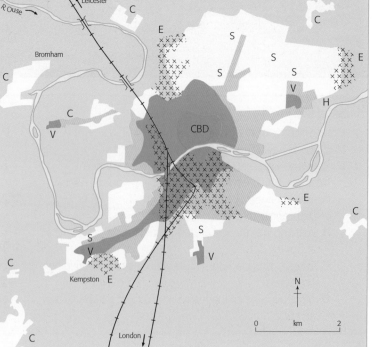

180

Is the CBD losing its charms?

The coffee shop, the solicitors and the factory owner in the cartoons opposite all wanted **good access** to the city centre, because that's where their customers were. But this has changed in the last 25 years or so.

In a way, the city centre has become too successful. People want to get there by car, and the older, narrower streets at the centre can't take the traffic. Street after street has been pedestrianised, car parks are now dotted around the CBD, and there are park-and-rides around the edge of the city, but for many shoppers getting into the city centre is too much of a hassle.

This is especially the case when out-of-town locations have vast superstores with free parking. Look again at the rents shown in the graph, and you can see that an out-of-town retailer will pay almost as much rent as companies in the city centre – but the store will be easily accessible (usually on a ring road) and will offer free parking. Now the buzzword is **accessibility**, especially by car.

▲ The centre of Bristol.

Activities

1 **a** What is an urban zone?
   b What does accessibility mean?
2 Look at the graph of rents.
   a What happens to the cost of land as you move away from the city centre?
   b What influence does accessibility have on the cost of land?
   c Why would HMV be prepared to pay for a city centre location?
3 **a** Using the cartoons opposite, explain why different 'bidders' will pay different amounts of money for locations within the city.

   b Why is Burgess' land use pattern:
      commercial → industrial → residential
      often found as you leave the city centre in an MEDC?
      (Hint: It's all about your answers to questions **2** and **3a**.)
4 **a** What is the anomaly (doesn't fit the pattern) in land prices in the graph?
   b Why do you think this is?
   c Explain the negative side of the CBD.
5 Draw and label a land use sketch of the photo above. You should be able to include four land use zones: CBD, industrial, residential, recreational.

In this unit you will find out about deprivation in cities.

Richer zones, poorer zones

Geographers are interested in the location of rich and poor people at several different levels:

◆ globally (where the MEDCs and LEDCs are)
◆ nationally (within a country)
◆ locally (for example within a city).

The **inner city** (look at Unit 9.5 to check its location) has high levels of **deprivation**. It is the poorest zone of most MEDC cities.

Deprivation in the inner city

Factories developed in the 19th century, and factory owners and developers built houses for the factory workers. These houses were terraced and small. In some cases, they were built back-to-back to cram in as many houses and people as possible.

In the second half of the 20th century, many of these factories closed because:

◆ other countries could make the same goods cheaper
◆ the local resources the factories needed ran out
◆ the machines and buildings were just too old.

Unemployment rose, and investors chose to put their money into more prosperous areas. This unemployment, together with cramped, ageing houses and schools, plus congestion as people tried to find parking spaces in the narrow streets, caused the better off people to move out to the suburbs.

Inner cities now have a higher-than-usual proportion of people who are:

◆ unemployed
◆ low-skilled and low-paid
◆ elderly
◆ single parents
◆ students
◆ ethnic minorities.

The rioting in Birmingham in 2005 highlighted some of the problems of the UK's inner cities. There can be tensions within the community. The unemployment, poverty, and lack of opportunities often result in high crime rates. Gangs develop to provide a sense of belonging, and as something to do. Adele's story highlights other difficulties.

My name is Adele.
Me and my mum live in a shared house. Our bit is not too bad, but some of the people who live here are scary. Sometimes there's used needles on the street. There's nowhere for young kids to play, and now the council want to close the primary school – they say it costs too much. And the council have agreed to build a new supermarket on our park. They say this will bring more jobs. My mum says these jobs will be low paid, low-skilled and mostly part-time.

Birmingham riots
A man was killed in clashes in the Lozells area of Birmingham last night. The riot, between Asian and black youths, broke out after a public meeting was held about an alleged sex attack on a teenage girl.

A group of more than 100 youths ran through the streets, attacking cars and motorists. Several cars were overturned and at least one was set alight. The mob was chased by police carrying riot shields.

The area has a strong African-Caribbean presence. Asian gangs have also sprung up in the area. There has been simmering tension between the two groups.

Adapted from newspaper reports, Sunday 23 October 2005.

Improving the inner cities

There has been a lot of **redevelopment** in the UK's inner cities.

Brindley Place in Birmingham is redevelopment on a grand scale:

- This part of Birmingham has a network of canals, which have been cleaned and smartened up.
- The accommodation runs from **social housing** to luxury flats. The buildings are roomy and modern.
- There are stylish bars and restaurants.
- There's the National Indoor Arena and the Sea Life Centre.

Brindley Place was started in 1994 and work is now complete. Brindley Place and the surrounding canal apartments cost about £400 million.

Developments like this provide many jobs. They try to mix the housing types, and provide lots to do in a safe, well-lit environment. This is one way to bring a higher quality of life back to our inner-city areas.

Before and after redevelopment at Brindley Place ▶

Activities

1 In theory, which zone of the city (see Unit 9.5) is most likely to be the most deprived? Why?

2 **a** Give three reasons why this zone in MEDC cities declined rapidly in the second half of the 20th century.

   b Why do you think industry left its location in the inner city?

   c Give three problems which would deter new industry from locating in the inner city.

   d Whereabouts in the city do you think industry has moved to?

3 Read Adele's story opposite. List five inner-city problems she mentions.

4 You are going to redevelop an inner-city area of your own. Make a large copy of the plan of an inner-city area on the right, but only copy the major roads, railway, and the canal. These things have to remain; everything else you can either knock down (**redevelop**) or keep but improve (**renewal**). Add labels to your map to show the changes you would make, explaining each one. Use the Brindley Place example to give yourself some ideas.

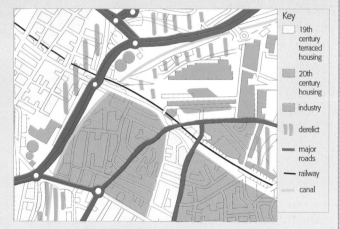

Key
- 19th century terraced housing
- 20th century housing
- industry
- derelict
- major roads
- railway
- canal

5 Now prepare a presentation (perhaps a PowerPoint presentation) saying how your plan helps:
- the local residents
- the environment
- the local heritage
- the city as a whole.

Urban problems in LEDCs

In this unit you will learn about deprivation in LEDC cities.

Rocinha

Rocinha is the biggest shanty town (*favela* in Portuguese) in Rio de Janeiro in Brazil. About 200 000 people live there.

Many *favelas* have no running water supply. Water comes in by truck, except in some areas where water is pumped in twice a week through recently laid pipes. Disposing of human waste is a big problem. Young children suffer very high rates of diarrhoea – on average, nine times a year for children under three.

The health risks are made worse by the overcrowding, the lack of clean water and toilets, and the lack of health care. Death rates in Rocinha are three times higher than the average for Rio.

The people of Rocinha have set up a complete alternative economy. They have their own businesses, banks, apartment buildings, and restaurants.

But street crime, drugs and violence are major problems. The *favela* is a dangerous place.

A local community worker is trying to increase the opportunities for children. He has built a small playground where the children can play safely. He's also trying to give them some of the skills they'll need to get jobs – for example, ICT skills. There is also a local radio station which is the focus of local community activities.

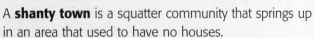

A **shanty town** is a squatter community that springs up in an area that used to have no houses.

A **squatter** is someone who settles on land without the legal right to stay there.

Shanty towns are also called **spontaneous settlements** – because spontaneous means unplanned.

Shanty towns

Shanty towns usually grow up in the less favourable parts of a city, such as steep hillsides or swampy areas.

- Homes are built from anything that's available – pieces of wood, cardboard, metal, plastic sheeting.
- The people are squatters. They are usually from rural areas, and have migrated to the city for a better life for themselves and their children.
- There's a lot of disease and poverty.
- The general level of education is quite low.
- Lots of shanty dwellers think that if you're old enough to walk and carry a bucket, you're old enough to work and earn your keep. Most children are sent out to earn money for the family.

Many parents really want their children to go to school, get an education, and get the good jobs that they themselves could never get. But they simply need the kids' money to keep the family going.

What can governments do?

In the 1990s, the Brazilian government decided to try and upgrade the *favelas,* rather than remove them. A major project, *Favela Bairro*, was designed to transform *favelas* with between 500 and 2500 households into lawful neighbourhoods, with legitimate property rights. It focused on improving the physical characteristics of *favelas* – paving roads, installing proper sewage systems, providing low-cost housing.

The program has had mixed results. The skills training for jobs wasn't very successful. What the *favela* population really needed was training in basic literacy and numeracy. The improvements in the *favelas* made house prices rise. Many residents cashed in by selling their suddenly valuable property and moving to other *favelas* which haven't yet been upgraded.

My name is Esat. I'm 14. I have four brothers and three sisters. I work at an outdoor market. My job is to wait and watch for people who buy things that are too heavy for them to carry themselves. I get their stuff home on a home-made cart. Other kids shine shoes, pick up scraps of paper to re-sell, or sell something like handkerchiefs, bread, tissues or razors – just about anything. I work about 16 hours a day, 7 days a week. I don't earn much, but what I earn goes straight to my parents.

Before

After

Activities

1 a What is a shanty town?
  b What is a squatter?
2 What do they call a shanty town in Brazil?
3 a Read Esat's story. Write down five questions you would ask him in a radio interview you're doing about conditions in LEDC cities.
  b Now write down the answers you think Esat would give.
4 a In an atlas, find Rio de Janeiro and describe its location in Brazil.
  b Where do people come from to make Rio de Janeiro so big?

5 a Where in an LEDC city would you find a shanty town?
  b Why do you think shanty towns developed here?
6 List six problems of life in Rocinha.
7 a What five things have been done to improve shanty town life in the Favela Bairro project?
  b Think of four further ideas to improve life in the Favela Bairro project – explain each one carefully.
8 Why would it help residents of favelas to have the legal right to stay put?

Urban models in LEDCs

In this unit you will learn about an urban model for LEDC cities, and compare it with actual land use in Rio de Janeiro.

The LEDC city

Just like MEDC cities, LEDC cities have land-use zones – and the CBD is at the centre for both – with entertainment, big shops, and the most important businesses.

When many people see a photo like this, they never guess it's of an LEDC city.

In fact, this is Nairobi, Kenya.

Major CBDs look very similar all over the world – lots of concrete, and flashy architecture. High-rise buildings were first developed in MEDC cities like New York and Chicago, because there wasn't enough available land in the CBDs, so the land had to be used more intensively. Lack of land is not a problem in Nairobi, but there are skyscrapers there, just the same.

Just as in MEDC cities, LEDC cities also have industrial areas, and high- and low-class housing zones, but the land-use pattern is different. What's more, many LEDC cities have shanty towns, like Rocinha in Rio de Janeiro (Unit 9.8).

The best housing starts near the CBD, often along a very smart street, sometimes called the **spine**. Along the spine you will find very expensive flats, with space for servants. Many of these apartments are protected by their own security staff.

Next to the high-class area, is medium-quality housing.

Shanty towns have developed on the unpleasant sites, like steep hillsides or swampy areas. Sometimes they are very close to the posh areas; sometimes right out on the edge of the city. There are also areas of social housing on the periphery (edge).

Industries are along the main roads.

Look at the urban model for LEDC cities on the right.

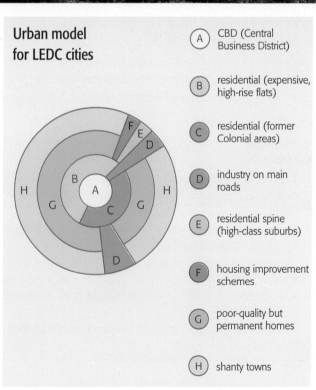

Urban model for LEDC cities

A — CBD (Central Business District)

B — residential (expensive, high-rise flats)

C — residential (former Colonial areas)

D — industry on main roads

E — residential spine (high-class suburbs)

F — housing improvement schemes

G — poor-quality but permanent homes

H — shanty towns

The model and Rio de Janeiro

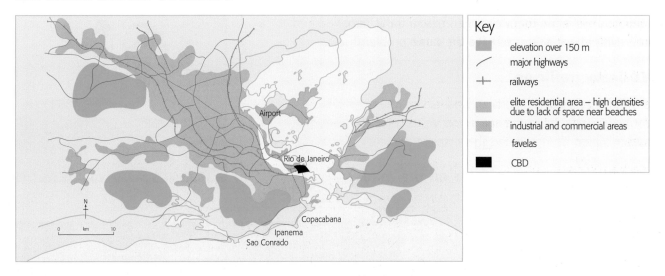

Key

- elevation over 150 m
- major highways
- railways
- elite residential area – high densities due to lack of space near beaches
- industrial and commercial areas
- favelas
- CBD

Activities

1 In what ways does the map of Rio de Janeiro (top) look like the urban model opposite?

2 In what ways does the map of Rio de Janeiro not look like the urban model?

3 Compare the LEDC urban model with the Burgess urban model in Unit 9.5.

4 Look at the cartoon of Rio (above). What does it tell you about Rio de Janeiro that the map doesn't – and what does it try to hide?

5 Why does the cartoon only show selected features of Rio?

Traffic – everybody's problem

In this unit you will learn that when it comes to traffic jams, every city, everywhere, seems to have the same problem!

There's heavy traffic on …

Do you ever listen to traffic reports on local radio? Whenever there's a rush-hour problem, the announcer will explain why there's a jam. Often it's 'due to the sheer weight of traffic'.

Why are there so many vehicles on the roads?

It's no fun reading the traffic reports, I can tell you …

Bangkok, Thailand

It's said Bangkok has the worst traffic jams in the world. It's not unusual for schoolkids to be woken at 5 am so they can be dressed and carried to the car, where they will fall asleep again – they will be dropped off at school at about 7 am. Then their dad will drive to his work. More than 2.6 million vehicles drive through the streets of Bangkok every day, and the resulting air and noise pollution has proved a constant headache for the city's population and the Thai government.

Every day the number of cars on the city's streets increases by 481, and Bangkok's drivers spend the equivalent of 22 days in their vehicles each year.

Bangkok's main problem, however, is that it has a severe shortage of roads – just 8% of its surface is covered with roads, compared with 20% in most other major cities.

On top of this, there is not enough public transport. Bangkok's elevated Skytrain system (pictured) is expensive and very short. Although an underground system was finished in 2004, the government is considering a 280-km extension to the Skytrain.

Has this improved public transport system helped? Let's dip into a weblog. Don't laugh at the English – your Thai might not be great …

By: Sukrit Tangwongtrakul Phy
Subject: Traffic Jam: Third reason of traffic jam in Bangkok.
First, Accident in the road. It is crashed cars and broken cars. Second, Building the road. Building construction prevents traffic, for example: building the bridge across the road. Finally, volume of the cars so much. The people have a lot of cars.

By: Kanha
Subject: Traffic Jam: Third reason of traffic jam in Bangkok.
In my opinion, Traffic jam in Bangkok is big problem. It's very difficult to solve because Bangkok has many cars and most of the people are selfishness.
The result of the traffic jam problem is:
- It causes air pollution.
- It causes respiratory sickness and people are bad health.
The way to solve traffic jam problem is:
- People should to go by bus, Skytrain and train.
- People have to observe the traffic law.
- People should cross the road by a flyover.
However, we should collaborate to solve the traffic jam problem in order to this problem is decrease.

Moscow chokes, drivers fume in mammoth traffic

Malkhaz nudged his Volga forward, stopped and sighed. He is one of the 3 million people who drive into Moscow every day and, like everyone else, he spends hours in traffic jams.

'It gets worse and worse, there are so many cars. People have got richer and richer. Now a husband has a car, his wife has a car, and his teenage son will get one when he's old enough' he said as he glowered at the Peugeot in front. 20 minutes and 600 yards of conversation later, he had calmed down a bit.

'This road was like this 100 years ago, and will be just the same 100 years from now. It can't be changed' he said, gesturing at one of the leafy and broad, but hopelessly clogged, boulevards of Moscow's historic centre.

Moscow's booming economy has allowed Russians to indulge in consumer spending which was impossible in communist times. Cars are at the top of their shopping lists.

Although only 1 in 10 Russians owns a car, car sales are booming and are expected to reach around 2 million a year by 2008, up from 1.6 million in 2005. Soviet citizens owned around 8 million private cars 15 years ago.

What can be done?

London has congestion charging. Other cities are considering it.

Tokyo has two projects designed to keep the traffic moving. Two main causes of traffic hold-ups have been identified there:

1 When people cross the road other than at proper crossings. So the plan is to stop this by putting up crowd barriers and improving legal crossings for pedestrians and cyclists (see right).
2 When buses stop to pick up passengers. So the plan is to make bays at bus stops, so the parked bus doesn't hold up the traffic (see right). Illegal parking will be savagely punished, but there will be more – and free – one-hour parking places.

Activities

1 Look at the graph on the right:
   a Describe the change in Russian car ownership between 1995 and 2002.
   b Why has this change happened?
2 The photo at the top of the page shows a Moscow traffic jam. Moscow already has a fantastic underground system. What changes could be made, using ideas from Bangkok and Tokyo?
3 Rank your improvements
   a by cost   b by environmental impact.
4 Why are your two rankings different?

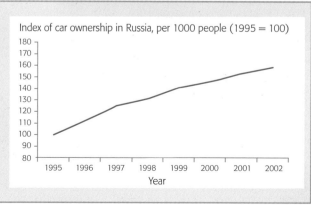

Index of car ownership in Russia, per 1000 people (1995 = 100)

Urban sprawl

In this unit you will learn how our towns and cities are growing, and about some of the problems this is causing.

Spreading out

New growth is happening at the edges of towns and cities. This area, where the town or city meets the countryside, is called the **rural-urban fringe**. Urban growth in this area is often called urban sprawl. The word 'sprawl' tells us this growth isn't seen as a good thing.

However, most MEDC cities are losing population – people are moving out to smaller towns and villages nearby. This is called **counter-urbanisation**.

Why are people moving out of cities?

Reasons for counter-urbanisation include:

◆ Inner-city problems, like pollution, traffic and crime.
◆ Businesses moving to office parks and science parks. (They're not real parks, just groups of offices and researchers located on out-of-town sites.)
◆ Better transport and more car ownership.
◆ The peace and quiet of the countryside.

The same pattern – moving from the city to beyond the city limit – is happening all over the UK. On top of this, most cities have out-of-town developments: garden centres, golf courses, country parks, superstores, and science and office parks.

The elderly lady on the right clearly hates the changes to her town. But other people want new developments in the urban fringe:

My town's under attack …
It's being destroyed. There's not much parking, and it's expensive. Queues stretch back along all the main roads at rush-hour and on Saturdays. All the traditional shops have gone: butchers, fishmongers, grocers, furniture shops – because the rents keep going up and parking is free at out-of-town shopping centres. Whole streets are full of bars and cafes. Young people everywhere; no oldies like me. I'm too scared to be in the town centre after 10 p.m.

We need free parking, and so do our customers.

Multiplex cinema owner

With a bigger stadium, we could get bigger crowds and increase our income.

Football club owner

Yes, the superstore is doing OK – but we need to develop megastores.

Supermarket boss

The government wants us farmers to develop new ways of earning money. What about a golf course?

Farmer

The split-up wasn't too bad, but now I have to find a new house.

Divorcee

We need a bigger house!

Parents of triplets

Problems and issues

You can see from the cartoons opposite that there are good reasons for building in the urban fringe. But there are a lot of people who want to ban any further building there:

◆ environmentalists – they worry about damage to wildlife
◆ walkers and naturalists – they have access to less and less open space
◆ people already living in villages at the urban fringe – demand for houses has gone up so prices have risen, meaning locals can't afford to buy houses in their own village
◆ 'greens' – an increase in commuting leads to increased greenhouse gas emissions, and air and noise pollution.

Green belts

The government has been trying to preserve the countryside. One plan was to create **green belts**. A green belt is a zone around an urban area. New building is not totally banned, but it's hard to get planning permission for any new development. In 2005, Brighton and Hove Albion Football Club got permission to build a new stadium on a site inside an Area of Outstanding Natural Beauty. Much of the M25 cuts through London's green belt.

One of the main problems of the green belts is that they have led to people commuting further into work.

An alternative is to redevelop brownfield sites – abandoned sites within existing towns and cities, such as Lewes in Sussex (below).

Chalgrove

Chalgrove is a village about ten miles from Oxford. Over the last twenty years, the number of households, car ownership and the average distance travelled per household has doubled. Lots of people have moved into the village, many looking for what they believe is a better quality of life in the countryside. Many live a 'commuter' lifestyle, travelling to work in Oxford, London, or other cities. These incomers often do their shopping or banking in the town they commute to.

In 2000, the Post Office said it was closing the post office because it was uneconomic. For pensioners in the village, the post office was the only way to get their pensions, because they were unable to get to their bank. The villagers in Chalgrove formed an action group to fight for their threatened post office. For now, the post office is still open.

▼ From this …

▼ … to this?

Activities

1 Define:
 a counter-urbanisation   **b** rural-urban fringe
2 Give three reasons why people are leaving cities.
3 Give four attractions of the rural-urban fringe lifestyle.

4 Name four land uses (other than housing) that develop on the rural-urban fringe.
5 Choose two of these uses, and explain fully why the rural-urban fringe is attractive to them.

The big picture

This chapter is about agriculture – or farming – in the UK, and in different parts of the world. These are the big ideas behind the chapter:

◆ All types of farming work as a system, with inputs, processes and outputs.

◆ Physical and human factors affect what type of farming happens where. And for most types of farming climate is the most important physical factor.

◆ Farmers, wherever they are in the world, face problems and challenges.

◆ Farming needs to be made more sustainable.

Your goals for this chapter

By the end of this chapter you should be able to answer these questions:

◆ What do these terms mean?

system, inputs, processes, outputs, factors, intensive, extensive, commercial, subsistence

◆ What type of farming happens where in the UK, and why?

◆ What problems and changes do the UK's farmers face? And how have some real farms changed?

◆ What do these terms mean?
CAP, SPS, quota, set-aside, agribusiness, sustainable, agri-environment scheme

◆ List some of the ways that farming in the UK can become more sustainable, and give some examples.

◆ What challenges do the market gardeners of the Netherlands, and farmers of Eastern Europe face?

◆ Farmers in LEDCs have problems too. What are they?

◆ What do these terms mean?
agro-tourist, Green Revolution, irrigation, salinisation

◆ How can farmers in LEDCs make their farming more sustainable? Give some examples.

And then . . .

When you finish the chapter, come back here and see if you've met your goals!

Did you know?
There are about 25 million sheep in the UK. That's nearly half a sheep for everyone!

Did you know?
2% of the UK's workers are employed in farming.

Did you know?
Farms are measured in hectares. A hectare is about the size of a football pitch.

Did you know?
◆ A cow will eat for about eight hours a day – the rest of the time is spent resting and chewing the cud.
◆ The cud is food the cow brings back from its stomach into its mouth and chews at its leisure. Clever cow!

Your chapter starter
Look at the photo on page 192.
What is this animal? What does it give us?
What type of farming is this?
What else do you know about farming?
Does farming have anything to do with you?

Stop looking at me like that.

Farming – what's it all about?

In this unit you'll start to think about farming, and find out about farming systems.

Celebrity chef Rick Stein criticised what he called 'cruel' British battery farming methods.

British battery hen farmers say their methods aren't cruel.

Did you know?
Britain is the largest producer of chicken in Europe.

Farming – or **agriculture** – it doesn't really matter what we call it. But what's it all about? What do farmers do? And how do they do it?

The answers are lots of different things, in different ways, in different parts of the world, as you'll see by the time you get to the end of this chapter.

Farmers produce the food we eat – from the beef that goes in our burgers, to the rice we have with our curry. Farming also includes things like flowers, fruit and fish. But farmers also look after the countryside.

Did you know?
In 2004, 68 000 people were employed full-time in farming in the UK.

Think about these

- How important is farming?
- How much food do we produce in the UK?
- Where does the rest of our food come from?
- How many people work in farming in the UK?
- **Farming**
- How far does our food travel?
- What do farmers do?
- How is it produced (and does it matter)?
- How does farming affect the environment?

Some of these questions will be answered in this chapter, or even on these two pages. You might need to do some finding out of your own to answer the others.

What goes in must come out

In geography we say that farming is a **system**. This is just a way of saying there are:

◆ **Inputs** – things that go into the system
◆ **Outputs** – things that come out of the system
◆ **Processes** – things that happen in the middle

There might be some **feedback**, e.g. where some of the profits (if there are any) are put back into the system. The farming system diagram below shows how inputs, processes and outputs fit together.

Inputs can also be called **factors**. These are the things which affect farming, and a farmer's choice of what to produce.

Systems can be applied to any farm anywhere in the world.

Did you know?
British farmers look after more than 70% of the total land area of the UK.

Did you know?
British farmers produce nearly 65% of the food we eat in the UK.

Did you know?
There are over 2 million dairy cows in Britain. They produce 14 billion litres of milk every year.

Did you know?
Dairy cows are kept indoors in the winter and they eat silage (pickled grass) and cow cake (dried cereal). Tasty.

In LEDCs farming may be subsistence (see Unit 10.2 for what this means), where there's no profit because the produce isn't sold – it's eaten by the farmer's family.

Physical inputs
Climate
Temperature
Length of growing season
Rainfall

Relief
High or low
Steep or flat

Soils
Deep or thin
Rich or poor

Human and economic inputs
Labour (workers)
Machinery
Buildings
Markets and transport
Capital (money)
Seeds, animals
Animal feed
Fertiliser, pesticides, etc.
Government/EU policies, subsidies, loans

Processes
Rearing animals
Grazing/feeding
Lambing/calving
Shearing/milking

Growing crops
Ploughing
Planting
Spraying
Harvesting

Outputs
Animals and animal products
Milk, wool, eggs
Lamb, beef, pork, chicken
Lambs, calves, piglets, chicks

Crops
Wheat, oats, barley, etc.
Vegetables, fruit, flowers

Feedback
In MEDCs there may be a profit which is reinvested.

Activities

1 Why do you think 'battery farming' (for example of hens in cages) has become an important method of farming in the UK?
2 Do you think Rick Stein's opinion on battery farming will influence either farmers or the people who buy the eggs?
3 Do you think 'farmers produce the food we eat' is an accurate description of farming in the UK?
4 Choose two of the physical inputs in the systems diagram. Explain why they are important in farming.

Farming – what happens where?

In this unit you'll learn how farms are sorted, and why farming varies around the UK.

Classifying farms

Geographers find it helpful to sort things into different groups. The technical word for sorting is 'classifying'. Farms can be classified in three ways.

1   By what is grown or produced (**processes**):
   - **Arable** farms grow crops.
   - **Pastoral** farms rear animals.
   - **Mixed** farms grow crops *and* rear animals. Some of the crops are used to feed the animals.
   - **Market gardening**. These are small farms growing fruit and vegetables.

2   By how much **input** there is:
   - **Intensive** farms have large inputs of labour, money or technology. They are usually quite small. Market gardening is intensive.
   - **Extensive** farms have smaller inputs and are usually larger. Hill sheep farms are extensive.

3   By **output**:
   - **Commercial** farms. The outputs are sold to make a profit, e.g. arable farms in East Anglia.
   - **Subsistence** farms. Farmers produce food for themselves and their family. There is nothing left to sell, e.g. rice growing in the Philippines.

Farming types in the UK

So, what type of farming happens where? It's not haphazard – there's a **pattern** to it all, as the map opposite shows. If you try to grow wheat in the Lake District, it won't grow very well – and there are good reasons for that. Different **factors** are at work. A farmer's choice about what type of farming to do depends on physical and human factors. For most types of farming, physical factors are more important than human ones – and **climate** is the *most* important.

Remember – the map is very generalised *and* it doesn't show any towns or cities.

The north and west

- Cool summers, mild winters (but cold on mountains).
- Lots of rain, snow in winter, strong winds.
- Lots of high land and steep slopes. Poor, thin soils.
- Small fields, sheep graze on moorland.
- Not a lot of machinery.
- Not a lot of money.
- Poor transport links.
- Markets not close by.

Hill sheep farms are found in parts of Wales, northern England and Scotland in areas with these physical and human factors. Land here isn't suitable for other types of farming.

Dairy farming

Dairy farms keep cows for milk. They are found where:
- there is a warm, moist (not *too* wet) climate
- land is not *too* steep
- transport is good (to get milk to the market quickly)
- markets are close.

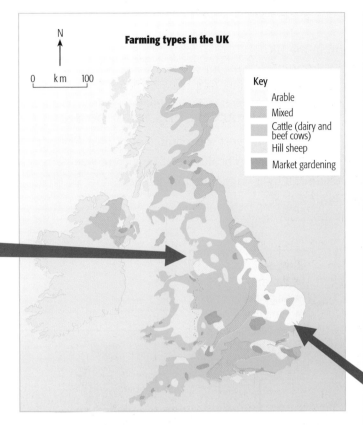

Farming types in the UK

Key
Arable
Mixed
Cattle (dairy and beef cows)
Hill sheep
Market gardening

Mixed farms

These are found:

- between the crop-growing areas in the east, and animal-rearing areas in the west
- where the climate is just right – not *too* wet and not *too* dry, and where soils are good.

The south and east

- Warm sunny summers, cold winters.
- Less rainfall (falls when crops are growing).
- Lots of low flat land.
- Fertile, deep soils.
- Large farms, with large fields.
- More machinery.
- More money.
- Good transport links.
- Markets closer.

Arable farms are found mainly in eastern England in areas with these physical and human factors.

Market gardening

This is found:

- where transport links are good
- close to markets.

Lots of money is spent on labour, seeds, fertiliser, sprays, heating and lighting (for greenhouses).

This photo shows strawberries being grown.

Activities

1 Farming in the UK is usually classified as commercial. Why?
2 Wheat is an arable crop.
   a What physical and human factors do you need to grow wheat?
   b Why can't you grow wheat in the Lake District?
3 Why do you think climate is often the most important physical factor influencing farming?
4 'Farmers in the UK decide what to grow and where to grow it – technology is more important than climate to the modern farmer.' How far do you agree with this statement?

Farming – on the flat ... and on the edge

In this unit you'll find out about an arable farm and a hill farm in the UK.

Arable farming – Lynford House Farm

Lynford House Farm as a system

Remember we said in Unit 10.1 that farming is a system? Every farm can be described like this. Lynford House Farm is an arable farm in East Anglia run by Robert and Charles Sears. The diagram below shows the inputs, processes and outputs of the farm.

Cereal harvest hits farm profits

A disastrous harvest was predicted for East Anglia's cereal growers. A healthy profit one year was followed by a staggering loss the next.

Inputs
- 570 hectares of flat fen land
- Farm is just above sea level
- Warm, sunny summers – 17 °C in July
- 560 mm rainfall a year
- Fertile soil
- Fertiliser and pesticide
- Fuel for tractors, etc.
- 4 full-time workers plus contractors
- Machinery – lots! Includes combine harvester, tractors, sugar beet harvester, mower.
- Subsidy paid on the amount of land farmed (a subsidy is money from the government or EU).

Processes
- Ploughing
- Sowing
- Applying fertiliser and pesticides
- Watering
- Weeding
- Harvesting
- Maintenance – machinery, hedges, ditches, etc.

Outputs
- Wheat
- Sugar beet
- Farm has produced potatoes, peas and winter linseed in the past

Feedback
Profit is reinvested in the farm

Lynford House Farm

What's changing?

With farm incomes down, and no crystal ball to predict the future, Robert and Charles have been simplifying things. They have:

- increased technology (they use computers for crop-recording, accounts, wages and banking)
- not replaced recently retired workers
- rented out fields to other farmers for growing potatoes, lettuces and onions
- sold 8 bungalows on the farm to pay off loans
- considered building wind turbines (they decided not to as too many people were against it).

Farm buildings

▲ *Lynford House Farm in the Cambridgeshire Fens, East Anglia.*

Hill farming – Herdship Farm

Hill farmers win wildlife honours

Maurice and Kath Toward from Herdship Farm in Teesdale, have been presented with a Hill Farming Award. Their farm is a haven for birds like black grouse, lapwing, yellow wagtail, snipe and golden plover.

Herdship Farm

Kath Toward was originally a city girl from Liverpool. Her business brain and Maurice's love of his land mean they have survived in difficult times. This is what Kath said about the farm:

'It's about 229 hectares. The land goes from 450–600 metres above sea level. Our local weather expert says we have about 580 mm of rain a year. We've got about 22 hectares of flowering hay meadow. The rest is *very* rough pasture. And we use moorland.

Animals – we keep 12 cows. We've been paid to change these to a traditional British breed. And we have *loads* of sheep. 268 Swaledales and 180 North Country Cheviots. We produce our own silage for the cows, and hay for the sheep. The sheep need dipping and shearing, and we're very busy when they're lambing! Lambs are sold for meat, or they replace older ewes.'

▲ *Herdship Farm in Teesdale*

What's changing?

The National Trust thinks the incomes of some hill farmers will halve by 2010. This is because of a change in subsidies. Farmers will be paid according to how much land they farm rather than the number of animals they keep. So, some farmers will be worse off.

At Herdship Farm, Maurice and Kath have seen lots of changes. They are paid by the Environmental Stewardship Scheme to:
- create breeding bird habitats
- look after wildflower sites
- maintain historic sites, e.g. old lead workings, on their farm
- organise farm tours and walks for the public.

Kath says 'We now call ourselves land managers, not just farmers.'

My days here could be numbered – people reckon hill farming is close to collapse.

Activities

1 What is a subsidy?
2 Why do you think farmers are paid subsidies?
3 What other ways can you think of for Lynford House Farm to make money?
4 Draw a systems diagram for Herdship Farm. Describe and explain the main differences between this and the Lynford House systems diagram.

Is farming in crisis?

In this unit you'll learn about some of the problems facing the UK's farmers.

Food in the shops

In early September, fruit and veg grown in the UK, like apples, carrots and green beans are in season. But in the supermarket we see apples from the USA, carrots from South Africa and beans from Kenya.

What's going on?

The food we eat has changed. We want different types of food to those that people ate 50 or so years ago. And, we want them cheaper.

◀ What's this . . .

. . . got to do with this? ▼

Most people shop at the supermarket. Everything's in one place, it's open for hours and seems to offer us bargains. Supermarkets are very powerful. They offer farmers and food producers the chance to sell to huge numbers of people. And for some farmers that's where it can all go horribly wrong.

The supermarkets' size means they can choose their suppliers and decide how much to pay farmers both at home and abroad. The food market has become **global**, and farmers in the UK compete with those abroad. A UK pig farmer spent lots of money to make his farm meet the needs of the RSPCA's Freedom Food Scheme. The supermarket he supplied with meat then bought cheaper Danish bacon instead, produced with lower welfare standards, so the supermarket could offer shoppers a better deal.

Farmers have other problems, such as money (income). Robin Spence is a dairy and livestock farmer in Dumfries, Scotland. Farmers there feel lucky if they make £12 000 a year – and they work every single day. Robin gets just over 18p a litre for his milk. Compare that with the price in the supermarket!

More problems

Increased demand for more, and cheaper, food has led to other problems.

Soil erosion

Repeated ploughing, especially in autumn and winter, means the soil is exposed at the wettest, windiest time of year. The Fens in East Anglia (where Lynford House Farm is) are flat, with little to slow down gales. So, the soil is eroded.

Removal of hedgerows in the past didn't help. The leaves and branches broke the fall of heavy rain, and the roots bound the soil together. When the hedges were removed, the soil was washed away by the rain, or blown by the wind.

Overproduction

Farmers used to be given subsidies which guaranteed them a minimum price for their produce. This meant they overproduced (produced food which wasn't needed). Since 1992, subsidies have been reduced, so this is no longer such a problem.

Use of chemicals

Farmers use a number of chemicals, including **pesticides** and **fertiliser**.
- Pesticides control pests, diseases and weeds in crops.
- Fertilisers replace nutrients removed from the soil. These need replacing for plants to grow well.

Pesticides, fertiliser, slurry (animal manure) and soil all end up in our water supply, and are a major cause of water pollution.

▼ *Soil erosion by wind in East Anglia.*

And there's more …

Hard up farmers quit the industry

More than 15 000 people left the farming industry in 2005, and the trend is likely to continue. Since 1999, 1 in 4 Scottish dairy farmers have gone out of business.

When a farm is put up for sale it's more likely to be snapped up by a city worker than taken on by a new farmer.

Activities

1 Find out where the food eaten in your home over a weekend is grown. List as many items as you can, particularly fresh food. Then describe what your survey tells you. How much of the food produced abroad is also grown in the UK?
2 Why could farmers in the UK have difficulty in competing with farmers abroad who wish to sell their produce here?
3 How far have environmental, economic, and social factors caused problems for UK farmers?
4 Find out about the problems caused for farming in the UK by *either* BSE in the mid-1990s, or the outbreak of foot and mouth disease in 2001.

All change for farming

In this unit you'll find out about changes in farming in the UK.

EU changes farm payments

EU agriculture ministers have agreed to change the money paid to farmers. The deal has been described as a 'historic agreement'. It has altered the Common Agricultural Policy (CAP) and will shape Europe's farming for the next 10 years.

What is the CAP?

The CAP was created in 1962 to:
- guarantee regular food supplies at affordable prices
- ensure a fair standard of living for farmers.

Under the CAP, Europe's farmers received £31 billion worth of **subsidies** a year. This was up to 70% of the whole EU budget. The subsidies meant farmers produced as much food as they could. This led to huge surpluses of food products (called 'mountains' and 'lakes') in the 1980s.

When the EU expanded in 2004, an extra 10 mainly poor, rural, countries joined. The EU couldn't afford to keep paying all those subsidies – something had to be done.

What's changed?

CAP reform began in 1992. Further changes were introduced in 2005. The main change is that farmers don't get several different subsidy payments. Instead they get one single payment a year. This is called the **Single Payment System** (or SPS for short).

Farmers must meet certain standards of animal welfare and land management to get the payment.

The new system means that farmers:
- spend less time filling in forms
- don't have to keep a particular number of animals
- will be paid depending on how much land they have.

Some things stay the same

- Dairy farmers have a **quota**. They are told how much milk they can produce, and can't produce more than this.
- Arable farmers must **set-aside** part of their land – so that it *isn't* used for growing crops or keeping animals on. There are strict rules about how much, and what type of land can be set-aside, and also about how it should be managed so that farmers get their payment under the SPS.

> **Did you know?**
> The SPS will break the link between CAP subsidies and the amount that farmers produce. They will not have to produce lots to get a subsidy. They can produce what the market wants.

▲ Kath Toward from Herdship Farm (centre) said 'For the new system the moorland that we use has been added to our farmland. So, for the SPS our farm doubled in size overnight and we get paid more!'

▲ Farmers can set-aside land at the edge of fields. This will encourage greater biodiversity on the farm.

Other changes in farming

Animal welfare

More people are concerned about the way animals are treated. The EU and UK introduced laws about animal welfare. Other organisations have set up their own schemes to improve conditions, e.g. the RSPCA Freedom Food Scheme.

Farms get bigger

Agribusiness is large-scale, capital-intensive farming.

It happens when small farms are merged into one large farm, and a lot of money is invested. Agribusiness farms tend to:

◆ have large fields, because hedgerows have been removed. (This makes it easier for machines to operate.)

◆ specialise in growing 1 or 2 types of crop, or rearing 1 or 2 types of animal.

◆ be owned by large companies or landlords.

◆ use the latest machinery.

◆ have high inputs of pesticides and fertiliser to get high outputs.

Agribusiness is popular in East Anglia, where there's a lot of fertile arable land.

> **Did you know?**
> Farmers plant more hedges than they remove.

> **Did you know?**
> Scientists are developing insect-like robots that could be used for crop pollination.

Mechanisation and the loss of jobs

Remember Robert and Charles Sears who run Lynford House Farm in East Anglia? They said 'On our farm we have gradually reduced the labour force. Larger machinery means the same work can be carried out by fewer people.'

Although machines such as tractors, combine harvesters and seed drills are expensive to buy, they do save time and money. The number of people working in farming continues to go down.

2001	2002	2003	2004
82 000	76 000	70 000	68 000

▲ *The number of people employed full-time in farming. (There are others who work part-time or seasonally, who add to the numbers.)*

Activities

1 Explain why the CAP led to food 'mountains' and 'lakes'.

2 How is the 'Single Payment System' different from CAP subsidies?

3 Do you think all farmers will benefit from changes to the system? Explain your answer.

4 Why do you think farmers are paid to 'set-aside' some of their land? Do you agree with this policy?

5 What are the benefits of 'agribusiness'? What are the disadvantages of this type of farming?

6 Why is increased mechanisation likely to benefit larger, more profitable farms? Which parts of the UK do you think are unlikely to be affected by increased mechanisation?

Making farming sustainable

In this unit you'll find out about some ways of making UK farming more sustainable.

What does 'making farming sustainable' mean?

The last few pages showed you some of the problems and challenges farmers in the UK have faced recently. Making farming sustainable means it needs to change and develop so that it meets people's needs today and can continue without harming the environment. There are a number of ways this can happen. Here are a few.

> **Did you know?**
> The National Farmers Union says that farmers are trying to minimise the environmental impacts of pesticides through a programme called the Voluntary Initiative.

Old methods help wildlife

Who'd have thought we'd see a scene like the one on the right in the twenty-first century?

Ty Brith farm near Welshpool is also farmed using traditional methods. The farm is run by Jonathan and Anna Khan. They use horses to cut the hay, as the small steep fields are surrounded by hedges. They would need to be removed if the Khans wanted to use modern machinery. Using traditional methods has helped to increase the numbers of bullfinches and thrushes. Ty Brith operates under the Tir Gofal Scheme.

Tir Gofal

This is an **agri-environment** scheme for Wales. Farmers are encouraged to:
- maintain and improve the landscape and wildlife
- provide new opportunities for people to visit the countryside.

Farmers are paid for this work. They can also go on courses to learn about managing different habitats, such as woodland, and to learn skills like dry-stone walling and hedge-laying.

Environmental Stewardship

This is an **agri-environment** scheme for England. Its aims are similar to Tir Gofal, to:
- conserve wildlife
- maintain and improve the landscape
- protect the historic environment and natural resources
- promote public access and understanding of the countryside.

What else?

As well as schemes like Tir Gofal and Environmental Stewardship, there are other ways that farming can become more sustainable.

- Go **organic**. Organic farms don't use artificial fertilisers, herbicides or pesticides. Organic farms and those converting to become organic made up 4% of the UK's farmland in 2005.
- **Diversify**. That means do other things as well as farming.

Herdship Farm

Remember Maurice and Kath Toward who run Herdship Farm in Teesdale? Look back at Unit 10.3 to remind yourself what else they're paid to do besides keeping all those sheep.

They, and other farmers in their area, work with other organisations to maintain and improve the environment, including:

- English Nature
- RSPB
- local authorities
- DEFRA (Department for Environment, Food and Rural Affairs)

Like many farmers, Maurice and Kath have had to diversify. They have a self-catering cottage called 'Frog Hall' which they let out for holidays.

The chipping news

Offering holiday cottages is a fairly common way of diversifying. Other farmers do things differently.

William Chase was an arable farmer in Herefordshire, growing potatoes on Tyrrells Court Farm. He supplied supermarkets with what they wanted – smooth-skinned potatoes, all about the same size. But he got fed up with dealing with the supermarkets' demands.

He wanted to use his potatoes in a different way. 'I decided to produce high-quality, pedigree potato chips – not mere crisps.' William said.

He uses old-fashioned varieties of potatoes grown without pesticides, and buys other vegetables from a neighbouring farm. 'We get the carrots that are too big or funny-shaped to sell.' William produces 160 000 packets of Tyrrells chips a week on the farm.

> **Did you know?**
> Farmers markets are where farmers can sell direct to the public. But in Devon farmers have opened their own farmers' supermarket.

▲ Who's a pretty boy? This Black Grouse is just one of many species of birds found on Herdship Farm.

Activities

1 Why is it important to make farming in the UK sustainable?
2 a Explain why farmers might be attracted to agri-environment schemes.
  b What do you think might be the disadvantages of these schemes?
3 Find out about some of the ways farmers diversify. Explain one type of diversification in detail.
4 Sustainable farming includes looking after the countryside. Do you think farmers should be paid to do this, even if they don't produce any food on their farms? Justify your opinion.

Farming in the EU

In this unit you'll learn about market gardening in the Netherlands and farming in Eastern Europe.

Market gardening in the Netherlands

- Market gardening is growing fruit, vegetables and flowers **intensively**.
- The Netherlands produces 60% of the world's commercially grown flowers.
- And 25% of European vegetable exports.
- The Netherlands is the most densely populated country in Europe. 16 million people are squeezed into 42 000 sq. km.
- Market gardening takes up 5% of the land area in the Netherlands.

Challenges

- The Netherlands faces competition for its flowers from LEDCs such as Kenya. (See Unit 10.8 for more on flower growing in Kenya.)
- The use of pesticides pollute water in flower-growing areas.

Market gardening in the Netherlands

Key

- market gardening
- main towns / cities
- railways
- Schiphol Airport

N

0   25   50 km

Haarlem   Amsterdam
North Sea
The Hague   Utrecht
Rotterdam   River Rhine
River Maas

About market gardening

The Netherlands is one of the most intensively farmed countries in the world. Land is scarce and expensive, so farming must be profitable to compete with other users.

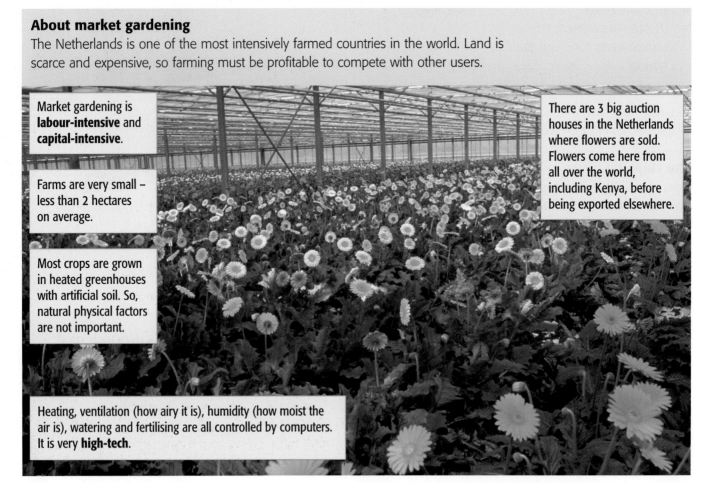

Market gardening is **labour-intensive** and **capital-intensive**.

Farms are very small – less than 2 hectares on average.

Most crops are grown in heated greenhouses with artificial soil. So, natural physical factors are not important.

Heating, ventilation (how airy it is), humidity (how moist the air is), watering and fertilising are all controlled by computers. It is very **high-tech**.

There are 3 big auction houses in the Netherlands where flowers are sold. Flowers come here from all over the world, including Kenya, before being exported elsewhere.

Eastern Europe

Did you know that 5 times as many people work in farming in the 10 countries which joined the EU in 2004, than in the original 15 countries?

The subsidy the farmers get from the CAP is only 25% of what farmers in the rest of the EU get. The subsidy is based on the size of the farm. Many farms in the 'new' EU countries of central and Eastern Europe are small, so the farmers won't get much money.

People are worried that farmers won't be able to compete with those in the richer EU countries, and that they will be forced to leave the countryside and move to the towns for jobs.

There could be a solution

Many farms in Eastern Europe are farmed using traditional methods (they seem old-fashioned to us). The low use of chemicals means there's plenty of wildlife around including big animals like elks and wolves!

> Szczepan and Helena Master's farm in southern Poland is only 5 hectares. They have a couple of cows, 4 pigs, 11 piglets and 2 horses. It's a hard life, but they wouldn't want to do anything else. Their farm is typical of many in Poland. They still use horses, rather than tractors.

If the farmers in Eastern Europe take the small step of going completely organic (they're nearly there anyway) then the higher price they could get for their produce at home, and abroad, could save their jobs, *and* produce high quality food for local people. Szczepan Master thinks this is the way forward. He has applied to be able to call his farm organic.

Some farms, like Szczepan and Helena's, are becoming involved in **agro-tourist** projects. Visitors can stay in the farmhouse and enjoy home-cooking for a handful of euros.

▲ *Back-breaking work. But keeping farming traditional could mean it has a future.*

Activities

1. Explain why physical factors are not very important in market gardening in the Netherlands.
2. Why do you think flowers are transported from all over the world to the Netherlands to be sold?
3. a Draw a systems diagram to show a typical farm in Poland.
   b Compare your diagram with the one you drew for Herdship Farm in Unit 10.3. Explain the main differences between the two farming systems.
4. Do you think that 'agro-tourism' would work in the UK? Which types of farms do you think would be most successful at agro-tourism?

Farming in LEDCs

In this unit you'll find out about subsistence rice farming in the Philippines, and commercial flower growing in Kenya.

Rice farming in the Philippines

'I'm Maximo Casiendo. I've got 7 children and we live in the Philippines. Our farm is really small – less than a hectare. We mostly grow rice. We also grow a bit of maize, and keep 20 hens and 8 turkeys for eggs and meat. There's usually only enough for the family – it's **subsistence farming** – nothing left to sell.

The land here is flat and low-lying with a rich, clay, loamy soil.

It's hot and wet – we've got a monsoon climate. Usually about 25 °C and tons of rain – 1800 mm a year. It rains most in the wet season – between June and December.

I use fertiliser, pesticide and herbicide on the rice. The hens and turkeys get maize to eat. I need diesel for my rice-threshing machine, and grow bamboo to burn for cooking.

My eldest two work on the farm – just look at all those jobs we've got to do! At threshing and harvesting time all the locals help each other out.

What problems have I got? Our rice yield is too low because of disease and those blasted snails and rats, so we can't afford to send the children to school. We can't rely on the weather like we used to – we can get droughts.'

▲ Maximo's farm is on the island of Negros in the Philippines.

Did you know?
Golden snails were introduced to provide protein. The farmers didn't want to eat the snails, but the snails love to eat the rice!

Did you know?
A lowland rice plant needs 2000 litres of water during its life.

Jobs, jobs, jobs
Maximo's year:

May
Plant first rice crop

June
Plant maize

July and August
Harvest first rice crop

September
Harvest maize
Plough for second rice crop

October
No planting, harvesting, etc.

November and December
Harvest second rice crop

January and February
Plant third rice crop

March and April
Harvest third rice crop

▲ Rice farming is **labour-intensive**, and very hard work.

Flower power in Kenya

Do you ever buy flowers? Probably not. But chances are, if you did happen to buy a bunch of roses from a supermarket, they'd have come from Kenya.

The Netherlands might produce 60% of the world's commercially grown flowers, but LEDCs like Kenya are hot on its heels. Kenya is among the top 5 exporters in the world, and provides a quarter of the EU's cut flowers.

What's the story?

◆ Flower growing needs lots of money, about £30 000 a hectare. It's very **capital-intensive**. But yields are high. In 2002 flower farms covered a tiny 20 sq. km (way less than 1% of Kenya's total area) but flowers made up 8% of the money Kenya earned from exports.

◆ Lake Naivasha is the centre of Kenya's flower-growing industry. Soil round here is very fertile, and the lake provides water for irrigation.

◆ Flower growers use lots of fertiliser and pesticides.

What problems do the flower growers have?

◆ Using water from Lake Naivasha for irrigation means that the level in the lake has dropped. What will happen to the hippos if all the water disappears?

◆ Using fertiliser and pesticides causes 2 problems: 1 - the chemicals end up in the lake causing pollution. 2 - they can make the flower workers ill.

◆ Some workers are badly paid.

What's being done?

The Kenya Flower Council has produced a Code of Practice for flower growers. It covers things like:

◆ welfare and safety – this is to do with wages paid, hours worked, protecting workers from the chemicals and so on

◆ use of pesticides

◆ environmental concerns – including pollution and the responsible use of water.

The idea is that together the flower growers, people who care about the environment, and the KFC will ensure that flower growing becomes a **sustainable** industry.

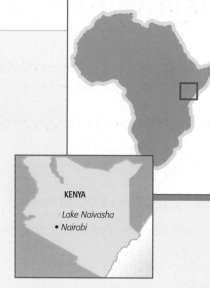

KENYA

Lake Naivasha
• Nairobi

▲ Lake Naivasha covers 150 sq. km. 15 000 hippos live here and lots of other wildlife.

Did you know?
Three-quarters of the flowers Kenya exports are roses.

▲ Flower worker in Kenya treating roses with pesticide.

Activities

1 **a** Draw a diagram to show a year in the life of Maximo's farm in the Philippines.

 b Add labels to your diagram to show the inputs, processes, and outputs of this farming system.

2 Why do you think so many farms in the Philippines are subsistence farms (there's little or no produce for sale)?

3 What advantages do flower growers in Kenya have over those in the Netherlands?

4 What problems are caused by the intensive growing of flowers in Kenya?

LEDCS – challenges and solutions

In this unit you'll learn about the challenges facing LEDC farmers and solutions to some of their problems.

The problem

Everyone has the right to be free from hunger, and to have safe and nutritious food to eat. But people are hungry. Look at the factfile.

Challenges for LEDC farmers

Yes, there are more problems than those mentioned in the factfile.

Problem 1: Climate change
Rain is becoming unpredictable (see the graph), growing seasons are shorter and water sources are drying up. The result? Lower yields and less food.

Problem 2: Soil erosion
- This happens where land isn't managed properly.
- Where the vegetation is removed soil can be washed away by the rain, or blown away by the wind.
- **Overgrazing** means there are too many animals for the amount of grass and the soil is exposed.
- Collecting **fuelwood** can cause deforestation. And again the soil is exposed and eroded.

Problem 3: More people
The 3 continents with the fastest population growth are the developing ones of Africa, Asia and Latin America. More people means more food is needed.

All those problems – but listen to this. There is enough food in the world to go around. No-one needs to be hungry, *or die, or* live with malnutrition. There are all sorts of problems to do with trade which need sorting out. But there are other things which can be done to make farming more sustainable so that farmers can produce the food they and others need.

Some solutions

Small and sweet, or big and brash? Some of the solutions to farmers' problems work and are sustainable, others can make things worse. Six possible solutions are looked at on the opposite page.

> **Factfile**
> - 6 million children under 5 die of hunger every year (that's like nearly everyone in London dying).
> - Over 800 million people in LEDCs go to bed hungry *every* night. They are badly **malnourished**.
> - Farmers in LEDCs often have small plots of land and lots of problems – insects destroy the whole crop; food prices go up and down; markets can be a long way away.

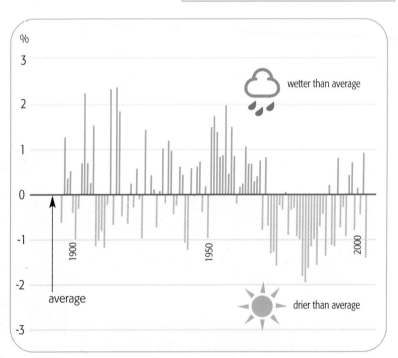

▲ The Sahel has mostly been drier than average since 1970.

> **Did you know?**
> It can take 400 years for 1 cm of soil to form, and between 3000 and 12 000 years for it to be deep enough for farming.

Diguettes and water harvesting ✓

In 1979 Oxfam encouraged local farmers in Burkina Faso to build **diguettes**, or stone-lines, along the contours of the ground. These hold back the rain so it soaks into the ground, and trap soil (**soil conservation**). Diguettes increase the depth of soil. Farmers can grow more crops, and have a better life.

Seed cross-breeding ✓

In the Philippines (and other countries) people are trying to cross traditional varieties of rice with new varieties to improve yields. These are called **hybrids**.

In Mali (West Africa) a hybrid type of millet increased yields by 13%. Doesn't sound much – but for a family on a small farm it can feed a child for a year.

Inappropriate technology ✗

Water may be needed to **irrigate** crops. This comes from wells, rivers and canals or reservoirs. Some reservoirs like the Narmada River Project in India can have advantages and disadvantages. Huge amounts of land are drowned; people lose their homes; they are really expensive to build. Irrigation can **waterlog** soil and cause **salinisation**. This is where the soil becomes very salty and plants die. So, the technology may be inappropriate.

Land reform ✓

In many LEDCs farms are *really* small. Maximo's farm (Unit 10.8) is minute. Farms can also be divided into tiny plots. Most of the land belongs to a few rich owners. Land reform in LEDCs tries to:
- increase the size of farm for small land owners
- set a maximum size of farm that the rich owners can have
- give land to people who don't have any (most don't).

Maximo is lucky – he owns his farm, thanks to the Land Reform Act.

High yield varieties ✗

These are types of grain like wheat, rice and maize which were developed to increase yields. It was called the **Green Revolution**. The seeds needed lots of expensive fertiliser and pesticides to produce high yields. As the price of rice fell some farmers became worse off.

Appropriate technology ✓

This is technology which suits local people's needs. In LEDCs it needs to be cheap and sustainable – things like:
- wells and water pumps
- renewable resources such as solar power
- involving people rather than machines.

Activities

1. a List the problems facing farmers in LEDCs.
   b Highlight those problems that are natural, or to do with the physical environment. Using a second colour, highlight those that are caused by people.
   c What conclusions can you draw from your list?
   d Are any problems difficult to place in a category?
2. Why does technology not always benefit farmers in LEDCs?
3. How will land reform benefit farmers in LEDCs?
4. Appropriate technology 'suits local people's needs'. Do you think that the use of technology in LEDCs is always appropriate? Explain your answer.
5. Research activity. Find out more about the Green Revolution. To what extent do you think this was appropriate technology for LEDC farmers?

The big picture

This chapter is all about industry – different types in different places. These are the big ideas behind the chapter:

◆ Industry and employment is classified as primary, secondary, tertiary and quaternary.

◆ As industry changes different location factors become more important, so industry locates in different places, and employment structures change.

◆ Some areas of traditional heavy industry, like South Wales and the Ruhr, declined, but have now attracted new industries and jobs.

◆ Industry is global – companies locate factories all over the world.

◆ Some countries in eastern Asia have industrialised very quickly.

Your goals for this chapter

By the end of this chapter you should be able to answer these questions:

◆ What do these terms mean, and can I give an example of each?
primary industry, secondary industry, tertiary industry, quaternary industry, inputs, processes, outputs, feedback

◆ Give an example of the location of one industry in the UK, and list the factors affecting its location.

◆ Why has the location of industry changed in the UK? Where is industry located now? And how has employment structure changed in the UK?

◆ Name an area where traditional heavy industry located and say why it declined. How has this area changed?

◆ What do these terms mean?
high-tech, footloose, deindustrialisation, employment structure

◆ Where can you find high-tech footloose industries, and why?

◆ What are TNCs? List the advantages and disadvantages they bring to the countries they locate in.

◆ Give one example of a TNC in an LEDC. Why did it locate there? Is its manufacturing sustainable?

◆ Draw pie charts to show employment structure in an LEDC like Kenya, an LEDC which is becoming more developed like Brazil, and an MEDC like the UK.

◆ What are NICs? Name the four Tiger Economies.

◆ How did South Korea develop its economy so quickly? What problems has rapid industrialisation caused?.

And then . . .

When you finish the chapter, come back here and see if you've met your goals!

Did you know?
◆ Computer games is a fast-growing industry.
◆ From 1995 to 2003 over 25 million gaming devices were sold in the UK – enough for every household in the country to have one.

Did you know?
The UK is the third-largest market in the world for computer games, after the USA and Japan.

Did you know?
About 60 million cars and trucks are made around the world each year, and the industry employs millions of people.

Did you know?
This book is a product of the publishing industry.

Your chapter starter

Look at the photo on page 212.
What is this man doing?
What are the white things in the photo? What are they for?
Where do you think these things have been made? Why?
What effect will making them have on the environment?

Scalpel please, nurse.

Industry, jobs and systems

In this unit you'll find out about different types of industries and jobs, and how industry works as a system.

Industry – what's it all about?

Making things? Partly – but it's about other things as well.

Industry provides jobs, or **employment**. There's different types of industry and different types of jobs. Think about these: baby-sitting, paper-round, hairdresser, teacher, carpenter, farmer, magician, mechanic, IT consultant – the list is endless. They're all types of jobs and someone's got to do them (even you)! We all need to work to earn enough money to live on.

But the world of work is changing. The job you do in 10 years time might not be the same as the one you do 10 years from then.

Classifying industry

Geographers (that's you reading this book, and me writing it) find it helpful to sort things into groups. The word for this is **classifying**. Industry and jobs can be classified in four ways.

> **Did you know?**
> - 2% of the UK's workers are employed in farming.
> - In 1999, 73% of the UK's workers were employed in service industries. By 2004, this figure was 80%.

> **Did you know?**
> We do still make some things in the UK – like cars, ships, planes, machine tools, electronics equipment, chemicals and so on.

Primary industry – people extract **raw materials** from the land or sea. Farming, fishing and mining are examples.

Secondary industry – this is where people make (or **manufacture**) things. Like turning iron ore into steel, making cars, building houses – and hard drives (like in this picture).

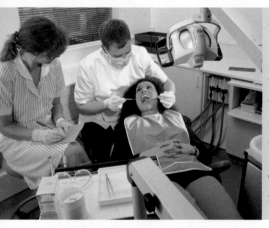

Tertiary industry. These industries provide a **service** for people. There are lots of them, for example the health service (doctors, nurses, dentists) and education (your teachers). Shop workers provide a service too.

Quaternary industries provide information and expert help. IT consultants and researchers work in these industries.

The names primary, secondary, tertiary and quaternary just mean, first, second, third and fourth. They refer to the order in which the industries developed.

The four types of industry aren't separate. They're linked together. Look at this example of car manufacturing.

| Mining for iron ore. | → | Making steel to turn into cars. | → | Car sales person orders cars using a computer. | → | IT expert fixes the sales person's computer when it goes wrong. |

In . . . out

In geography we say industry, or a factory where something is made, is a **system**. This is a technical way of saying there are:

◆ **Inputs** – things that go into the system
◆ **Outputs** – things that come out of the system
◆ **Processes** – things that happen in the middle

There might be some **feedback**, for example where some of the profits (if there are any) are put back into the system. The profits will buy more raw materials, new machinery and pay the workers. If there isn't any profit, the factory or industry will go bust!

The system diagram below shows how inputs, processes and outputs fit together. Inputs can also be called **factors**. These are the things which affect where an industry, or factory, will locate. Systems can be applied to any industry, or factory, anywhere in the world.

Physical inputs
• Raw materials
• Energy supply
• Site and land
Human and economic inputs
• Labour (workers)
• Transport
• Capital (money)
• Markets
• Government policies
• Environment

→

Processes
• Processing
• Assembling
• Packaging
• Administration

→

Outputs
• Finished product
• Profit
• Waste

Feedback
Profit which may be reinvested.

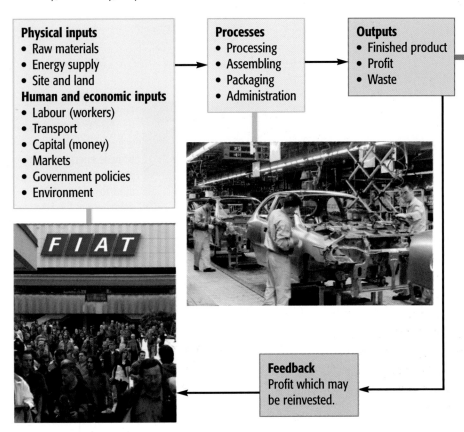

One of the outputs from the system isn't really wanted – **waste**. It can be a real headache. It can cause pollution, and can be difficult and expensive to get rid of.

Activities

1 a Make a list of any thirty jobs.
 b Against each job, note which sector of industry it belongs to (primary, etc). Did you have difficulty classifying any of your jobs?
 c Add up the total number of jobs in each sector of industry. How does this compare with national figures for the UK, where 3% are employed in primary and 80% in tertiary?
2 If a factory manufacturing cars closes down, it affects the factory and many others that are linked to it. Using examples, explain why this is.

215

Industry – deciding where to put it

In this unit you'll learn how industry decides where to locate, and how location changes.

Burnaston

Cars – love them, or hate them?

Most of us use them. They've all got to be made somewhere – but where? How do people decide? Read this. It's adapted from the Toyota UK website and explains why Toyota decided to build their car assembly plant at Burnaston, in Derbyshire (that's the Toyota plant in the photo).

File Edit View Favorites Tools Help

Back ▪ ○ ▪ ▪ ▪ ▪ ▪ Search ☆ Favorites ▪ ▪ ▪ ▪ ▪ ▪ ▪

Address ▪ ▪ ▪ Go Links »

We were offered a site of almost 600 acres, about 7 miles from Derby city centre. The land was relatively flat and easy to develop. The site provided electricity, gas, water and phone lines. There were good transport links to the rest of the UK and Europe. There was a large, skilled and flexible workforce nearby. And they had engineering and manufacturing backgrounds.

What else? The British government and local authority supported our investment. Burnaston was a great environment to live and work in. And there was a large market in the UK for our cars. So that's why we located at Burnaston.

Did you know?
Toyota have another site in north Wales where they produce engines. They employ over 5500 people at their two UK sites.

Industrial location factors

Toyota and Burnaston is a real-life example of how people decide where to **locate** their industry or factory. The photo and text boxes below break it down to show *exactly* what location **factors** people have to think about.

Did you know?
Toyota is the third biggest car manufacturer in the world.

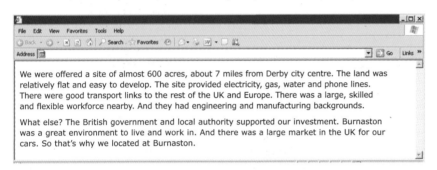

Raw materials
If these are heavy and bulky to transport – like coal and iron ore – the factory needs to be close to them. This is less important than it used to be.

Site and land
Modern industry needs large, flat sites with space to expand.

Energy supply
Early factories had to be close to fast-flowing water or coal fields to provide energy to work machines. Now electricity is available anywhere in the UK.

Labour (workers)
Some industries need lots of workers, others need workers with special skills.

Environment
A good environment – nice surroundings with lots of things to do – will attract workers.

Transport
A good transport network (road, rail, air and sea) is important to get the finished product to the market.

Capital (money)
Industry needs money to set up factories and produce things. Banks, governments and local authorities can provide money.

Markets
This is where the finished product is sold. It might be nearby in the UK, or abroad.

Government policy
The UK government can attract industry to some parts of the country by giving grants and subsidies.

Changing industries and changing locations

Nothing stays the same forever, and that includes industry. As industry changes, different location factors become more important.

Many of the old traditional industries in the UK – things like coal mining, ship building and textiles – began in the 19th century in the Industrial Revolution. They needed:

◆ raw materials – often heavy and bulky
◆ energy – provided by coal

So, they were usually found near coal fields, or ports (so raw materials like cotton could be imported, and finished products like cloth could be exported). The maps show where the traditional industries used to be found in the UK before 1970 (top map) and where industry is now (bottom map). What's happened?

◆ During the 20th century coal mines, textile mills, shipyards and steelworks all closed.
◆ New industries, many to do with electronics and computers, have developed.

For newer industries, being in a good environment with a trained workforce, close to large markets and with good transport links is important.

Changes to the type of industry, the way it works, or where it locates, can mean that businesses and factories close. People lose their jobs and way of earning a living. And that can affect families and the whole community.

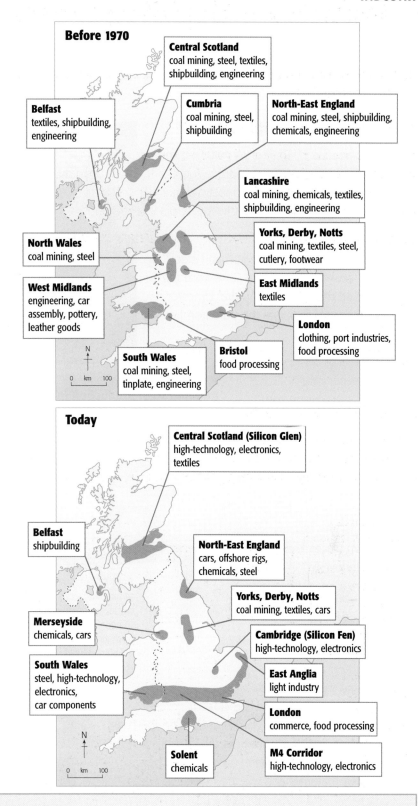

Before 1970

Central Scotland
coal mining, steel, textiles, shipbuilding, engineering

Belfast
textiles, shipbuilding, engineering

Cumbria
coal mining, steel, shipbuilding

North-East England
coal mining, steel, shipbuilding, chemicals, engineering

Lancashire
coal mining, chemicals, textiles, shipbuilding, engineering

North Wales
coal mining, steel

Yorks, Derby, Notts
coal mining, textiles, steel, cutlery, footwear

West Midlands
engineering, car assembly, pottery, leather goods

East Midlands
textiles

London
clothing, port industries, food processing

South Wales
coal mining, steel, tinplate, engineering

Bristol
food processing

Today

Central Scotland (Silicon Glen)
high-technology, electronics, textiles

Belfast
shipbuilding

North-East England
cars, offshore rigs, chemicals, steel

Yorks, Derby, Notts
coal mining, textiles, cars

Merseyside
chemicals, cars

Cambridge (Silicon Fen)
high-technology, electronics

South Wales
steel, high-technology, electronics, car components

East Anglia
light industry

London
commerce, food processing

Solent
chemicals

M4 Corridor
high-technology, electronics

Activities

1 Describe the distribution of industry before 1970, as shown by the first map.
2 Explain why the location of industry in the UK has changed since 1970.
3 During the 20th century, industries such as coal mining and textiles closed down. Why?
4 Explain why the factors important for locating an industry are different now compared to the 19th century. How important was the natural environment, then and now?
5 Do you think that companies such as Toyota would choose to locate in the UK without help from the government? Give reasons for your answer.

Industry – traditional and heavy

In this unit you'll find out why traditional heavy industry located in South Wales, and in the Ruhr in Germany.

Iron and steel in South Wales

> This is my job – my life. Tower Colliery is the only deep coalmine left in South Wales. My dad was a miner, and his dad before him. Our communities were built around the mining and steel industry. And that's almost disappeared now.

Q What do you need to make iron and steel?

A Iron ore, coal and limestone. Coke from the coal is used to smelt the iron ore. Limestone is added to help separate the pure iron from what isn't pure.

South Wales

In the nineteenth century, South Wales became important for producing iron and steel. The three raw materials needed to make iron and steel were all found locally. The steep valleys with fast-flowing rivers provided power to begin with, and also transport. The iron industry developed in places like Ebbw Vale and Merthyr Tydfil.

After 1860, steelworks began to replace ironworks. Fast forward to the 20th century. The local raw materials had run out, and only Tower Colliery remained working. By the 1990s, all the steelworks had closed – except two. These were Port Talbot and Llanwern, both on the coast. They were **integrated steelworks**. All the stages in the steel-making industry happened on one site. They imported raw materials and exported steel. Llanwern closed in 2001, and 3000 jobs were lost.

But these days it's not all doom and gloom in South Wales. Read Unit 11.8 to find out what's happening there now.

Iron and steel production in South Wales

BRECON BEACONS (limestone)

Ebbw Vale

Merthyr Tydfil

Llanelli

Aberdare

Pontypool

Steel to car assembly plants in the Midlands

Swansea

Neath

Rhondda

Newport

Key
- coal field
- rocks with iron ore
- ironworks in 1800
- Tower Colliery
- integrated steelworks
- motorway
- main towns

Pontypridd

Cardiff

M4

Port Talbot: large area of flat land; large workforce nearby; good motorway links; money from government and EU helped build the steelworks.

Llanwern: closed in 2001 because of competition from other countries; too much steel produced worldwide and falling prices.

Penarth

Barry

When industry declines, people lose their jobs. It affects the whole community. People leave. Shops close. Crime goes up. ▶

The Ruhr industrial region – Germany

Factfile

◆ The Ruhr coal field is Europe's largest energy supply. There's a huge amount of coal and it won't run out in the near future.

◆ Local supplies of iron ore meant that the iron and steel industries developed.

◆ There was an excellent system of rivers and canals. They were used for power (the rivers) and transport.

◆ Other industries were attracted to the area, like the chemical industry (used coal as one of its raw materials); engineering (used the iron and steel); textiles (used some of the machines produced by engineering).

◆ In 1956, nearly half a million people had jobs in coal mining.

But, like South Wales, this area has suffered too.

◆ Since the 1970s, coalmines, steelworks and other heavy industries have closed.

◆ By 1999, there were only 53 000 jobs left in coal mining.

◆ Half a million people have left the area since the mid-1980s.

◆ Lots of people have no jobs. In 2001, 12.5% of workers were unemployed – far more than in the rest of Germany.

◆ The environment was ruined. Slag and waste heaps were left by coal mining and other industries. And both air and water were massively polluted.

◆ There is still a large local population – 5.4 million people live in the Ruhr region. This means there is a big workforce, and big market for goods produced here.

Did you know?
One-third of the EU's coal is still produced in the Ruhr.

Key
- - - - coal field
───── motorways
───── canals
───── rivers

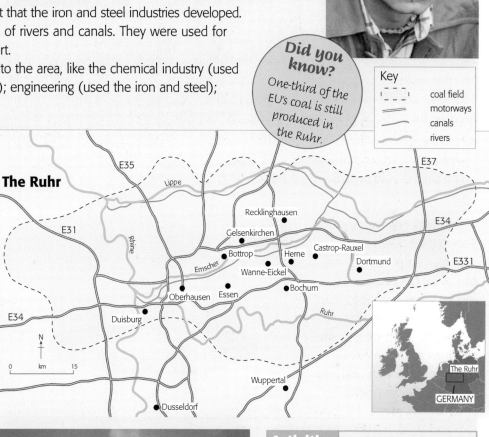

The Ruhr

Industry can be bad for the environment. This is Duisburg. ▶

Activities

1 The natural environment – through raw materials – helped industry to develop in South Wales. What are the disadvantages of the South Wales natural environment?

2 Why do you think the steelworks at Port Talbot and Llanwern remained open while others closed?

3 Why do you think that competition from other countries would be a reason for the Llanwern steelworks closing?

4 Draw a 'consequences map' to show how people in South Wales have been affected by the decline of traditional industries.

5 Why do you think industry has declined in the Ruhr, even though there's still plenty of coal?

6 What are the similarities and differences between the examples of South Wales and the Ruhr?

Industry – footloose (and fancy free)

In this unit you'll learn about high-tech and footloose industries.

What's the photo on the right got to do with geography? At first glance not a lot. But someone's got to make the computer. And it's got to be made somewhere. Making electronic equipment, computers – those sorts of things – are **high-tech** industries, and they're **footloose**.

High-tech and footloose

The new industries that have developed and begun to replace traditional heavy industries are often high-tech. They tend to make expensive things. They employ fewer people than traditional manufacturing industries. Because they don't use lots of heavy raw materials, because the national grid provides power, and because of improved transport and communications, they can choose where to locate. In geography we call this being footloose.

But, if they have more of a choice about where to locate than the old industries, how *do* they decide? What's important?

- Locate in areas with good transport links – close to motorways, railways and with good access to airports.
- Need workers with special skills close by.
- Use small, light parts to make products.
- Don't cause pollution like traditional industries do.
- Final products are small, and easy to transport to markets.
- Locate in a nice environment.

Footloose industries

- Power is provided by electricity (just plug into a socket).
- Are close to other industries so they can swap ideas and information.
- Need cheap land with large sites to expand.

Footloose industries are often found on the edges of towns and cities, in specially built 'parks', or estates. These might be:

Science parks
These have links with universities. Businesses are high-tech and might concentrate on R and D. A lot of land isn't developed. Instead it's landscaped with lots of trees and grass to make a good environment for people to work in.

Business parks
These are like science parks – but they don't have a link with a university. They have high-tech industries, as well as offices, hypermarkets and leisure facilities. And, like science parks, they're landscaped.

Industrial estates
These can be found towards a city centre, as well as on the edges of towns and cities. Some businesses are high-tech, but more are likely to be involved in manufacturing. There are more buildings and less trees and grass than in science and business parks.

Did you know?
Many high-tech companies have two parts. One involves lots of R and D (research and development) and is to do with developing new products. The other is to do with making things. They put together parts made somewhere else.

Areas where footloose industries have located include:
- the M4 corridor (aka 'Sunrise Strip')
- Silicon Glen in central Scotland
- Silicon Valley in California.

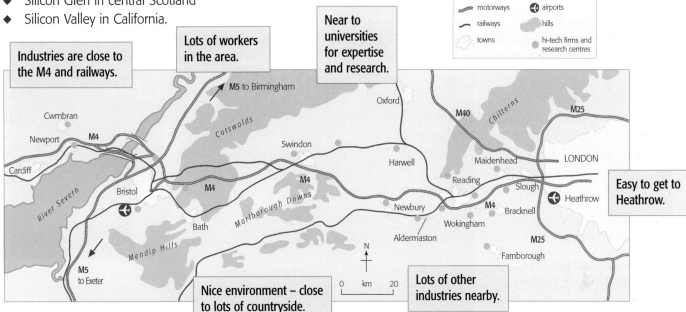

Industries are close to the M4 and railways.

Lots of workers in the area.

Near to universities for expertise and research.

Easy to get to Heathrow.

Nice environment – close to lots of countryside.

Lots of other industries nearby.

▲ Advantages of the M4 corridor

Aztec West Business Park

This was developed in the 1980s and 1990s. It is:
- on the edge of Bristol
- at the western end of the M4 corridor
- on a large area of flat land next to the M5.

And:
- Lots of houses have been built nearby.
- There are 100 businesses. They provide jobs for more than 6000 people.
- It covers 63 hectares.
- It's landscaped to look like a park.
- You can find a hotel, pub, cafes, a wine bar, a newsagent and a hairdresser there.

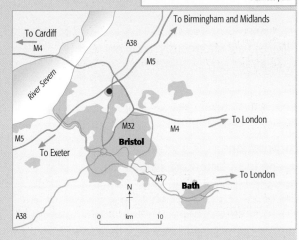

This table shows just a few of the businesses there.

Name of business	What they do
Aardman Animations – have part of their business here	Animated film makers (of Wallace and Gromit fame)
GHR Partners	Human Resource Consultants
Stat Plus	Legal and commercial stationery supplier

Activities

1 Make a list of ten high-tech products. Find out where each of them is manufactured. Comment on what you find.
2 There is no perfect location for an industry. Look at the spider diagram and choose the three factors which you think would be most important for a company manufacturing high-tech products. Justify your choices.
3 Name three industries that would be able to locate virtually anywhere. Now choose two that are tied to a certain location. Explain why you have chosen each industry.
4 If footloose industries can locate almost anywhere, what problems could this bring to the UK economy?
5 For one of the businesses at Aztec West, find out where else the company is located. Are the reasons the same for all locations, or are there any differences?

Industry – going global

In this unit you'll find out about transnational corporations.

Chen Ernu's story

I'm 42 years old. I came to Beijing with my husband and our 3 children 10 years ago. We used to be farmers, but got fed up with not being able to grow enough to eat.

I make clothes. Do you know how much I get paid? In your money it's 33p an hour. Not much is it?

The factory's not much fun. I'm expected to work longer and faster than ever. It's a job. I suppose it's better than nothing. But if you people in the UK don't buy enough of our clothes, I could lose my job overnight.

CHINA

Beijing

Britain may be an island, but we're part of a **global market**. Look at your jeans, your mobile – who made them, and where? Probably someone like Chen Ernu, in somewhere like China.

People who make things have to be paid. Wages vary enormously. Look at the wage rates in the table. Would you fancy working for 33p an hour?

Transnational corporations

Some businesses are now so large that they have offices and factories around the world. They're called **transnational corporations** (TNCs for short) or multinational companies. The headquarters and main factory are often in an MEDC, like the USA or Japan. Smaller offices and factories are in LEDCs where workers are cheaper. And, because of that, it is cheaper to make things there.

Country	Average wage rates per hour (manufacturing) 2003
USA	£12.09
UK	£10.92
Japan	£10.64
Spain	£7.72
Korea	£5.54
China	£0.33

TNCs can be huge. Some of the biggest make more money in one year than some countries do. Some of the first businesses to become TNCs were car manufacturers. They found that by locating in different countries, they could:

◆ make their cars more cheaply (workers were paid less and raw materials might cost less)
◆ be nearer to large markets (places with big populations).

But it's not just car manufacturers that are TNCs as the table on the next page shows.

Did you know?
Half the women who work in garment factories in Bangladesh don't have a contract – so no job security.

Did you know?
Because our fashions change so quickly, workers in garment factories in LEDCs have to work harder.

Revenue for 10 TNCs, 2000			
TNC	Type of business	Based in	Revenue ($ billions)
Wal-Mart	supermarkets	USA	244
BP	Oil/petrol	UK	233
Exxon Mobil	Oil/petrol	USA	180
Toyota	cars	Japan	168
Nestle	foods	Switzerland	49
Microsoft	software	USA	32
Coca-Cola	Soft drinks	USA	21
McDonald's	Fast food	USA	17
Gap	clothing	USA	15
Nike	Sports goods	USA	11

Total GDP for 8 countries, 2000	
Country	GDP (or total wealth produced) ($ billions)
USA	10 980
India	3022
UK	1664
Bangladesh	259
Nigeria	111
Tunisia	68
Ghana	44
Jamaica	10

Are TNCs good or bad?

It depends who you are. Some people are for TNCs, some are against them.

They help to develop mineral wealth and improve energy production.

The money we earn goes into the local economy.

They invest in big projects.

They can improve education and our work skills.

They improve roads, airports.

They give us jobs.

Most of the profits go abroad.

Few of the managers are local people.

Sometimes we're badly paid.

They can cause pollution.

Minerals are exported.

TNCs might pull out with little warning.

The things we make are no use to us, or they're too expensive.

Activities

1 Why are most TNCs based in MEDCs?
2 Explain why many TNCs manufacture their products in LEDCs.
3 a What are the costs and benefits for a country of having a branch of a TNC located there.
  b Overall, do you think TNCs bring more benefits or problems?
4 Now consider Toyota, a Japanese TNC located in the UK (see Unit 11.2).
  a Do you think the UK benefits from having a Toyota factory in Derbyshire?
  b Are the arguments 'for and against' the same as for an LEDC? If not, why are they different?
5 What is your opinion of the 'increasing trend towards globalisation'? Is it right that some TNCs earn more than some countries?

Did you know?

Globalisation means the way companies, ideas and lifestyles spread around the world. TNCs create world markets for their products.

223

Industry – Ford in India

In this unit you'll learn about one TNC in India.

In the last unit we looked at TNCs. The Ford Motor Company is just one example of a TNC which has located factories in different parts of the world.

Ford factfile

◆ The Ford Motor Company is the world's second largest car manufacturer.

◆ Ford employs over 300 000 people worldwide.

◆ Ford makes Jaguars, Land Rovers, Aston Martins and other ranges of cars. It also makes lots of trucks.

◆ The Ford Motor Company was started by Henry Ford in Detroit in 1903, with 10 employees. Hardly the global company it is today.

By the late 1990s, Ford was:

◆ manufacturing, or assembling, cars worldwide

◆ locating new factories in LEDCs

◆ making different parts, for different models, in different countries

◆ facing competition from other manufacturers.

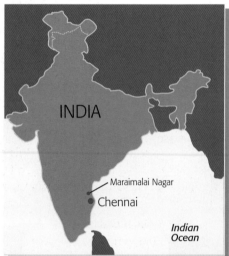

INDIA

Maraimalai Nagar
● Chennai

Indian Ocean

Ford India

In 1995 Ford went into partnership with Mahindra & Mahindra Limited in India. They opened an integrated high-tech manufacturing plant at Maraimalai Nagar, 45 km north of Chennai, in 1999. The site is huge. It covers 140 hectares. It can make up to 100 000 vehicles a year.

Ford India:

◆ employs about 1800 people at the plant at Maraimalai Nagar

◆ has 94 Indian suppliers

◆ has 33 dealerships in India.

The launch of the Ford Endeavour Special Edition in September 2005. This vehicle was specially designed for Asian markets. ▶

Ford chose India because:

◆ it has a huge population – over 1 billion people (so there's a big market for cars)
◆ it may be an LEDC, but it has a high-earning middle class
◆ labour costs are much cheaper than in MEDCs.

What about people and the environment?

◆ Ford India pays its workers more than other workers in similar industries in India.
◆ All workers are offered training.
◆ Almost three-quarters of the goods and services that Ford India buys, come from India. And over 70% of these come from the Chennai area.
◆ Ford India contributes to development projects. Like a health centre for people around Maraimalai Nagar, and disaster relief for victims of earthquakes and floods.
◆ Ford India is working towards the sustainable use of resources, such as water and energy, in its production processes. (There is a shortage of water around Chennai.)
◆ Ford India treats all the waste water from its plant. It is then reused. Other waste products are sold and recycled. And its cars are designed to be more environmentally friendly too, both during use and at the end of their lives. 85% of the materials used in the cars can be recycled or dismantled.

Did you know?

India had the world's 12th highest GDP in 2003 (and it was growing faster than the UK's).

Activities

1 Explain why Ford decided to locate in India.

2 a Write down your opinion about each of Statements A–C.

   A 'Ford wants to make money, and the Indian market is huge. That's all they care about.'

   B 'The benefits to the local economy have been tremendous. Even people not directly involved in the industry have benefited from things like a new health centre and help with the recent flooding – all from Ford's money.'

   C 'Ford does not benefit India – it benefits the middle classes who can afford to buy new cars.'

   b Overall, do you think Ford has benefited the Indian economy?

3 How far do you think that Ford has tried to make its car manufacturing in India sustainable? Explain your answer.

All change for industry

In this unit you'll learn how industry has changed in the UK.

Don't we make anything any more?

Leaving school soon? Fancy a job? How about manufacturing? You'll be lucky. It's in decline in the UK. Over half a million manufacturing jobs were lost between 1997 and 2004. What's left? Lots of jobs in service industries. Want a job that's got something to do with IT? No problem. There's lots out there.

Deindustrialisation

This is the name given to the decline in manufacturing (secondary) industry, and the growth in tertiary and quaternary industry. In the UK, this has happened because:

- machines replaced people in most manufacturing industries

- other countries produced goods more cheaply
- prices for UK goods were too high – not enough were produced (low **productivity**), lack of investment in new machinery, high interest rates.

Changing industry in the UK

What's happened? Before 1800, most people worked in farming, or things to do with farming. The Industrial Revolution in the 19th century changed all that. Lots of people moved to the towns for work – making steel, ships or textiles. Others worked in mines.

In the 20th century it all changed again (but not overnight). There was a shift to jobs in service industries, and more recently to quaternary industries.

▽ *Changing employment structure in the UK.*

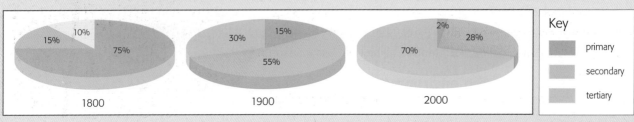

		Key
1800	10%, 15%, 75%	primary
1900	15%, 30%, 55%	secondary
2000	2%, 28%, 70%	tertiary

Where are the 'new' jobs?

In Unit 11.4 we looked at high-tech and footloose industries. Lots of these are found on the edges of towns and cities. (In geography we call that the **rural-urban fringe**.) They're found on specially built 'parks' or estates. And shops have moved to out-of-town shopping centres on the rural-urban fringe.

Why build there, and what are the consequences? Look at the table.

Why?	Consequences
◆ Land is cheaper	◆ Urban sprawl (towns keep growing)
◆ Big sites with space to expand	◆ Nearby villages become **suburbanised** (and more like towns)
◆ Less traffic and pollution	◆ **Greenbelts** disappear
◆ Close to good transport links	◆ People often need to travel by car to get there – so pollution increases
◆ Close to workers	◆ Traffic congestion – especially at out-of-town shopping centres
◆ Nice environment with open space	◆ Town and city centres have become 'urban deserts', with fewer businesses and shops.

What does the government do?

Key

Development areas

Intermediate areas

Special status for Northern Ireland

Assisted areas in the UK

N

0 km 100

The example above is from 2005, but it's in places like South Wales where lots of people have lost jobs over the years that the government has tried to help. They have encouraged industry to move to areas of high unemployment to create new jobs, for example by providing government grants and subsidies, and have tried to protect existing jobs.

The map shows the places that most needed help in the late 1990s.

But the way the government helps is going to change. The EU is changing the rules. From 2007 they want there to be less aid. And they want it to be better targeted.

Cleaning up industry

The oil and chemical leak in the article to the right might have been an accident, but industry causes all types of pollution in its normal day-to-day business. Air pollution can result in global warming and acid rain. Water pollution can upset ecosystems, kill fish and affect our health. There's masses of legislation (laws) which are intended to help industry clean up its act and reduce pollution.

The Environment Agency is responsible for maintaining and improving water quality in England and Wales. It plays a major role in monitoring air quality, along with local authorities. But all industries are responsible for the impact they have on the environment.

Activities

1 Look back to the list of jobs you wrote for activity 1 in Unit 11.1.
   a Does your list suggest that deindustrialisation is taking place?
   b How many of your jobs are in some way connected with IT? Does this fit in with your answer to **a** above?
2 Explain why deindustrialisation has happened in the UK.
3 Look back to the maps in Unit 11.2. What is the relationship between the changing location of industry and the information shown in the pie charts opposite?
4 The table opposite shows the negative effects of industry setting up on the edges of towns. Can you think of any positive impacts?
5 Why do you think the government should help industries that are declining or struggling?

Firm fined over water pollution

A firm in Rugby was fined £6000 after oil and chemicals leaked from drums and entered Sow Brook. The charges were brought by the Environment Agency.

Industry – about turn

In this unit you'll find out how two declining areas have changed.

The new South Wales

We've looked at declining heavy industries in South Wales and the Ruhr. Industry in decline is bad news. But things can get better.

Attracting new industry to South Wales

- The Welsh Development Agency was set up in 1976 to attract industry to Wales, and to encourage people to set up businesses.
- Urban Development Corporations were set up, for example Cardiff Bay.
- The region became a Development Area and had help from the government and the EU.

Did it work?

- In the 1980s, lots of companies came to South Wales, including 130 American and 130 European ones, as well as over 20 from Japan.
- New industry attracted to South Wales included biotechnology, IT, electronics, and financial services.
- Most urban areas in South Wales now have modern business parks.

Valleys town to receive facelift

A five-year regeneration project in Ystrad Mynach (a South Wales valley town) will include:

- The transformation of the Penallta colliery (which closed in 1991) into a new 'urban village'.
- Improvements to recreation facilities at Penallta Country Park.
- Better public transport.
- New business developments at Tredomen Business Park.
- Refurbishment of colliery buildings.

Swansea

Swansea Waterfront has had a makeover. The latest news is:

'Insurance group Admiral will create 250 jobs in Swansea over the next 3 years. The company will move to purpose-built offices in the city's waterfront area.'

Admiral's move was helped by a £1.9 million grant from the Welsh Assembly.

One of the aims of developing the waterfront is to attract jobs in the tertiary and quaternary sectors.

But not everyone is happy. Swansea's city centre has been in decline for 20 years. Businesses and shops have left. People think the city centre won't benefit from the development. A member of the city's civic society said:

'The projects on the waterfront might split the city. Development will concentrate things there and everyone else will lose out.'

▲ New building at Swansea Waterfront

Cycles

You can look at what's happened in South Wales like this:

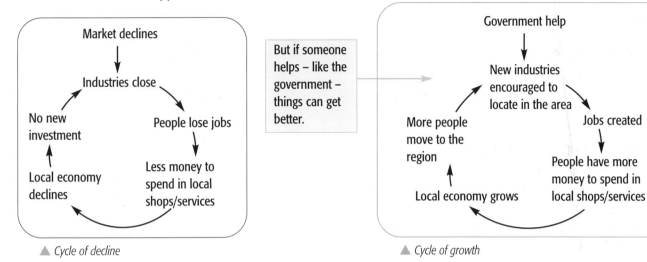

Market declines

Industries close

No new investment

People lose jobs

Local economy declines

Less money to spend in local shops/services

▲ Cycle of decline

But if someone helps – like the government – things can get better.

Government help

New industries encouraged to locate in the area

More people move to the region

Jobs created

Local economy grows

People have more money to spend in local shops/services

▲ Cycle of growth

Much the same has happened in the Ruhr.

What's new in the Ruhr?

The Ruhr – heavy industry was in decline, and it had an image problem. Rivers and the atmosphere were polluted, the landscape was ruined. Something had to be done. The state and central government wanted to encourage new types of employment and improve the environment. Work began in the 1960s.

- ◆ Now 65% of the Ruhr's workers are employed in the tertiary sector. Jobs range from those in shops, health and veterinary services, to transport, legal and business consultants and telecommunications.
- ◆ New universities and colleges were set up to educate workers with new qualifications and skills.
- ◆ Business parks were developed for light and high-tech industries.
- ◆ The environment has been cleaned up.

Activities

1 Do you think new industries would have located in South Wales without government help? Explain your answer.
2 Most industries that have chosen to locate in South Wales are from outside the UK. Why do you think this is?
3 What do you think might be the advantages and disadvantages of large foreign companies locating in South Wales?
4 Compare the changes that have taken place in South Wales and the Ruhr. What are the main similarities and differences?
5 Find out about one other area in the UK where new industries have chosen to locate. Are the factors causing the decline, and the reasons for re-growth, the same as in South Wales, or are they different?

Emscher Landscape Park

A whole area along the River Emscher has been transformed to create Europe's largest regional park. It stretches 70 km from east to west and covers 320 sq. km. The aim was to improve the working and living environment for the 2 million people who live in the region.

Lots of work has been done, ranging from developing large areas of derelict land to planting trees. Old industrial buildings have been deliberately included in the park. The park includes 230 km of cycle tracks and 130 km of footpaths, and a golf course.

Work began on the park in 1989, but it's still not finished. It'll continue until 2020.

▲ Where's that gone?

Industry and LEDCs

In this unit you'll learn about industry in LEDCs.

I'm Maximo Casiendo – a rice farmer from the Philippines. You can read more about me in Unit 10.8. There's lots of people like me in LEDCs – about half of us work in farming.

Brazil is becoming more developed. Fewer people work in farming (they've been replaced by machines). More people work in towns and cities in factories (secondary activities). As the country becomes richer, there's an increase in tertiary jobs.

The **UK** is an MEDC. Lots of people work in tertiary activities. Secondary activities still exist but lots of workers have been replaced by machines. Few people work in primary industries.

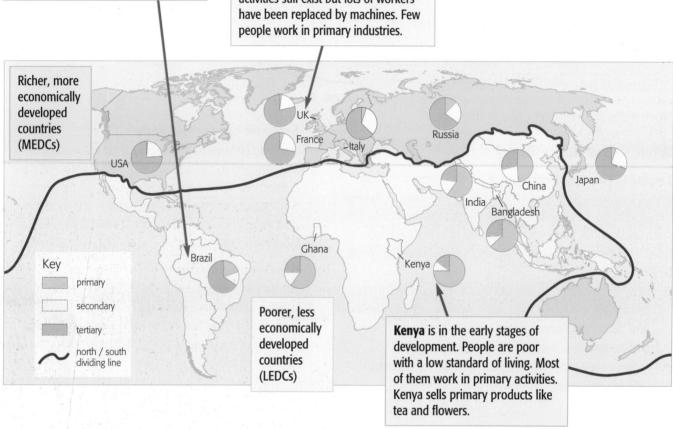

Richer, more economically developed countries (MEDCs)

Key
- primary
- secondary
- tertiary
- north / south dividing line

Poorer, less economically developed countries (LEDCs)

Kenya is in the early stages of development. People are poor with a low standard of living. Most of them work in primary activities. Kenya sells primary products like tea and flowers.

The map shows the proportion of people working in primary, secondary and tertiary industries (aka the **employment structure**) for 12 countries at different stages of development. It also shows the world split into two parts. Countries to the north and east of the thick black line are richer and more developed, and those to the south and west are poorer and less developed.

But maybe things are changing.

The BRICs are coming

Brazil, Russia, India and China are the so-called BRICs. It's predicted that by 2050 only the USA and Japan are likely to remain in the G7 (the group of the world's top 7 richest nations). Brazil, Russia, India and China will replace the UK, Germany, Italy and France. At current rates of growth, China's economy will be bigger than the USA's by 2041. And it will keep growing.

▲ China is emerging as a global heavyweight.

Industry and pollution

China and India might be changing, but this change is coming at a price – pollution.

China's economy is growing fast. That means its energy demands are huge. This has caused big problems:

◆ two-thirds of China's power comes from coal and coal products – the cheapest and dirtiest forms of energy
◆ 400 000 Chinese people die each year from diseases related to air pollution
◆ 16 of the world's 20 most polluted cities are in China.

In India, 2000 factories in Delhi discharged untreated waste into the River Yamuna. The 20-km stretch of the river in Delhi is only 2% of its total length but it accounted for 71% of its pollution. The culprits were detergent, textile, engineering and auto factories. The Supreme Court banned the discharge of untreated waste to try to stop the pollution.

Other industries act differently. Ford India (Unit 11.6) treats all the waste water from its plant, and is working towards the sustainable use of resources.

▲ Pretty in pink – China's largest iron and steel works at Anshan.

Sustainable development

Sometimes people need help. Practical Action is a British charity. It works with people in LEDCs helping to provide practical answers to poverty, and sustainable solutions. One of the projects it's involved with is the Jua Kali engineering workshops in Kenya (see right). The project aims to increase production from the workshops so that people earn more money and more jobs are created.

Practical Action ensures that the equipment, tools, information, skills and organisation needed to make the workshops run well are in place.

The workshops use scrap metal. They are supported by the Kenyan government, as well as Practical Action. Schemes like this are **sustainable** – they can continue for years without using up resources, or harming the environment.

> **Did you know?**
> Sustainable development means improving people's lives without wasting resources or harming the environment.

Activities

1 a Describe the differences in employment structure between the MEDCs and LEDCs shown on the map.
  b Give reasons for the differences you have identified.
2 Describe the differences that exist
  a within the six MEDCs
  b within the six LEDCs.
3 Are the differences within LEDCs greater than the difference between them as a group and the MEDCs? Explain your answer.

4 a Suggest what the employment structure of the BRICs might look like by 2050.
  b Explain why the employment structure of these countries is likely to change in the future.
5 The Industrial Revolution in Europe during the 19th century created a lot of pollution. Do you think it's fair for countries industrialising now to be criticised for the pollution they're creating?

The NICs in east Asia

In this unit you'll find out about industrialisation in developing countries.

→ What's a tiger got to do with geography? Read on, and find out.

What are NICs?

NICs – that's short for **newly industrialised countries**. They're countries that have developed very large manufacturing industries very quickly. The process is called **industrialisation**, and it's happened much faster in the NICs than it did in Europe and North America.

The NICs economies have grown and they've become richer. The countries in eastern Asia have seen the largest growth. They include countries like Japan, Singapore, Thailand and Malaysia. The four countries whose economy grew the fastest are known as the 'Tiger economies' – South Korea, Taiwan, Singapore and Hong Kong.

China could well be the next NIC.

How did the NICs develop so quickly?

- ◆ **Labour** – people were prepared to work for long hours for little pay to begin with, so things were produced cheaply.
- ◆ **Government** – introduced long-term industrial planning and tried to attract new industry with financial incentives.
- ◆ **Transport** – all the countries were close to main shipping lanes. Ships are the cheapest way to transport goods long distances.
- ◆ **Markets** – goods were produced for a global market. Markets within Asia are increasing as people have more money.

Economic growth continued in the NICs during the 1980s when it was slowing down in MEDCs and world manufacturing was declining.

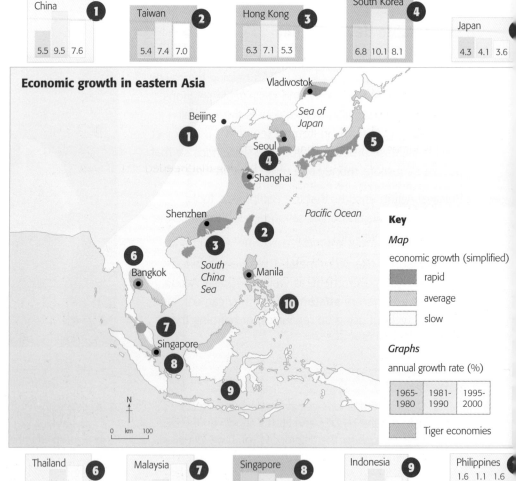

China ❶ 5.5 9.5 7.6

Taiwan ❷ 5.4 7.4 7.0

Hong Kong ❸ 6.3 7.1 5.3

South Korea ❹ 6.8 10.1 8.1

Japan 4.3 4.1 3.6

Economic growth in eastern Asia

Vladivostok

Beijing ❶

Sea of Japan

Seoul ❹

Shanghai

Shenzhen

❸

❷

Pacific Ocean

❺

❻

Bangkok

South China Sea

Manila

❿

❼

Singapore

❽

❾

N

0 km 100

Key

Map

economic growth (simplified)

- rapid
- average
- slow

Graphs

annual growth rate (%)

1965-1980	1981-1990	1995-2000

Tiger economies

Thailand ❻ 4.0 7.6 8.4

Malaysia ❼ 4.0 5.1 8.2

Singapore ❽ 7.2 7.0 6.1

Indonesia ❾ 3.2 6.3 4.8

Philippines 1.6 1.1 1.6

Hyundai to build new Indian plant

South Korea's Hyundai Motors plans to build a second plant in India. It will produce 150 000 cars a year and will be built close to their existing plant in Chennai.

The company is South Korea's top car manufacturer and aims to become one of the top 5 car manufacturers in the world by 2010.

Samsung to expand

Samsung announced a major expansion plan. It aims to become one of the three largest electronics companies in the world by the end of 2010.

Samsung produce memory chips, semi-conductors, flat screen TVs and display panels, as well as mobile phones.

Not bad for a company which began by exporting black and white televisions to Panama in 1969.

▲ *Seoul, capital of South Korea – the heart of a tiger.*

South Korea

Hyundai and Samsung are just two of South Korea's big industrial companies. Their names and products are known around the world. And yet in the 1960s South Korea was an isolated war-ravaged country. How did it, and its companies, grow so fast?

The government planned a series of five-year economic plans. South Korea has developed in 3 stages:

◆ **Stage 1 – 1960s.** South Korea had few natural resources and little technical expertise. Early development focused on manufacturing that needed lots of workers, for example textiles.

◆ **Stage 2 – 1970s.** Investment grew in heavy industries like shipbuilding, iron and steel and cars. The government planned to export these abroad.

◆ **Stage 3 – 1980s and 90s.** Since the 1980s there has been a move towards high-tech industries like computers and electronics.

What's the downside?

People's standard of living has improved, but it's not all good news. Rapid industrialisation has caused air and water pollution. There are fewer jobs in farming so people have moved to towns and cities to find work. And that causes all sorts of problems. People aren't prepared to work for little pay any more, so industrial disputes like strikes for better pay and working conditions are common. Some of the biggest companies are chaebols started by families. And some of them have been accused of corruption.

South Korea: employment by sector (%)		
	1970	2004
Primary	50	8
Secondary	15	19
Tertiary	35	73

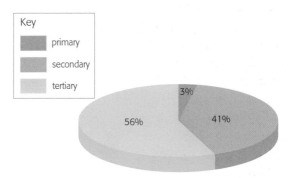

GDP by sector

▲ *GDP is a measure of a country's wealth. This pie chart shows how farming (primary), industry (secondary) and services (tertiary) contributed to South Korea's wealth in 2004.*

Activities

1 Explain why the economies of the NICs grew so quickly.
2 Why do you think these economies have developed much more rapidly than those of Europe in the 19th century?
3 Is the rapid growth of the South Korean economy due to government planning? Explain your answer.
4 Explain, with the use of examples, some of the problems brought about by rapid industrialisation in NICs.

The big picture

This chapter is about resources and how we use them. These are the big ideas behind the chapter:

♦ A resource is anything – natural or man-made – which humans can use.

♦ As population grows, and as countries develop economically, there is an increased demand for resources.

♦ Increasing demands for resources affect the environment.

♦ We need to tackle global warming and find alternative sustainable sources of energy.

♦ Tourism has grown dramatically, and tourists have a major impact on holiday destinations.

♦ Tourism can help to preserve the environment, and be sustainable.

Your goals for this chapter

By the end of this chapter you should be able to answer these questions:

♦ How does population growth affect the use of resources?

♦ How has changing technology affected the development of energy resources?

♦ What is the impact of increased energy production in an LEDC like China?

♦ What is the evidence for global warming, and does everyone agree it is happening?

♦ List the possible effects of global warming.

♦ What can you do to use energy more wisely, and how can governments tackle global warming?

♦ Give an example of alternative energy being developed in the UK.

♦ Give three reasons why tourism has grown in the last twenty five years.

♦ List at least four impacts (more if you can) of tourism in an MEDC and an LEDC.

♦ How can tourism be made more sustainable?

♦ What do these terms mean?
materialism, fossil fuel, global warming, greenhouse gas, green tourism

And then . . .

When you finish the chapter, come back here and see if you've met your goals!

Did you know?
Levi Strauss jeans were invented as work trousers for American miners looking for gold.

Did you know?
A slant well is an oil well drilled on a slant so you can drill oil that is under someone else's property.

Did you know?
Cars and trucks are responsible for almost half the world's oil consumption.

Did you know?
Just as we have created rubbish mountains, we've also accumulated a blanket of junk around the Earth. There are over a million bits of debris orbiting our planet.

Your chapter starter

Look at the photo on page 234.
What do you think the man has in his hand?
What could it be used for?
Is it a renewable resource?
What effect might getting it, or using it, have on the environment?

Where's my pick and shovel?

The rate of resource use

In this unit you will learn why resource use is growing at a faster and faster rate.

Population growth increases resource use

A resource is anything – natural or man-made – which humans can use. The more people there are, the more resources we need. Between 1980 and 2005, total world population grew from 4.4 billion to 6.4 billion. By 2015, the world's population will be over 7 billion. All 7 billion people will need water and food. Already, trying to feed growing populations has put pressure on soil and water resources.

The photograph on the right was taken in Burkina Faso, a country in West Africa, in the Sahel. Burkina Faso has suffered as a result of:

◆ a rapidly growing population – and the people use wood as their basic fuel
◆ rapidly growing numbers of animals.

Trying to increase food output has caused **overcultivation** and **overgrazing**.

A newspaper described the changes:

The landscape is a wreck. Until 20 years ago, it was thick, dry forest teeming with wildlife, and plants and trees that local people used for all aspects of their lives. Now it is dust and bits of scrub.

Water is an even bigger problem in Burkina Faso. The total yearly rainfall has gone down from 500 mm to 400 mm in the north, and from 1400 mm to 1100 mm in the south of the country. What has caused this change in the climate? It's possible that as the trees are cut down, there's less **evapotranspiration** to pump water vapour into the air.

Many scientists believe that the carbon dioxide that comes from our cars and lorries, and from our oil-, coal-, and gas-burning power stations, has helped to cause the **droughts** that have harmed the Sahel region of Africa. The droughts have been the worst the world has ever seen, and have often led to famine.

▲ The effect of overcultivation and overgrazing in Burkina Faso.

▲ These women have to walk for four hours a day to get water – even during a sandstorm.

Economic development increases resource use

In the last 30 years, the population of the UK, in common with most MEDCs, hasn't grown very much. But energy use per person in the UK has gone up from 82 to 195 G-joules. Your granny could tell you why …

The richer a country gets, the more energy it uses – the more we have, the more we seem to want. The more we want, the more we buy. The more we buy, the more resources are used up. Some people call all of this **materialism**.

Materialism is wanting only belongings or comfort, and having no interest in morals. To be called materialist isn't really a compliment!

But LEDCs understandably want to improve the living standards of their populations through economic development. You can see the link between **economic development** and energy use per person if you look at what's happening in China:

When I was your age we didn't have computers ... nor those play stations ... nor these empeethree things – we made our own music. Switch the kettle on love – it's time for Countdown.

China's earnings per head (US dollars)	
1981	$285
1986	$275
1991	$351
1996	$667
2001	$921
2006*	$1553
* forecast	

Key

― total
▬ oil
▬ gas
▬ other

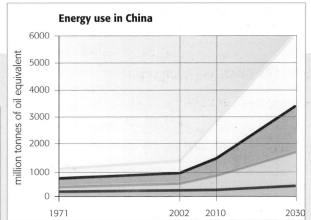

Energy use in China

million tonnes of oil equivalent

---

1 'Overgrazing' means there are too many animals on the land. What does 'overcultivation' mean?

2 Between 1950 and 2005, the population of Burkina Faso grew from 4 million to 14 million. Copy out and complete the flow diagram below to show how population increase can damage the environment:

3 **a** Use the numbers in the table (above left) to draw a bar chart to show China's earnings per head.

b What has happened to China's earnings per head? Use figures in your answer.

c How is your bar graph connected to the graph showing fuel use (above right)? Explain your answer.

4 Describe three ways in which economic development leads to increased resource use.

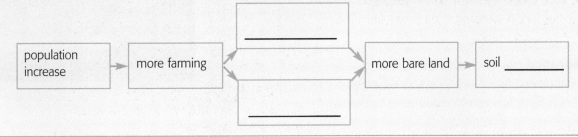

| population increase | → | more farming | ⇒ | _____ | → | more bare land | → | soil _____ |

_____

Resource use and new technology

In this unit you will learn how resource use changes with new technology – and about the results of this.

Changing energy technology

Different types of energy have been used in the last half million years. Look at the timeline on the right.

It's clear that we have developed new technologies to meet our expanding needs. What will the new technology of the 21st century be?

Energy use in the UK

Look at the graph below. You can see that while the use of one energy source has gone down, the use of others has gone up. These aren't just 'dead' numbers. Geographers look at the effect of these changes on *places* and *people*.

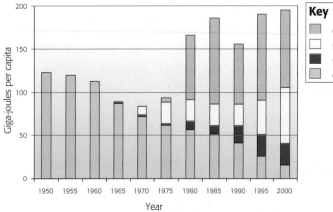

Energy use in the UK

Key
- oil
- natural gas
- nuclear power
- coal

(y-axis: Giga-joules per capita, 0 to 200; x-axis: Year, 1950 to 2000)

In the 1950s, many important British industries were run by the government. These nationalised industries – coal mining, water, gas, and steel, for example – needed large **subsidies** of taxpayers' money to keep people in work. These subsidies got more and more costly for the government.

Other countries could produce coal more cheaply – they paid their workers less, and spent next to nothing on the health and safety of their labour force.

It made sense, then, for the British government to start closing down the UK's coal mines and start importing coal instead. Thousands of British miners lost their jobs from the 1980s onwards.

But **deindustrialisation** has other costs. Without work, people need to claim benefits. Local shops and industries suffer when money's tight. And communities have to change.

---

500 000 BC: Man makes fire

20 BC: Roman watermills

The earliest known description of a vertical watermill is in the writings of Vituvius, a Roman engineer.

500 AD: Persian windmills

The first windmills were developed to automate the tasks of grain-grinding and water-pumping. The earliest known design was developed in Persia (modern-day Iran).

19th century: steam power

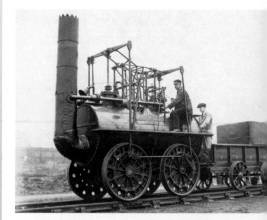

20th century: coal-fired power station for electricity

20th century: nuclear power station for electricity

What did it feel like when the pits closed?

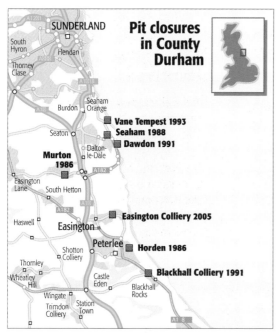

▲ Pit closures in a small area of County Durham. The movie Billy Elliot was filmed at Easington.

I'm Bob, and I was a miner

When my pit closed in 1993, the younger lads were too young to retire – but in their minds too old to do anything else. They still had twenty years before they retired. Having been a miner all their working lives, that's all they knew, and any new job they took would be at a lower wage – if they were lucky enough to get a job at all. Fortunately, most of them did find jobs.

I took it very badly because I was older – who would employ me? I was losing a well-paid job, and it was the only job I wanted to do. The greatest fear was the uncertainty – was I going to lose what I'd worked all my life to achieve? I still had a mortgage to pay and had a good lifestyle. Could I still keep them up?

Ellington Colliery closed in 2005.

So, no more pits in the North-East, then?

Nope.

Because there's no coal left?

Nope. There's 3 million tonnes at Ellington.

But coal's just too dirty?

Nope. They can turn it into gas underground.

That's great news – North Sea gas is running out. When does it start?

They're still thinking about it …

Activities

1 Using the time-line and graph, copy out this text and add in the correct dates.

Humans probably worked out how to make fire in _____ BC. Watermills were developed by the _____, around 20 BC. Windmills were developed around _____, but steam power only began in the _____ century. Electricity stations burning coal, gas or oil were built in the _____ century. The UK started to use nuclear power around _____, and natural gas around _____.

2 Look at the graph of energy use in the UK.

a In which year did oil first become an important source of energy for the UK?

b Why do you think natural gas is a popular type of fuel?

c Describe the fall in the use of coal. Use figures in your answer.

d Why has the use of coal fallen so much in the UK?

3 Using the graph and the text:

a Give three reasons why the number of coal mines in Britain has fallen since the 1980s.

b Give three reasons why people protested against these pit closures.

c Write an interview with a miner in the 1980s. Make up four questions a reporter might ask, and then four answers the miner might give.

Changing resource use in an LEDC: China

In this unit you will learn about the huge increases in energy production in China – and the impacts this is having.

Coal use in China

'Coal consumption in China went up from 610 million tonnes in 1980 to 1393 million tonnes in 2002. Coal quality – the average heating value – has also greatly improved. About two-thirds of China's power comes from coal and coal products – the cheapest and dirtiest forms of energy.'
He Youguo, China Coal Industry Development Research and Consulting.

Coal and pollution

77-year-old Liu Hongkui is the leader of retired workers in Tangshan, 150 km east of Beijing. Just behind their houses is a coke plant, which pours out poisonous fumes day and night. They're sure it's causing lung and heart disease, and cancer. They are victims of China's thirst for energy. Air pollution – including acid rain and greenhouse gas emissions – is one of several problems. 16 of the 20 most-polluted cities in the world are in China.

▲ China has faced power cuts because energy supply can't keep up with demand. This is a coke plant, like the one at Tangshan.

Despite a fine, the factory continues to pump out pollution. The coke plant is playing a part in China's rapid economic development. It turns coal into coke, which is then used in steel-making. Steel, in turn, is needed for the construction of new roads, buildings, cars, and home appliances for China's 1.3 billion people.

Air pollution expert Liu Xiang says 'Often these polluting activities are the main industries and important taxpayers, so local governments don't want to see them closed down because that would slow down economic development.'

Can China use coal forever?

About 80% of the world's energy supply comes from fossil fuels.

'We have to change the efficiency of fossil fuel use so we have more energy services from the same amount of coal. We have to make clean coal technology. We have to fight pollutants like sulphur dioxide and mercury, and capture carbon dioxide emissions.'
The head of the UN Environment Programme.

China has a big project to produce electricity without pollution: The Three Gorges Dam.

Did you know?
China's economy has been growing very quickly in recent years – and this has increased the demand for energy.

Did you know?
Gunpowder, paper, the compass, and paper money were all invented in China.

The Three Gorges Dam

The huge Three Gorges hydroelectric power project has been built to manage the mighty Yangtze River.

Supporters say China's economic development depends on it. They say it will provide a clean source of energy for future generations. The dam is expected to generate one-ninth of China's power. That's equal to 50 million tonnes of coal a year, or 15 nuclear power plants. The project will lower greenhouse gas emissions.

▲ The nearly completed Three Gorges Dam in 2005. It will be the largest dam in the world when finished.

The dam's huge system of locks will allow ocean-going ships to travel inland, boosting trade and development.

The dam will also help control the terrible flooding of the Yangtze River – in the 20th century, the river's floods killed about 300 000 people. Experts say the dam will reduce the frequency of flooding disasters from once every ten years to once a century.

BUT!

◆ About 1.3 million people have to be relocated from 1400 towns and villages, which are being flooded by the new dam's giant reservoir lake. There's the hardship of resettlement for these people, and many of them are being moved to much less fertile land.

◆ Rubbish from the flooded towns and villages will also leak into the lake's water.

◆ The area to be 'drowned' is famous for its breathtaking scenery, and is home to archaeological sites including burial grounds and ancient temples.

Wu Deng Ming is president of the Green League of Chongqing. He is worried that, in spite of the Chinese government's promise to clean it up, the lake behind the dam will become a dumping ground for the sewage, wastewater and agricultural run-off produced by the 15 million people living nearby. Each year, says Mr Wu, the area around Chongqing will dump 350 million cubic metres of wastewater and 400 million cubic metres of industrial waste into the reservoir – enough to fill the whole reservoir in 50 years.

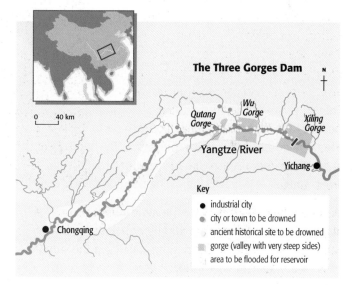

The Three Gorges Dam

N

0   40 km

Wu Gorge

Qutang Gorge

Xiling Gorge

Yangtze River

Yichang

Chongqing

Key

● industrial city
● city or town to be drowned
○ ancient historical site to be drowned
■ gorge (valley with very steep sides)
 area to be flooded for reservoir

Activities

1 **a** Look at the diagram in unit 12.2. Why did people invent new ways of creating energy?
   b People say that 'necessity is the mother of invention'. What does this mean?

2 **a** Design a poster for Liu Hongkui's protest.
   b Write a possible reply to him from the Chinese government.
   c What arguments could be given in favour of increased resource use?

3 Many Chinese think the costs of The Three Gorges Dam project are too high. How far do you agree? (Hint: 'How far do you agree' means give the advantages and disadvantages of the project, and then decide, on balance, if the project should have been allowed.)

Global warming

In this unit you will learn about the evidence for and possible effects of global warming.

It's getting hot in here

One of the problems with making energy by burning coal, oil, or gas – **fossil fuels** – is that they give off sulphur dioxide, which can make acid rain, and carbon dioxide, which is a **greenhouse gas**.

Most scientists agree that human activities are adding to **global warming**. We're pumping large amounts of heat-trapping greenhouse gases into the atmosphere. The main source of these gases is the burning of fossil fuels.

Every time we drive a car, use electricity from coal-fired power plants, or heat our homes with oil or natural gas, we release carbon dioxide and other heat-trapping gases into the air.

Another important cause of global warming is the cutting down of trees, especially the tropical rainforests. This is because trees absorb carbon dioxide from the atmosphere.

Since 1800, the amount of carbon dioxide in the atmosphere has gone up by 31%. Over the same period, methane in the atmosphere has risen by 151%, mostly from farming activities like growing rice and raising cattle.

As the volume of these gases grows, more heat is trapped by the atmosphere and less escapes back into space. This increase in trapped heat changes the climate - it increases **global warming**.

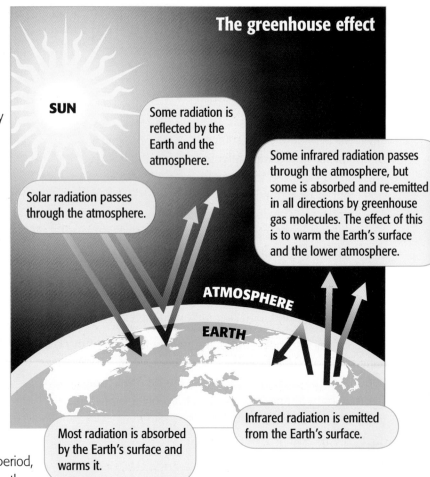

The greenhouse effect

SUN

Some radiation is reflected by the Earth and the atmosphere.

Solar radiation passes through the atmosphere.

Some infrared radiation passes through the atmosphere, but some is absorbed and re-emitted in all directions by greenhouse gas molecules. The effect of this is to warm the Earth's surface and the lower atmosphere.

ATMOSPHERE

EARTH

Most radiation is absorbed by the Earth's surface and warms it.

Infrared radiation is emitted from the Earth's surface.

What's the evidence for global warming?

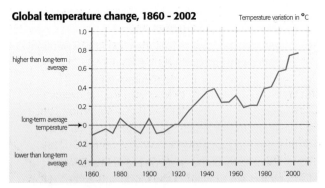

Global temperature change, 1860 - 2002

Temperature variation in °C

higher than long-term average

long-term average temperature →

lower than long-term average

▲ The graph shows the average increase in global temperatures. Many scientists think this rise has been caused by the increasing amount of greenhouse gases, particularly carbon dioxide.

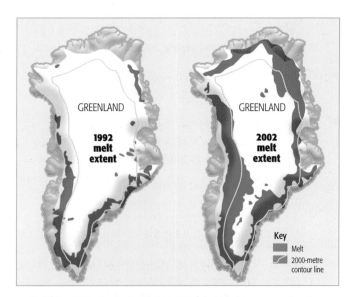

GREENLAND
1992 melt extent

GREENLAND
2002 melt extent

Key
Melt
2000-metre contour line

▲ Glaciers and ice sheets are shrinking because temperatures are rising. The two maps show the changes in the ice cover on Greenland in just 10 years. The white shows solid ice, and the orange shows melted ice. When glaciers and icecaps melt, more water pours into the sea.

What might happen?

Although a few researchers disagree, most scientists predict that global temperatures will rise between 2.5 °C and 10.5 °C over the next 100 years. Nobody knows for sure what *will* happen – but here are some predictions about what *might*:

◆ Sea levels could rise between 9 and 88 cm. This would mean:
  - more coastal erosion
  - more coastal flooding
  - the loss of vital fertile land in low-lying areas like Bangladesh or the Mississippi delta.
◆ In many parts of the world, warmer weather would mean a longer growing season.
◆ More carbon dioxide (CO_2) in the atmosphere should make plants grow more energetically. Experts reckon the extra CO_2 would improve food output by 17%.
◆ People like warm climates; heating bills are lower and clothing costs are reduced.
◆ Many natural ecosystems could be lost – perhaps forever.
◆ There could be greater threats to human health as mosquitoes and other disease-carrying insects spread infection over wider areas.

So, not all the possible consequences of global warming are negative – some can even be benefits.

Is it happening everywhere?

Not all the evidence points to a rise in temperatures. Here's a different point of view – from Antarctica:

It's not like climate hasn't changed before.

Antarctica getting colder?

US scientists say they have found that much of Antarctica is actually getting cooler.

This is different from earlier reports, which say that Antarctica has got slightly warmer recently.

The researchers say the cooling is causing soil organisms to fall in number by more than 10% a year. They also found that organisms have been taking in significantly less carbon dioxide.

They say their findings are different from most models of climate change:

'The average air temperature at the Earth's surface increased by 0.06 °C per decade during the 20th Century, and by 0.19 °C per decade from 1979 to 1998. Climate models generally forecast warming in polar regions. Although earlier reports were of a slight warming, our analysis of Antarctic weather shows an overall cooling on the continent between 1966 and 2000, particularly during summer and autumn.'

Activities

1 Fit the correct 'tail' to each of the 'heads'.

head	tail
The sun's radiation …	… greenhouse gases, which warm the atmosphere.
Some of this solar radiation …	… passes through the atmosphere.
But most solar radiation …	…long-wave, infra-red radiation.
The Earth then begins to send out …	… is absorbed by the Earth.
Some of this radiation is trapped by …	… is reflected by the Earth and its atmosphere.

2 Look at the graph of global temperatures.
  a Describe the changes, including the times when temperatures went down.
  b How much has the average temperature risen since 1860?
3 Look at the possible effects of global warming. Sort the effects into positive and negative.
4 What evidence is there that global warming may not be happening **globally** – over **all** the Earth? Use your own words.

What can I do about global warming?

In this unit you will find out how we can tackle global warming.

You've had this lesson already – probably more than once. You know what to do, but don't switch off; this affects all of us, now.

Every day you see cars, lorries, buses, trains, factories – they're all burning fossil fuels. Lots of other people are hurting the planet more than you are.

WALK TO SCHOOL

We have seen that most – but not all – scientists believe that our increasing output of greenhouse gases – carbon dioxide, methane, ozone and some others – is causing global warming.

But just look at a typical day …

Jed's Day

07.28: (as late as possible) Alarm rings on mobile. Switch on radio. Batteries dead. Chuck old batteries.

07.30: Stumble out of bed, go to loo – long flush. Pressure shower.

07.40: Get dressed, go downstairs.

07.45: Fill kettle. Boil kettle. Make cup of tea. Breakfast.

07.55: Run tap. Clean teeth. Turn off tap.

08.00: Get lift to school.

08.45 - 15.30: School – lessons, send texts, school dinner, fizzy drink from vending machine, chuck can in bin, listen to some MP3 tracks. Brain on screensaver.

15.45: Bus home. Buy drink in plastic recyclable bottle. Chuck bottle in bin. Download a ring tone; some more MP3 tracks.

16.15: Switch on computer to start homework. Actually use Playstation/TV.

18.00: Leave TV on standby, computer on screensaver. Have tea.

No, not **this** sort of car-sharing!

So what can you and I do to slow down the emission of greenhouse gases? Basically, use less energy based on fossil fuels.

This spider diagram shows some of the ways to use energy more wisely. Which ones do you do now, and which ones could you do if you wanted?

Low-energy light bulbs cost around £3 each. They can save £10 on electricity per year. A bulb used for 4 hours a day will last 10 years.

USING ENERGY WISELY

If your TV is on standby 18 hours a day, and electricity costs 5 pence per kWh, you'll save £3.29 per year on your electricity bill just by switching the TV off!

Full loft insulation covering an area of up to 51 square metres costs about £220 and saves £92 in heating costs each year.

The average UK family spends £574 on central heating each year. Lowering the thermostat on the central heating by 2°C can save 15% or more on your heating bill.

The average UK family uses 380 kWh of electricity each year on lighting, at 5 pence per kWh. Turning out a light that would otherwise have been left on can cut the lighting bill by 31%.

What can governments do?

A lot of governments have been working really hard to cut down emissions of greenhouse gases. In December 1997, more than 160 nations signed an agreement called the **Kyoto Protocol**.

The Kyoto Protocol is an international agreement on climate change. Countries which have signed this protocol have decided to reduce their emissions of carbon dioxide, methane and other greenhouse gases.

The aim is to keep the level of greenhouse gases in the atmosphere at a level that would prevent dangerous changes in the climate.

Other organisations – like the European Union – agree that substances released into the atmosphere by human activities lead to many current environmental problems, like:

- acid rain
- poor air quality
- global warming and climate change
- damage to and dirtying of buildings
- holes in the ozone layer
- poisoning ecosystems
- exposure to hazardous substances.

The UK government is one of the countries which has signed the Kyoto Protocol. Here's a speech by a government minister, explaining the plans for cutting the release of greenhouse gases in the UK:

Call **ME** a polluter?

'In the UK, we have set as our first goal obtaining 10% of our electricity from renewable sources by 2010, with the hope of doubling this by 2020 … Wind energy, as the form of renewable energy with by far the best immediate prospects for growth in the UK, will play a very big part … This is true of both onshore and offshore wind generators. There are currently wind generation projects amounting to more than 2000 MW … To put this figure in context, total UK windfarm capacity is currently around 650 MW. We estimate that nearly 500 MW of capacity will be built this year, or about four times as much as last year … We are also encouraging the development of other forms of renewable energy, such as biomass, solar cells, and wave and tidal energy … to create a much more varied renewable energy sector.'

Activities

1 List every resource you used today, from when you got up until this lesson. Make a two-column table showing your activity and the resource used.
2 Send a text to Jed about his typical day, with three ways he could use resources more carefully.
3 Look at the spider diagram.
   a Rank the methods of cutting down energy usage from biggest to smallest savings per year, looking at the costs as well as the savings.
   b Now rank the methods as you did in (**a**), but this time over 25 years.
4 a Which resources used in your house are being recycled?
   b Which could be?
5 List the five renewable resources being developed by the UK. Which of these methods do you think would be best for the UK. (Hint: think about both positive and negative impacts.)
6 What's an offshore windfarm?

Wind power in the UK

In this unit you will learn how the UK is developing
wind power – and how it splits opinion.

North Hoyle Wind Farm

▲ North Hoyle Wind Farm being built.

- ◆ North Hoyle windfarm is located 4-5 miles off the North Wales coast, between Rhyl and Prestatyn.
- ◆ It's made up of 30 wind turbines, each producing 2 megawatts of power.
- ◆ It's the UK's first important **offshore** (built at sea) wind farm.
- ◆ It is part of the UK's move to cleaner sources of power.

North Hoyle was built in 2003, and is now fully operational. It produces enough clean 'green' electricity to power about 40 000 homes a year. This clean electricity will offset the emission of about 160 000 tonnes of carbon dioxide – the main greenhouse gas contributing to global warming – every year.
Together, Greenpeace (the 'green' campaigners) and the electricity generating company npower have developed *npower Juice*, a clean electricity product available to home customers at no extra cost.

Now it's fully operational, North Hoyle is the main source of npower Juice. Householders signed up to npower Juice notice no difference in the electricity they receive, but know that the electricity they are paying for is generated from a renewable source. This is because, for every unit of electricity they use, npower feeds the same amount in to the electricity network from the North Hoyle Wind Farm.

North Hoyle Wind Farm working. ▶

Not everyone believes that wind power is the answer – some people think it's just too noisy.

Is wind power noisy?

Did you know?
- In 2003, windfarms generated 0.4% of the total UK electricity supply.
- By 2010, this should rise to 8% of total UK electricity supply.

No!

Almost everything with moving parts will make some sound. Well-planned wind turbines are usually quiet as they operate, and compared with road traffic, trains, aircraft and construction noise, the noise from wind turbines is very low.

Outside the nearest houses, which are at least 300 metres away, the sound of a wind turbine generating electricity is likely to be about the same level as noise from a flowing stream about 50-100 metres away, or the noise of leaves rustling. This is similar to the sound level inside a typical living room with a gas fire switched on, or the reading room of a library, or in an unoccupied, quiet, air-conditioned office.

British Wind Energy Association

Yes!

The noise, says Les Nichols, is a low thump-thump-thump that reverberates up to 22 times a minute.

'It's not there all the time, but you're always waiting for it,' he says. 'It's like a water torture, totally infuriating.'

Les lives beside a windfarm in Furness, the scenic area between the Lake District and the town of Barrow. For the past three and a half years, he and his neighbours have had to put up with noise pollution that disrupts their sleep and causes constant stress.

Yet when the developers sought permission for the seven giant turbines, they guaranteed there would be no noise nuisance, he says.

More people in Britain could now face similar problems as a result of government plans announced last week to double the number of windfarms in an effort to derive 20 per cent of the country's electricity from renewable sources by 2020.

Adapted from newspaper reports, 2003.

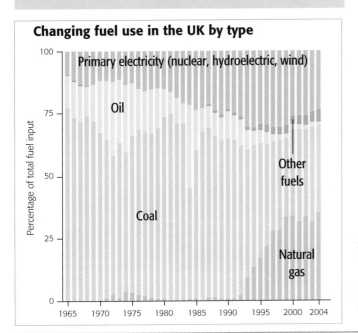

Changing fuel use in the UK by type

(Graph: Percentage of total fuel input vs years 1965–2004, showing Primary electricity (nuclear, hydroelectric, wind), Oil, Coal, Natural gas, and Other fuels.)

Activities

1 Look at the graph above. Did the use of primary electricity (nuclear, hydroelectric and wind power) grow between 1990 and 2004?

2 You are an official for the British Wind Energy Association. How would you convince Les Nichols that windfarms are the future?

3 Use the photo and the text to explain why some people don't like windfarms on land.

4 What are the advantages of offshore windfarms?

5 'The use of fossil fuel right now is unavoidable.' Do you agree or disagree with this statement? Justify your answer.

Going anywhere nice on your holidays?

In this unit you will learn how the holidays people take have changed.

What kind of tourist are you?

Different people want different things on a holiday. Thinking about whether you agree with the statements below or not will tell you what kind of tourist you are, and also help you consider different tourist attractions.

What kind of tourist are you?

1   I like to work on my tan on the beach.
2   I don't like foreign food.
3   I hate those artificial tourist attractions, like 'local' dancers.
4   Most of the photos I take are of views.
5   Being lost in a town where they don't speak English is a nightmare.
6   I need satellite TV to watch my football team.
7   I really want to see ancient ruins in faraway countries.
8   I love extreme sports, like kite-surfing.
9   I would never visit a museum on holiday.
10 There's no such thing as a holiday that's too cheap.
11 Holidays are the perfect times to be on the pull.
12 I really don't mind hill walking in the rain.
13 Why are the places I like full of tourists?

Tourism has grown a lot in the last 25 years

Here are some of the reasons:

◆   People have more leisure time.
◆   In 2005, UK workers earned four times as much as they did in 1980!
◆   People have more of their income available for holidays.
◆   Pensioners are richer and healthier than ever before.
◆   Cheaper travel.
◆   Book online – and save! The Internet has helped bring down the cost of travel and holidays.

Cheapflights™ .co.uk

When we were younger, we only got one week's holiday.

I always watch the holiday programme.

> Road fuel tax rates on the main types of petrol and diesel are lower now than they were six years ago, and, since then, the main rates of road fuel tax have fallen nearly 12 per cent in real terms, saving the average motorist about 6p per litre every time they fill up. "
> *UK Treasury*

If you are planning on travelling to Taiwan, the assistance from 'Marco Polo' travel agency is unquestionably the best you will find. Our love for the island, combined with our exclusive experience of tourism in Taiwan, enables us to assist you in planning your trip and fulfilling your utmost desires.

Further and further

So, people in MEDCs have more free time and more money. And there's the technology to let holidaymakers travel much further than they did fifty years ago.

What about the future? What will we be doing, and where will we be going?

... and the future?

Activities

1 **a** Look at the list of 13 holiday statements opposite. What types of tourist attractions are mentioned?

 b Now divide your list into physical and human factors.

2 **a** Group the holidays shown in the cartoons A to D into 'low impact' and 'high impact'. You should be thinking about impacts on the environment, and on the people involved – both the tourists and the people who look after them.

 b Which outcome – E or F – do you think is more likely by 2045? Explain your answer.

3 The graph shows the number of foreign trips made by UK residents between 1980 and 2000.

 a Describe the changes between 1980 and 2000.

 b Why did the number of trips increase so much?

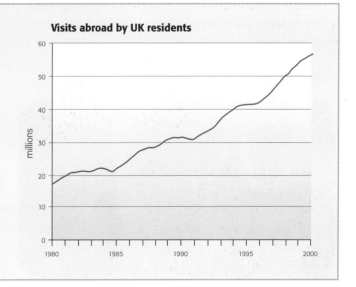

Visits abroad by UK residents

The impacts of tourism

In this unit you will learn about the impacts of tourism on one of Europe's most popular holiday destinations.

I'm going to Ibiza!

All tourists have an impact on the place they go to on holiday. The photo diary below sums up some of the impacts of tourists on Ibiza, a popular holiday island in the Mediterranean.

... picture of Danni, the barman. He says Ibiza is one of the richest places in Spain – but lots of the jobs are done by bar staff and holiday reps from the UK. He wants to come back with us for a better job ...

... traditional bling! You see less and less of the original culture ...

Apparently, some famous singer owns this big house. Lots of rich people have houses here and they have maids and gardeners and chauffeurs, even though they're hardly ever there. The first time I saw this house, I really wanted to find out who lived there.

... watch out for the beach, especially at night – sea urchins are quite common here, and Jem accidentally stood on one and was in agony for a few days. You can't pull out the spines – when you pull them they crumble. He got some cream to get them out, so it didn't ruin his holiday!

The clubs are great, BUT it's really hot, so you get thirsty and you can't drink the water – it's too salty. There's no kettle in the flat. Apparently the water sometimes runs out. So you have to buy water all the time. And I don't even want to think about the loos: you can't flush anything down them!
See you soon,
Love, Susie

Clampdown on Ibiza nightlife

The 'anything goes' lifestyle on Ibiza could be changing. Two million tourists go to Ibiza every year – 700 000 of them British – and with clubs open all night, many go simply to party. Ibiza provides the cutting edge of music, but many also go to the island for drink, drugs, sun, sand, and sex.

Now the local government wants to introduce tighter controls. It wants a 65-decibel sound-limit to cut down noise pollution, all clubs to be fitted with noise-limiters, and strict limits on the number of people in each club.

Many people in the music industry are against the new rules. They think the 'anything goes' atmosphere of the island has created a special brand of Ibiza music, now a major export product in itself.

But many locals support the government's efforts, and sympathise with the difficult balancing act it has to achieve. After all, Ibiza still needs the money tourism brings – $939 million a year – and doesn't want to drive the tourists away.

Winning back the island is also a question of image. The government wants to attract a different type of tourist in the future – one who is interested in the island's culture and wildlife. The government says there's more to do on Ibiza than dance all night and sleep all day.

Ibiza's Tourism Minister says:

" Everyone is welcome in Ibiza, but we have to make sure they behave themselves. We want people who come to Ibiza to enjoy themselves, but within certain controls. We can't be swamped by groups of young people, who sometimes go beyond the limit. "

Jules, a British girl, says:

" If you come to Ibiza, this is what you come for – parties till 6 in the morning. I think it's crazy to introduce controls. Ibiza has been like this for more than 20 years – a place for people to let their hair down with all their friends. There's no trouble at all here. "

Lenny, a music producer from Denmark who makes his own CDs under the name Ibizarre says:

" Everyone is soaking up that vibe, that Balearic feeling as it's been termed. "

He's typical of many foreigners who come to Ibiza and love it so much that they never go home.

Nito Verdera, a local journalist who has been campaigning for years to clean up Ibiza, says:

" Here we live off tourism, but people are fed up. If you have bars making noise and you can't sleep, and you see your children getting used to bad behaviour, it's too much. We have always been tolerant, but now we want to sleep, we want to rest, we want our island back. "

Activities

1 Write a postcard from Jules (above), describing her holiday.
2 Using the photo diary and the text on this page, list the advantages and disadvantages of tourism for Ibiza. Make two columns headed Advantages and Disadvantages.
3 What is the 'difficult balancing act' that Ibiza has to pull off?
4 'Ibiza needs tourists, and tourists need Ibiza; they are interdependent (depend on each other).' Explain why.

Tourism in the UK

In this unit you will learn about the impacts of tourism on one of the UK's National Trails.

The English Tourist Board says there are lots of things to do in England:

Experience	Discover	Explore
The British Grand Prix	Stay on a Farm	England's National Parks
Music festivals	Tate Galleries	England's Wooden Kingdom
Musical short breaks	England's best pubs	Horse riding in England
Wimbledon	The Da Vinci Code	Take a Walk
England's theme parks	England's Castles	Leave the Car at Home!
Celebrity Connections	English Railway Journeys	Pedal Power
Novel locations	King Arthur's England	
Romantic film locations	Gorgeous Gardens	
Myths and Legends	Pride and Prejudice Movie locations	
Scared of the Dark		
On the Brewery Trail		

In this unit, we look at one attraction – the Pennine Way, a long-distance footpath. It's very popular – but that's the problem!

The Pennine Way National Trail

The Pennine Way became the UK's first National Trail in 1965. It's now one of the most famous and popular walks in the country. Average time to complete it: 16 days.

The 429-km (268-mile) trail runs from Derbyshire, through three National Parks, over Hadrian's Wall, and on to the Scottish Borders.

The trail uses old miners' tracks, packhorse routes and drove roads. Clear signposts make it easy to follow. It is well looked after. It's one of the best walking experiences in Britain.

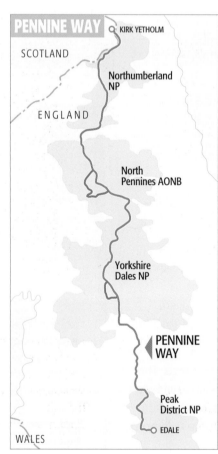

There are lots of hotels, bed and breakfasts, hostels, bunk barns and campsites close by, with good public transport links to nearby towns and cities. To make things as easy as possible, you can book accommodation in advance and your luggage can be taken ahead for you.

Along the trail you can see some of the best landscape features in Britain. These include:
- Malham Cove – sheer 80-metre high limestone cliffs topped by a limestone pavement (see below).
- High Force – a thunderous waterfall that crashes over a shelf to a deep dark pool 21 metres below.
- High Cup Nick – a deep-sided gorge.

Problems on the Pennine Way

Wind, rain and frost are natural forces of erosion – and they have their greatest effect on bare ground. So the causes of widespread erosion include:

◆ accidental (sometimes deliberate) summer fires that destroy the vegetation
◆ overgrazing by sheep which prevents the renewal of vegetation. There are now three times as many sheep grazing the moorlands as there were in 1950.

But the greatest cause of erosion on and around the Pennine Way is **people pressure** – the thousands of walkers who cross the moorland every year.

◆ When the exposed peat (the moorland soil) is wet, it's easily churned up by tramping feet and is washed away by heavy rain. When it's dry, it's blown away as a fine dust.
◆ Walking over soft waterlogged peat, particularly after heavy rain, is difficult and unpleasant – even dangerous – and walkers try to avoid the worst sections by walking on the firmer ground to the sides of the path. This increases the size of the damaged area.
◆ Some paths are not well marked, so the trampled area spreads as walkers try to find the easiest path.
◆ Organised events, like sponsored walks and fun runs, can put as much pressure on a path as a whole year of normal use.

Where's the path then?

Can it be managed sustainably?

A **restoration project** has been set up to:

◆ protect and restore the fragile soil and vegetation
◆ provide a long-lasting walking surface
◆ make sure that all the work is in harmony with the wild and unspoilt landscape.

In one summer, 750 tonnes of recycled Pennine sandstone slabs were airlifted in by helicopter to provide the surface material for new stretches of path.

Once the trampling pressure has been restricted to these hard surfaces, attempts can then begin to replant the surrounding bare ground. Lime and fertiliser (applied from the air by helicopter) encourage the growth of vegetation.

Activities

1 Choose two things you'd like to do or see from each of the lists opposite, and explain why.
2 List three attractions of the Pennine Way.
3 Look at the causes of erosion on the Pennine Way. Think of ways each of these causes could be reduced.
4 Do you think that making a harder-wearing footpath along the Pennine Way will solve all the problems of over-use? Justify your answer.
5 The Yorkshire Dales National Park has asked you to design an information board to inform walkers about the sustainable use of the Pennine Way. Make sure you highlight the problems, and the many ways in which walkers can reduce their impact on the environment.

Tourism in an LEDC: Phuket, Thailand

In this unit you will learn about the impacts of tourism on Phuket.

Asia's top beach destination ...

◆ Phuket is often called a tropical paradise, and is well known for its natural beauty.

◆ It offers warm seas, good snorkelling, great beaches, and lively nightlife.

◆ The island was featured in the film *The Beach*.

◆ It's Thailand's largest island – it covers 540 sq. km.

◆ 50% of the island is still forested.

◆ It has a population of 250 000 – but gets 4 million tourists a year, three-quarters of them coming from overseas.

The photos show some of the things Phuket is famous for.

If you're tempted, and wondering where to stay, how about this offer?

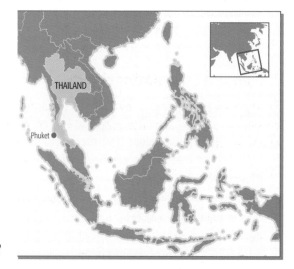

Royal Meridian

Deluxe ocean-front villa, French chef, British holiday reps who really know the island, £1000.

Offer based upon 2 people sharing for 10 nights.

Flights with British Airways; return private car transfers.

'You can rent a water-jet for half an hour and go wild in the waves. Or you can rent a bog motorcycle, even if you don't have a license, and drive around the island. Or you can rent a big four-wheel drive and go around the island.'
A tourist.

'I think Phuket was great. The beach and the nightlife are so close to each other. The street sellers can be a bit of a nuisance but I just smiled at most of them and said no in a very polite way.'
A tourist.

'Because of the record travel and tourism boom over the last decades, the smuggling and illegal trade in exotic plants and animals has already become a multi-billion-dollar business. So-called biopirates, often pretending to be harmless tourists, steal local plants and animals during their trips in foreign lands and easily pass through the nothing-to-declare green channels at airports to take them home or sell them abroad.'
A reporter.

Phuket Bay International City

There are plans to build a mini-city on reclaimed land in the bay off Saphan Hin. The proposal has come from a Japanese urban developer.

The project would include:

- a spaceship-shaped structure called Anabasis, which will contain a 2000-room hotel and a convention centre;
- a lotus-shaped resort called Marina City;
- The Tower, which will include hotel rooms and office space;
- Sport World, featuring international-level sports facilities;
- Good Luck Island – a casino.

All of these would be built with protection against tsunamis in mind. There are also plans for a marina project, focusing on yachts and cruising.

Details and costs haven't been revealed. Companies in China are also interested.

Activities

1 Look at the photos of Phuket and read the text again.
   a List as many reasons as you can for visiting the island. Aim for a minimum of 8 answers.
   b Now colour code your list: use blue for physical/natural attractions and red for human/cultural ones.
   c Which type of attractions – physical or human – do you think are most important to Phuket's tourist business?
2 Why might increased visitor numbers be successful in the short term, but harmful in the long term? Explain your answer fully.
3 Read the hotel offer carefully, and try to work out how many Phuket locals are benefiting from the package offered. Is this good or bad? Explain your answer.
4 Write a letter to the *Phuket Gazette* local newspaper, expressing *either* your support for *or* concern over Phuket Bay International City. Explain why you are for or against the development. Write at least 150 words.

Green tourism

In this unit you will learn how tourism can help to preserve the environment.

What's it all about?

You have seen that tourism can have negative impacts. **Green tourism** has developed to try to limit the negative impacts of our holidays. It's also known as **ecotourism** or **sustainable tourism**.

This diagram shows what green tourism is all about:

... minimise damage to the environment

... minimise damage to local culture

... promote conservation

... help social justice

... limit and control the number of tourists in an area

Green tourism aims to ...

... be 'environmentally friendly'

... protect wildlife

... protect the well-being of local people

... help to generate income and employment

Green tourism includes:

- **Agro-tourism** – this is when people stay on working farms. The farms have basic facilities for visitors. The tourists work with farm animals, or crops.

- **Cultural tourism** – this is where tourists learn about local culture and traditions. They stay in local villages or even with local people.

How green is my hotel?

Some hotels are more 'green' than others. Read about these hotels in Ibiza. Can you find the ways each hotel **fails** to be truly sustainable?

The *Finca Agricultor* stands on a hilltop in Ibiza, surrounded by its own fruit and vegetable fields, which are farmed with the latest environmentally-friendly methods to provide guests with fresh natural food.

We farm olives, plums, apricots, table and wine grapes, satsumas, tangerines, oranges and lemons, nectarines and apricots, avocados, figs, cherries, pomegranates, almonds and walnuts, wheat, and beans – and we use all of them in our cooking.

The *Finca Agricultor* is surrounded by woods, and rocky cliffs with fabulous views as far as the eye can see. Each double room has a wonderful view, a private balcony, air conditioning, satellite TV, a mini-bar, and a fully equipped bathroom with hairdryer.

The reading room and living rooms have original farmhouse fireplaces for when the nights are cold.

We can organise trips to nearby places of interest, country walks, horseback and bike riding, scuba-diving, and sailing trips to nearby sights.

In the heart of rural Ibiza, in a wonderful, quiet valley surrounded by beautiful, ancient pine, almond and olive trees, you will find *Can Zangamanga*.

Our rooms, carefully equipped down to the last detail, have all mod cons, so that you can enjoy a pleasant stay. *Can Zangamanga* rooms have:

- complete bathrooms with jacuzzi or hydro-massager
- air conditioning (hot/cold)
- telephone
- mini-bar
- satellite TV

There are many paths around the farm, which immerse you in a luxuriant forest of pines. Inside the farm grounds there is a swimming pool, and a solarium.

In *Can Zangamanga* we can arrange for you to hire cars and boats, so that you can go round the island, enjoy its picturesque coastline, and dive into the crystal-clear waters.

Sustainable tourism in Turkey: a success?

The tourist resort of Antalya is on Turkey's Mediterranean coast. It has switched from mass tourism to sustainable tourism. Here are the changes that were made:

♦ The Ministry of Tourism has decided against the building of any more hotels.
♦ All tourist hotels are connected to three wastewater purification plants. Some of the wastewater is used for irrigation, while the rest is completely cleaned and released back into nature.
♦ Low-energy light bulbs are used throughout the resort.
♦ All waste is composted, and there are plans to set up a generator fuelled by refuse.
♦ 90% of mosquitoes, houseflies and sand flies have been eradicated.
♦ Research is still going on to investigate the ecology of the area.
♦ Using this research, ecologists will plan the future development of the resort. The plan is to preserve, or even increase, the biodiversity of the area.
♦ Three books, and a lot of posters, have been produced to raise the awareness of visitors about sustainable development.
♦ There is piped water available at many sites in the forest, in order to fight forest fires, and a fire engine which can cover rough terrain has been bought. Two firemen are on duty through the year, with four more during the season when forest fire risks are high.

golf course

Activities

1 **a** If you had to go on a holiday to Ibiza, which of the hotel options opposite would you choose, and why?
   b Which of the holidays would you least like, and why?
   c Think about the last holiday you went on. In what ways was it sustainable and/or unsustainable.
2 Copy the sustainable tourism checklist on the right, and fill it in to decide which of the two hotels in Ibiza is more sustainable. Give each a score out of 80, and explain your findings.
3 Look at the photographs of the resort at Antalya.
   a Is this resort truly sustainable?
   b What new regulations would you make for the resort?
4 'Will tourism eat itself?' Explain what you think this question means, and then try to answer it.

Sustainable tourism checklist	Marks out of 10
♦ Develops good relations between tourists and locals	
♦ Supports learning about other cultures	
♦ Mixes land use to allow varied habitats	
♦ Uses local materials and local businesses	
♦ Minimises water use	
♦ Minimises electricity use	
♦ Provides worthwhile jobs in tourism	
♦ Minimises pollution from motor exhausts	
Total score	

The big picture

This chapter is about development – improving people's lives. These are the big ideas behind the chapter:

◆ Some countries are more developed than others, and there's a big gap in development between the most and least developed.

◆ Development can be measured in different ways.

◆ Huge numbers of people around the world don't have access to clean water, or enough food to eat.

◆ There's an imbalance in trade. The rich North gets richer, and the poor South gets poorer.

◆ Different types of aid have advantages and disadvantages.

◆ Fairer trade and more effective aid can help countries develop.

Your goals for this chapter

By the end of this chapter you should be able to answer these questions:

◆ You can measure development using indicators. How many can you list?

◆ What does the UN's Human Development Index measure?

◆ What has helped to cause the gap in development between MEDCs and LEDCs? Name three MEDCs and three LEDCs.

◆ Why does it matter if people don't have access to clean water? Give an example of a large scale scheme, and a small scale one to increase water supply – both in LEDCs.

◆ Where in the world are people suffering from malnutrition? Why?

◆ What is trade? What trading problems do LEDCs have?

◆ Why isn't trade fair, and how can it be made fairer?

◆ What do these terms mean?
GDP per capita (PPP), NGOs, appropriate technology, sustainable development, dietary energy supply, trade balance, trade surplus, trade deficit, tariffs, quotas, free trade, trading blocs, World Trade Organisation

◆ Aid can provide short-term emergency relief, or long-term sustainable help. What other types of aid are there, and what advantages and disadvantages do they have?

◆ What else can help LEDCs develop their economy and reduce poverty?

And then . . .

When you finish the chapter, come back here and see if you've met your goals!

Did you know?
If the world was a village of 100 people ...
◆ 14 wouldn't have enough to eat
◆ 31 wouldn't have electricity
◆ 17 wouldn't have clean safe water to drink
◆ 29 would be aged under 15.

Did you know?
During the 1990s, clean drinking water reached an extra 1 billion people in LEDCs – that's roughly one-sixth of the world's people.

Did you know?
◆ Bananas are the world's most popular fruit.
◆ But flying them around the world takes a lot of fuel and adds to global warming.

Did you know?
◆ Deaths from diarrhoea have gone down by 60% in the last twenty years.
◆ But diarrhoea remains a leading killer in LEDCs, causing the deaths of 2 million people a year, mostly children.

Your chapter starter

Look at the photo on page 258.
What sort of ship is this?
What sort of place is it leaving? Where do you think it might be going?
What might it be carrying?
Do ships like this have anything to do with you?

I'd like to apply for the job of ship's cat.

Development – a world of two halves

In this unit you'll learn what development means, and see how it is measured.

School – *boring*. What's the point? I have to go every day.

If I fancy a cuppa what do I do? Turn on the tap and fill the kettle – no problem.

School – you're lucky. You can learn to read and write. Some of us are too busy earning a living to go to school.

If I want a drink I've got to fetch the water from the river. Takes me hours – and it's dirty.

Development

It's about improving people's lives, so the Indian girl in the photo *can* go to school, and *can* have clean water to drink. Sounds simple? Read the rest of this chapter and you'll find it's not quite as easy as it sounds.

How **developed** a country is is affected by things like history, industry, politics, hazards, etc. – you'll find out more about these in Unit 13.2.

Can you measure it?

Yes, in all sorts of ways. One of the easiest is GDP per capita (PPP). This shows how wealthy a country is. Look at the map. It shows the world divided in two, according to levels of development.

- ◆ **GDP** stands for **Gross Domestic Product**. It's the total value of goods and services a country produces in a year.
- ◆ GDP is measured in dollars.
- ◆ GDP is divided by a country's population to give **GDP per capita**.
- ◆ **PPP** means **purchasing power parity**. GDP is adjusted because a dollar buys more in some countries than others.

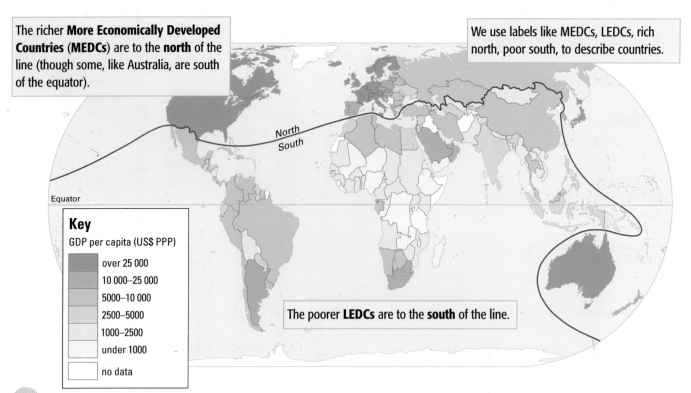

The richer **More Economically Developed Countries (MEDCs)** are to the **north** of the line (though some, like Australia, are south of the equator).

We use labels like MEDCs, LEDCs, rich north, poor south, to describe countries.

North South

Equator

Key

GDP per capita (US$ PPP)

- over 25 000
- 10 000–25 000
- 5000–10 000
- 2500–5000
- 1000–2500
- under 1000
- no data

The poorer **LEDCs** are to the **south** of the line.

How else can you measure development?

You measure development using **indicators** (that's the technical word). So, GDP per capita (PPP) is one indicator, but there's more.

◆ **Social indicators**. You can split these into population and health. The table below shows which is which.
◆ Then there's **others**. These can include all sorts of things, like the percentage of the adult population who can read and write (adult literacy), and so on.

Although these indicators aren't the same as wealth, a lot of them will depend on how wealthy a country is.

The table below shows some indicators for different countries. All those numbers look a bit baffling. But try looking at them one column at a time and compare the numbers for different countries and you'll see some patterns.

| Country | SOCIAL INDICATORS | | | | | | | | Others | | |
| | Population indicators | | | Health indicators | | | | | | |
	GDP per capita (PPP) US$	Birth rate	Death rate	Natural increase	Infant mortality	Life expectancy	People per doctor	% adults with HIV/AIDS	% adult literacy	% in farming	% urban population
USA	40 100	14	8	6	7	78	182	0.6	97	0.7	80
UK	29 600	11	10	1	5	79	476	0.2	99	2	89
Japan	29 400	9	9	0	3	81	500	Less than 0.1	99	5	65
South Korea	19 200	10	6	4	7	77	714	Less than 0.1	98	8	80
Brazil	8100	16	6	10	30	72	476	0.7	86	20	83
China	5600	13	7	6	24	72	625	0.1	91	49	39
India	3100	22	8	14	56	64	2000	0.9	60	60	28
Kenya	1100	40	15	25	61	48	10 000	7	85	75	39

Spot the difference

The table shows you that:

◆ LEDCs like Kenya usually have higher birth, death and infant mortality rates than MEDCs like the UK.
◆ LEDCs like India have a lower level of literacy, and fewer doctors for the population than MEDCs like the UK.
◆ LEDCs like China have more jobs in the primary sector (for example farming) than MEDCs like Japan.

Activities

1 Look at the map. Describe the distribution of wealth shown. Explain any anomalies (countries that don't fit the general pattern).
2 Why do you think that GDP is measured in dollars? What doesn't a measure of wealth per person show (hint – think about people like yourself)?
3 List three indicators you think are good measures of development, and three you think aren't so good. Explain the reasons for your choices.
4 Look at the table. Describe, and explain, the main differences between
   a Kenya and the UK
   b Japan and China.
5 How far do you think it's possible to divide the countries in the table into MEDCs and LEDCs? Why is this?

Mind the gap

In this unit you'll find out why some countries are more developed than others. And about the Human Development Index.

What's caused the gap?

There's a gap in terms of levels of development between the LEDCs and the MEDCs. All sorts of things have caused it, and they're linked. Here's just a few for starters.

History

Europeans began colonising large areas of the world from the 16th century onwards. The economies of the colonies were altered, and new country borders were created, so that raw materials could be sent from them to Europe. The development of the colonies was restricted, and they were left with economic and political problems.

Industry

The Industrial Revolution of the 19th century, meant that things started to change in countries like the UK. People changed from working in farming to working in manufacturing industry. In the 20th century, there was a shift to jobs in service industries.

Lots of LEDCs still have a lot of people working in primary industries, like farming. As they develop, more people will work in secondary and tertiary industries.

Debt

LEDCs have often borrowed lots of money to try to develop, and it has to be repaid (plus interest). If they can't repay the money, they get into debt. Add on the interest and the debt grows, leaving less and less money for things like schools, developing industry, and improving people's standard of living.

Politics

Political instability, poor management of the economy, and inefficient government haven't helped some LEDCs. For example, Nigeria changed from military rule to a civilian government in 1999. The country's economy is based on oil. It was mismanaged and now needs rebuilding.

Other countries have planned their economic development. South Korea has gone from being an LEDC to an NIC in 40 years (see Unit 11.10).

Environment and hazards

Natural hazards affect both MEDCs and LEDCs, but their overall impact can be different – depending where they occur. For example, if we have too much or too little rain in the UK, we can cope. But it's different in LEDCs. They lack the money and technology to cope with major hazards.

Tropical storms, earthquakes and volcanic eruptions hit both MEDCs and LEDCs. For instance, Hurricane Katrina left about 1000 people dead and caused $125 billion of damage in the USA in 2005, which the US economy could cope with. However, in the same year, an earthquake in Pakistan had a much greater human cost – it killed nearly 80 000 people. And the country struggled to cope with helping the survivors without major international support.

How else can you measure development?

In Unit 13.1 we looked at how you could measure development by wealth. But development is about more than that. The UN measures **quality of life**. They produce the **Human Development Index** (**HDI** for short) which combines three aspects of human development:

◆ A long and healthy life – measured by life expectancy.
◆ Knowledge – measured by the adult literacy rate combined with the number of years spent at school.
◆ Standard of living – measured by GDP per capita (PPP).

Each of the three aspects is given a score. 1.000 is the best. 0.000 is the worst. The HDI is the average of the three scores. Countries are ranked according to their overall score.

> **Did you know?**
> The HDI was developed in 1990 and has been used by the UN since 1993.

The HDI 2005 factfile

Country	Rank	HDI
USA	10	0.944
Japan	11	0.943
UK	15	0.939
South Korea	28	0.901
Brazil	63	0.792
China	85	0.755
India	127	0.602
Kenya	154	0.474

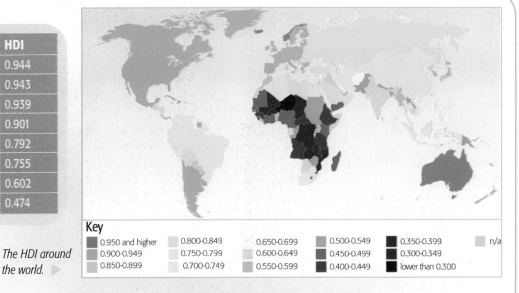

The HDI around the world. ▷

Key

0.950 and higher	0.800-0.849	0.650-0.699	0.500-0.549	0.350-0.399	n/a
0.900-0.949	0.750-0.799	0.600-0.649	0.450-0.499	0.300-0.349	
0.850-0.899	0.700-0.749	0.550-0.599	0.400-0.449	lower than 0.300	

The top 3 countries

◆ Norway
◆ Iceland
◆ Australia

And the bottom 3

◆ Burkina Faso
◆ Sierra Leone
◆ Niger

The HDI for countries around the world is improving, with two exceptions:

◆ The new countries of central Asia, e.g. Kazakhstan – worsening education, economies and mortality rates have caused the decline in their HDI.
◆ Sub-Saharan Africa – HIV/AIDS is the biggest reason for the decline in the HDI in these countries.

Activities

1 Describe the pattern of development shown on the HDI map.
2 Compare the pattern on this map with the map in Unit 13.1. Explain any differences you can see.
3 Differences in development were much less before the 19th century than they are now. Why?
4 Do you think the HDI is a better measure of development than other indicators, such as GDP? Explain your answer, referring to named indicators of development.
5 How do you think the ranking of the countries in the table (2005 HDI factfile) could change in the next century. What reasons could lead to these changes?

Water – a matter of life and death

In this unit you'll learn about the difference in
availability of clean water in MEDCs and LEDCs.

Bring me water

The world's population is growing fast.
There's about 6.5 billion of us now, and
by 2050 there'll be nearly 9 billion. And
although population continues to grow,
the supply of water doesn't. It's finite.

Uneven supplies

The amount of water varies from place
to place, and from time to time.

◆ The wettest parts of the world are
those with equatorial and monsoon
climates.
◆ The world's biggest dry area
stretches from the Middle East
across North Africa to the Atlantic
Ocean.
◆ Places with monsoon climates get
most of their rain in one season.
For the rest of the year, they get
barely a drop.
◆ Rainfall can be unreliable.

How clean is our water?

In some parts of the world, water is very
clean; in others it's filthy. 1 billion people
don't have access to clean piped water.

The map on the right shows the
percentage of the world's population that
does have access to safe (clean) water.
Compare it with the map in Unit 13.1.
Notice anything?

Does it matter if people don't have
clean water? Yes!

◆ More than 5 million people die from
water-borne diseases every year.
◆ People spend hours every day
walking to fetch water. Time they
could be spending in school, or
working and earning money to
improve their lives.

Did you know?
You can live for about 2 months without food, but less than a week without water.

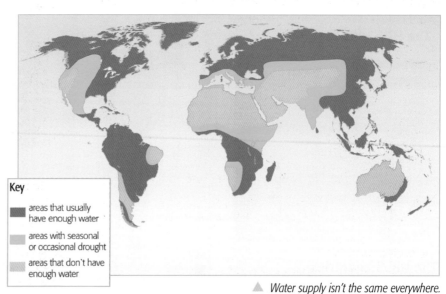

▲ Water supply isn't the same everywhere.

Key
- areas that usually have enough water
- areas with seasonal or occasional drought
- areas that don't have enough water

▼ Percentage of population with access to safe water.

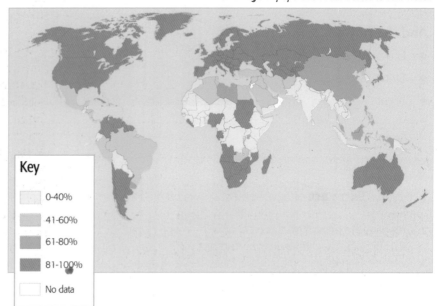

Key
- 0-40%
- 41-60%
- 61-80%
- 81-100%
- No data

Water use and abuse

The graph on the right shows some staggering differences in water use around the world.

The UN recommends that people need a minimum of 50 litres a day for drinking, washing, cooking and sanitation. But not everyone has that much.

Now look at the pie charts for individual countries. Compare India and the UK. Bit of a difference isn't there?

And it's going to get worse …

For countries to develop, they need more water – for irrigation (to produce more and better food), and for industry. And they need cleaner, safer water for people to use.

And, as they develop, they'll use more water as people's lifestyles change. Plus, the world's population is growing. But there's only so much water to go around.

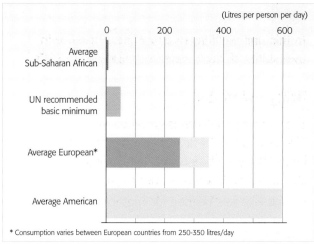

* Consumption varies between European countries from 250-350 litres/day

▲ Water use around the world.

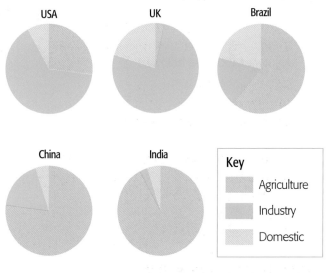

▲ Water use for individual countries.

So, what can be done?

Get technical
◆ Change to drip irrigation, which uses less water.
◆ Treat waste water so it can be reused.
◆ Tackle pollution to make more water useable.

Increase supply
◆ Build dams and other large-scale projects.
◆ Use underground supplies.
◆ Build wells and supply pumps – small-scale projects.

Do deals
◆ In 2004, Israel signed a deal with Turkey to ship 50 million cubic metres of water a year for 20 years in return for arms.
◆ In 1999, Egypt, Ethiopia and Sudan agreed a strategy for the sustainable development of the River Nile.

Use less
◆ This might mean using and reusing water more efficiently.

Get the UN to act
◆ The UN launched an International Decade for Action called 'Water for life', in 2005, to try to halve the number of people without access to safe drinking water and basic sanitation by 2015.

Activities

1 Describe the pattern of access to safe water shown by the bottom map opposite.
2 Compare this pattern with the map of global population distribution in Unit 8.1. What problems will this cause?
3 Contrast the ways in which water is used in the countries shown in the pie charts above. Give an example of at least one type of water use from each sector of the graphs.
4 The box on the left shows what can be done about water shortages. For each solution, suggest whether you think it would be more suitable in MEDCs or LEDCs. Explain why.

Water – increasing supply

In this unit you'll find out about two different approaches to increasing water supply.

Is big best?

By 1950, Egypt had a water crisis. Why?

◆ It depended on the River Nile for all its water.
◆ Urbanisation and industrialisation were increasing and needed more water.
◆ The Nile was needed for irrigation. And more land needed irrigating to feed the rapidly rising population.

Egypt needed more water and power, and decided to build the High Aswan Dam to provide both. Work started in 1960 and, by 1968, the reservoir, Lake Nasser, was full. Like all big schemes, the High Aswan Dam brought benefits, but there are disadvantages too (see below).

> **Did you know?**
> Most of Egypt gets less than 125 mm of rain a year.

> **Did you know?**
> The Nile is the only river in Egypt.

Key
- Irrigated land (also area where most people live)
- ◻ Towns with new industries

0   300 km

Mediterranean Sea

N

Benefits

Agriculture – it increased:
◆ the amount of irrigated land
◆ crop yields
◆ crops grown for export
◆ food processing industries and cotton textile production

Lake Nasser – provides:
◆ protection against flooding and famine
◆ a large reliable supply of water
◆ fishing, giving food and jobs
◆ tourism-based jobs

HEP – means:
◆ electricity for agriculture, industry and villages
◆ farmers can use electric pumps to get more water from wells

Jobs and the economy
◆ have both grown fast

Cairo

E G Y P T

River Nile

Aluminium smelting
Nag Hammadi ◻

Sugar refining
Kom
Ombo ◻

Fertilisers
Aswan ◻

High Aswan Dam
and HEP station

Lake Nasser

LIBYA   SUDAN

Red Sea

Disadvantages

Declining water quality
◆ water pollution is caused by the use of fertilisers (see below)

Floodplain
◆ no silt is deposited now
◆ farmers have to use expensive chemical fertilisers instead
◆ the shallow water helps to spread the diseases bilharzia and malaria

Lake Nasser
◆ evaporation causes water loss
◆ silt is deposited here

Resettlement
◆ 120 000 people were forced to move home because the new lake covered their villages
◆ many resettled in Kom Ombo and Cairo

... And now Toshka

This is Egypt's new plan to create habitable land in the desert. Why? The population has soared from 20 to 70 million in the last 20 years. It's predicted to reach 120 million in the next 20. The plan is to create a second Nile valley to:

◆ increase the amount of arable land and so produce more food
◆ create nearly 3 million jobs
◆ attract 16 million people to the planned new towns.

The Mubarak pumping station – which pumps water out of Lake Nasser – is already operating. Toshka will cost $70 billion.

Did you know?
Egypt is 95% desert.

Did you know?
A hand-dug well costs about £1200.

Or is small beautiful?

Imagine having a small, muddy pool as your only source of water. Every day you wait for hours in a long queue. Wait as water slowly seeps through the mud. And wait until enough water has collected to fill your bowl. Then lug it home.

Apoyanga's story

Apoyanga Nash from northern Ghana doesn't have to imagine waiting by that muddy pool. It was what she did, day in, day out, for years.

The muddy water could be lethal. Animals drink from the same pool. When Apoyanga and her children drank the water, it gave them diarrhoea and stomach cramps.

Water Aid, a UK charity, and their partners Rural Aid, helped Apoyanga's community to build a well with a pump to provide clean water.

Apoyanga says 'Now we have the well our lives have improved. We're much healthier. I don't spend so much time collecting water. I've got time to weave baskets to sell so that I can afford to send my children to school.'

You can find stories like Apoyanga's in many countries. Little by little, people's lives can be improved. Small projects like providing wells and pumps to ensure a safe, clean supply of water for a community are often supported by **NGOs**. They are examples of:

◆ **Appropriate technology** – suitable for the people who are using it. It's not expensive and complicated. It's cheap and simple. And allows people to manage things for themselves.

◆ **Sustainable development** – they improve people's standard of living and quality of life without wasting resources or harming the environment.

Did you know?
NGO stands for non-governmental organisation. They include charities like Oxfam, Water Aid etc.

Activities

1 Using information on this page, and other sources if you need to, explain why Egypt relied so heavily on the Nile for its water.
2 What are the benefits and problems caused by the Aswan Dam? To answer this, make a cost-benefit table, like the one here. List the effects of the dam in the columns. Use your completed table to evaluate the overall impact of the dam.

Cost	Benefit

3 Explain why using pumps to provide water in Ghana is an example of 'appropriate technology'.
4 Compare the advantages of the schemes in Egypt and Ghana. Which do you think is the most suitable
  a for the people in an LEDC?
  b for the environment?

Food

In this unit you'll learn why some people don't have enough to eat.

How much food do we need?

The amount of food we need, or consume, is measured in calories. The **dietary energy supply** (DES for short) is the number of calories each person needs. People living in temperate climates (MEDCs like the UK) need at least 2600 calories a day. People living in tropical climates (many LEDCs) need at least 2300 calories. Why the difference?

◆ There's a greater proportion of adults in MEDCs (they need more than children).
◆ In temperate climates, people need more energy to keep warm.

And what type?

You know about healthy balanced diets. Everyone needs:

◆ protein – like meat, eggs, and milk, for their bodies to grow and repair themselves
◆ carbohydrates – like cereals, potatoes, sugar and fat, for energy
◆ vitamins and minerals – found in all sorts of fruit, vegetables, fish, and meat, to help prevent disease.

But we don't all eat a balanced diet, do we? For many people in LEDCs, their basic diet is based on carbohydrates like rice, wheat and maize, and it lacks protein, vitamins and minerals.

What happens if you don't have enough?

You'll be hungry and you'll suffer from malnutrition if you don't have enough food, or the right kind. You'd only die in extreme conditions, but it would reduce your ability to work, and your resistance to disease. If you're a child, you might not develop properly and you might have:

◆ **marasmus** – caused by not eating enough food. A child would be very thin and wouldn't grow.
◆ **kwashiorkor** – caused by eating too many cereals and not enough protein. A child's body would be swollen, their skin would be very dark and peeling. Their hair would turn orange.

Did you know?
Up to half a million children go blind every year because they don't get enough vitamin A.

Did you know?
◆ Lack of vitamin B can cause beri-beri (wasting of the limbs).
◆ Lack of vitamin D can cause rickets (deformities in the bones, especially the legs and spine.

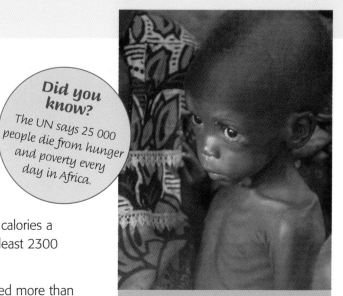

Did you know?
The UN says 25 000 people die from hunger and poverty every day in Africa.

Niger 2005
It wasn't a famine – but it was a crisis. The cause? Not enough food. Or was it? Drought in 2004, was followed by a plague of locusts, then another drought.

People – adults, children, babies – died from **malnutrition**. There was some food from the local harvest, but few people could afford it. So the developed world stepped in with food aid.

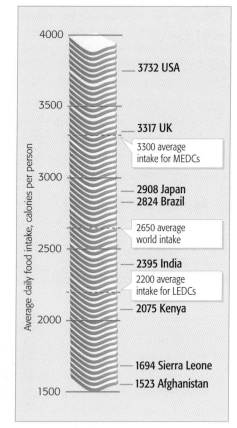

How much food people have.

Who's suffering?

Look at the map and table. The table shows that the percentage of malnourished people has fallen since 1970 everywhere *except* sub-Saharan Africa. But what it doesn't show is that the actual *number* of people has increased. This is because of the rise in world population.

Region	1970	2000
Sub-Saharan Africa	35	42
Near East and North Africa	23	12
Central America and Caribbean	24	11
South America	17	9
South Asia	34	22
East Asia	35	16
China	46	14
All developing regions	36	19

Percentage of people suffering from malnutrition. ▽ ▷

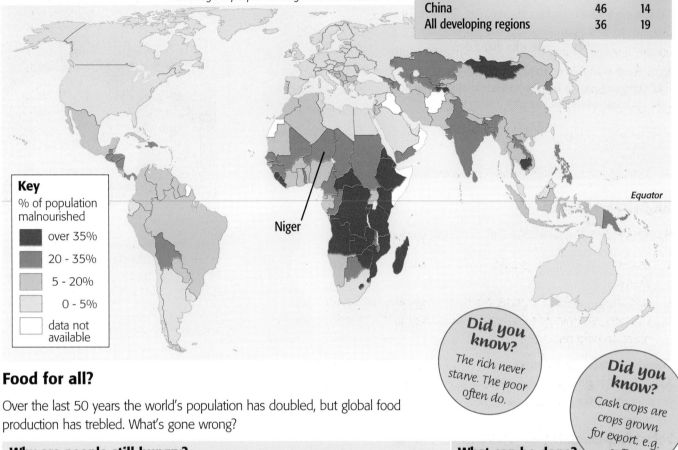

Key
% of population malnourished
- over 35%
- 20 - 35%
- 5 - 20%
- 0 - 5%
- data not available

Niger

Equator

Did you know?
The rich never starve. The poor often do.

Did you know?
Cash crops are crops grown for export, e.g. coffee

Food for all?

Over the last 50 years the world's population has doubled, but global food production has trebled. What's gone wrong?

Why are people still hungry?

- Poverty. People are too poor to buy the food they need.
- Some LEDCs have been encouraged by MEDCs and TNCs to grow cash crops, so fewer crops are grown for local people to eat.
- MEDCs export subsidised crops, which works against farmers in LEDCs.
- Food production is uneven across the world.
- Local physical factors. In some places, the climate means crops might fail; soil erosion has reduced the amount of land available for farming; a lot of good irrigated land has been damaged by salinisation and waterlogging.

What can be done?

- Make farming more sustainable (see Unit 13.4).
- Make trade fairer (see Unit 13.8).
- Provide short-term aid – food.
- Help countries develop so people can afford to buy the food they need – year after year.

Activities

1 What were the causes of the crisis in Niger in 2005?
2 The UK government provides food aid for countries such as Niger. What long-term problems might this cause?
3 Charities raise money to help people such as those in Niger. Do you think people should raise money through charities, or do you think only governments should give aid?
4 'Poverty and hunger are problems for Africa, not all LEDCs'. Using information from this page and any other sources, explain why you agree or disagree with this statement.

In this unit you'll find out what trade is, and who has the lion's share.

Trouble brewing

As you made your cup of tea this morning, Elizabeth Miheso will have been at work for hours picking tea on a small Kenyan tea estate – for 30p a day.

And as you stirred in the sugar, Ibrahim Shikanda will have been helping his parents harvest the sugar cane that no longer provides them with a living wage.

You're unlikely to meet Elizabeth or Ibrahim. But your life and theirs are linked – by trade.

Did you know?

More than 165 million cups of tea are drunk in the UK every day. And half the tea we drink comes from east Africa.

So, what is trade?

If someone wants something that someone else has, they have to trade for it. Tea, sugar, trainers, mobiles – they're all traded. A country buys goods and services that it either doesn't have enough of, or can get more cheaply from somewhere else. These are **imports**. **Exports** are things which one country sells to another. Take Kenya and Japan. The diagrams on the right show their imports and exports.

The difference between imports and exports is called the **trade balance**.

What most countries want is a **trade surplus**. This should mean the country will become richer and people's standard of living should improve.

If it's the other way round, there'll be a **trade deficit**. A country with a trade deficit will stay poor, get into debt and people's lives won't improve.

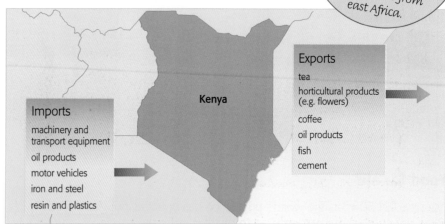

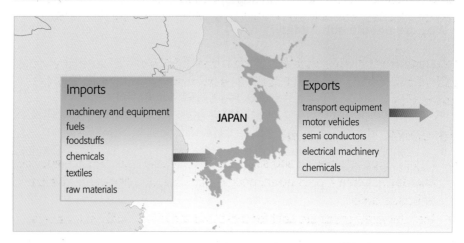

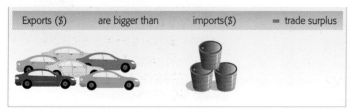

Look at Kenya and Japan again.

> **Kenya – 2004**. Exports = £2.6 billion. Imports = $4.2 billion. You don't need to be a maths genius to see that the sums don't add up. Perhaps that's one of the reasons why Kenya is 154th in the HDI rankings.

> **Japan – 2004**. Exports = $538.8 billion. Imports = $401.8 billion. That's a healthy surplus. And that's what countries want. That's one reason why Japan is high up (11th) in the HDI rankings.

Patterns of trade

Kenya's an LEDC. Japan's an MEDC. Generally:

◆ MEDCs *export* 'expensive' manufactured goods, and *import* 'cheap' primary products to make into manufactured goods.
◆ LEDCs *export* 'cheap' primary products (like tea, coffee, flowers, fish) and *import* manufactured goods they can't make (when they can afford them).

Look at the two pie charts.

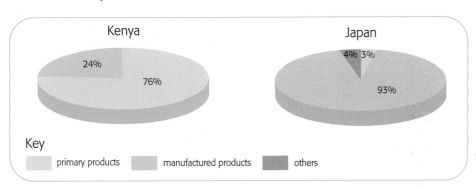

Exports by type of product.

Have you spotted the pattern? Add to this the fact that most trade – 80% – is between MEDCs, and only 20% is between LEDCs, and things look a bit unbalanced.

One reason why LEDCs trade foodstuffs is that MEDCs can afford to buy them. Lack of purchasing power in LEDCs is a major reason why so many people continue to live in poverty.

So, what's the problem?

◆ Primary products like tea and sugar are sold cheaply, and the price goes up and down. When it goes down, people like Elizabeth Miheso and Ibrahim Shikanda suffer.
◆ Manufactured goods are sold for more and the price usually stays steady.

There's an imbalance in trade. This results in:

◆ a trade deficit for many LEDCs, like Kenya – look at those import/export figures again – making it hard for these countries to develop
◆ a trade surplus for MEDCs – look at Japan's figures again
◆ a bigger share of world trade for MEDCs, and less for LEDCs
◆ the rich North getting richer, the poor South getting poorer.

Did you know?
Countries that trade with other countries are **interdependent**.

Activities

1 Explain the difference in Japan and Kenya's exports.
2 Why is it unlikely that every country in the world will have a trade surplus?
3 What problems are caused if a country has a trade deficit?
4 Why do you think the prices of primary products, such as tea and sugar, often go up and down? What effects will this have on people in countries exporting these products?
5 Why do you think the 'imbalance in trade' doesn't show any signs of improving, and may even be getting worse?

271

Trade – problems and partners

In this unit you'll learn about some of the other trading problems LEDCs have, and about trading partners.

Problems for traders

Ibrahim Shikanda (see Unit 13.6) helps his parents grow sugar in Kenya. The cost of fertiliser is rising rapidly and the price of sugar is falling. The poor are getting poorer.

Now scale that up. If a country has only one or two goods to sell, they can end up in real difficulty if:

◆ prices fall – like sugar (and it's the same for tea)
◆ other countries can produce the same thing more cheaply
◆ a crop fails, or a natural raw material runs out
◆ demand falls for their product.

Lots of LEDCs, especially those in Africa, rely on just one or two goods, as this map shows. If any of the things in the list above happens, it's seriously bad news for the country concerned. The economy will be affected, and people will suffer.

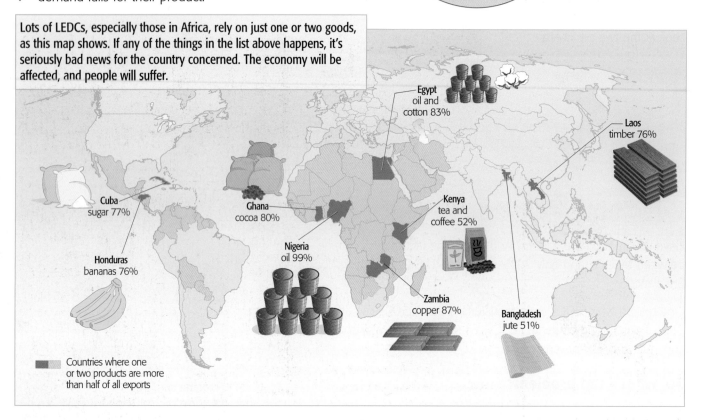

Egypt
oil and cotton 83%

Laos
timber 76%

Cuba
sugar 77%

Ghana
cocoa 80%

Kenya
tea and coffee 52%

Honduras
bananas 76%

Nigeria
oil 99%

Zambia
copper 87%

Bangladesh
jute 51%

Countries where one or two products are more than half of all exports

Who wins? Who loses?

There are always winners and losers – especially when it comes to trade and development. How does it look to you so far? Look at the text on the right and make your mind up.

MEDCs

1 We can get cheap imports of foodstuffs and raw materials, and export expensive manufactured goods. So we've got a trade surplus.

2 We've got the money to improve the environment if we damage it by mining etc.

3 We can put pressure on the LEDCs.

4 Our imports can come a long way – so we've got high transport costs.

5 And manufacturing causes pollution.

LEDCs

1 MEDCs provide a market for our cheap exports. And producing primary goods provides lots of jobs.

2 We've got a limited range of exports. Our imports cost more than we get for our exports, so we have a trade deficit.

3 Mining, deforestation and over-grazing damage the environment.

4 We might be able to get aid from MEDCs, but it might be tied (see Unit 13.9)

Trading partners

Trade makes the world go around. Ships, planes, lorries and trains are taking goods all over the world from one place to another – day in, day out. So, who trades with who?

KENYA

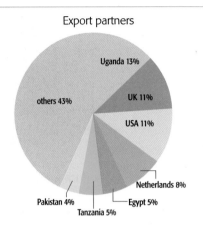

Export partners

Uganda 13%
UK 11%
USA 11%
others 43%
Netherlands 8%
Egypt 5%
Tanzania 5%
Pakistan 4%

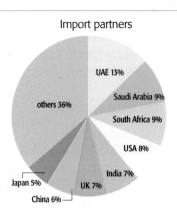

Import partners

UAE 13%
Saudi Arabia 9%
South Africa 9%
USA 8%
India 7%
UK 7%
China 6%
Japan 5%
others 36%

Kenya:
- imports 22% of its goods (oil) from the UAE and Saudi Arabia
- had to start buying more Japanese goods in the 1990s as Japan became Kenya's largest overseas investor (see bilateral aid in Unit 13.10)
- exports things like cement and refined oil to Uganda and Tanzania
- exports goods such as cut flowers and vegetables to Europe by air.

JAPAN

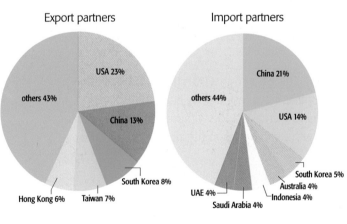

Export partners

USA 23%
China 13%
others 43%
South Korea 8%
Taiwan 7%
Hong Kong 6%

Import partners

China 21%
USA 14%
others 44%
South Korea 5%
Australia 4%
Indonesia 4%
Saudi Arabia 4%
UAE 4%

Japan:
- has few natural resources and has to import lots of raw materials, food and energy resources
- imports most from China (an LEDC)
- exports most to the USA (an MEDC).

Activities

1 Explain what problems LEDCs might have if they rely on a small number of export products.
2 Why are the prices of primary products more likely to vary over time than the prices of manufactured goods?
3 Divide the statements in the MEDC and LEDC boxes opposite into social/economic, environmental and political. Which group seems to be the most important? Are there any differences between the MEDC and LEDC examples?
4 Describe and explain the pattern of import and export partners for Kenya and Japan.

Trade – it's not fair

In this unit you'll find out some reasons why trade isn't always fair, but that it can be made fairer.

Bananas

Fancy a banana? Trading anything – including bananas – should be easy. Somehow the world has managed to make trade complicated, and at times unfair. But increasing trade is an important way for LEDCs to develop.

Free trade, tariffs and quotas

Most countries have tried to control trade by creating barriers to protect their own jobs and industries. They do this with **tariffs** and **quotas**.

◆ Tariffs are taxes or customs duties paid on imports. This is usually done to make the imported goods more expensive.
◆ Quotas are limits on the amount of goods that can be imported. They are usually restricted to primary goods, and so work against LEDCs.
◆ **Free trade** is when countries don't discourage, or restrict, the movement of goods.

So, how does this affect bananas? The box on the right shows you.

Trading blocs

These are countries which have grouped together to improve their trade balance. The UK belongs to the EU, which has grown to 25 countries. When the EU began, it cut duties on goods traded between member countries – making them cheaper.

You need to know that:

◆ World trade isn't shared evenly. The EU and the USA have over half the world's trade. Developing countries have less than a quarter.
◆ As trading blocs like the EU try to increase trade within the bloc, developing countries lose out – increasing the gap between the rich North and the poor South.

> The tariff on Latin America bananas (from countries like Ecuador, Colombia and Brazil) is £126 a tonne.
>
> There is a limit (quota) on the amount of bananas those same countries can export to the EU.
>
> There is no tariff on bananas from African, Caribbean and Pacific countries (mainly former EU colonies) exported to the EU.

Did you know?
60% of the EU's bananas come from Latin America. 20% come from Africa and the Caribbean. The other 20% come from the EU (mainly from Spanish and French islands).

▼ Trading blocs.

Key
(25 = number of member countries)

Major trading groups
■ EU (European Union - 25)
■ NAFTA (North American Free Trade Association - 3)

Other developed countries group
■ EFTA (European Free Trade Association - 4)

Important developing countries groups
■ Mercosur (4)
■ ASEAN (Association of South-East Asian Nations - 10)
■ OPEC (Organisation of Petroleum Exporting Countries - 11)

The World Trade Organisation (WTO)

The WTO makes the rules on world trade. It polices free trade agreements, settles trade disputes and organises trade negotiations. So, when countries argue over bananas and beef it's the WTO who sorts it out.

The WTO promotes free trade by persuading countries to get rid of tariffs and other trade barriers.

Some people are for free trade. They say:

◆ it will help countries' economies to grow and will reduce poverty
◆ developing countries will earn more money from exports.

Others are against it. They say:

◆ it means that developing countries will import food that puts their own farmers out of work
◆ that while developing countries have imported more food, the USA and EU haven't.

At the WTO talks in Hong Kong, in December 2005, little progress was made. Rich countries agreed to end export subsidies to farmers by 2013 (most were being phased out anyway).

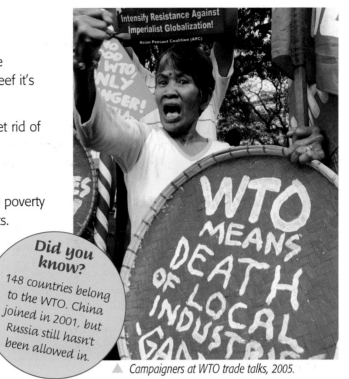

Did you know? 148 countries belong to the WTO. China joined in 2001, but Russia still hasn't been allowed in.

▲ *Campaigners at WTO trade talks, 2005.*

Making it fairer

Fair trade is where producers in developing countries get a guaranteed price for their product. This gives them a decent return for their work, even when world prices are low. Take Renson (pictured with his family on the right). He's a banana farmer from Ecuador. He's been able to build a new home for his family since selling bananas to the Fairtrade market. He hopes to be able to give his children the education he missed.

Fairtrade started with coffee, chocolate and tea. There are now over 800 Fairtrade products which support farmers in 49 developing countries.

Did you know? Global citizenship is the idea that we should all try to improve the quality of life for everyone. Fairtrade is one way of doing this.

Activities

1 Explain why some countries have introduced tariffs and quotas on some products.
2 Would you expect MEDCs or LEDCs to create tariffs and quotas? Which type of imports are most often affected?
3 Why have countries joined together to form trading blocs?
4 'Free trade will never happen. MEDCs are all-powerful, and it's in their own interest to keep things as they are.' What is your opinion of this statement?
5 Why do you think Russia isn't a member of the WTO? Does this matter?
6 Would you buy Fairtrade products, even if they were more expensive?

Aid – closing the gap?

In this unit you'll learn about different types of aid and why it's needed.

Food aid for Niger

Food shortages in Niger reached crisis point. An urgent appeal by the Disasters Emergency Committee raised an impressive £5.4 million on its first night. Food aid was sent to Niger.

Niger's prime minister agreed with the UN's plans to stop large-scale food aid. He said it needed to stop so that Niger didn't rely on aid.

The UN said that cutting food aid would allow food prices in Niger to come down to normal levels. They had risen dramatically during months of desperate food shortages.

September 2005

Urgent appeal for Zimbabwe

The situation was dire, and getting worse. 4.8 million people in Zimbabwe needed help. If the rains failed again they'd be staring famine in the face.

Practical Action helps people like those in Zimbabwe to help themselves. By sharing techniques with farmers such as building earth dams – contour ridges and furrows to trap water for crops – they can make the difference between food and famine, life and death.

They know the techniques work. When the harvest comes in families have enough food to last a year. Practical Action says 'If there's one thing we have learnt about famines in Africa it is this: listen to the early warnings and respond quickly'.

November 2005

The examples above are just two types of aid. Food aid to help in an emergency, and long-term sustainable aid – helping people to help themselves to prevent an emergency happening. There are other types, as this diagram shows (see also Unit 13.10).

2
International organisations (multilateral)
From organisations like the World Health Organisation (WHO) and International Monetary Fund (IMF).

1
Government (bilateral)
Given from one country to another. Often 'tied' – which means the receiving country has to buy goods from the donor country.

AID

3
Voluntary
These are NGOs like Oxfam and Comic Relief.

Aid can be:

◆ **Short term / emergency** – to cope with the immediate problems of hazards such as earthquakes.

◆ **Long term / sustainable** – organisations like Practical Action help people to help themselves.

Why is aid needed?

◆ LEDCs often get very low prices for their raw materials.

◆ There are differences in levels of development. LEDCs need to develop to improve people's quality of life and standard of living.

◆ To recover from natural hazards like floods, drought, earthquakes and hurricanes, and hazards of our own making, like wars.

▲ *Refugees like these in Sudan are given medical help.*

What exactly is aid?

Aid is when one country, or organisation, gives resources to another country. It comes in different shapes and sizes:

◆ Money – it might be grants or loans which have to be paid back.
◆ Goods, food, machinery, technology.
◆ People with special skills like engineers, teachers etc.

Aid should help countries to develop their economies and services, and so improve people's lives.

Did you know?
The **donor** is the country giving the aid. The **recipient** is the country receiving the aid.

How much do we give?

MEDCs like the USA, UK and Japan are in the top 15 countries when it comes to quality of life. The UN set a target that MEDCs should give 0.7% of their income in aid to LEDCs. The table shows what these three MEDCs gave in 1990 and 2003.

Hardly generous was it? The USA's and Japan's percentage went down! Only the UK's went up, and that's still only half the UN's target.

Aid given as a percentage of a country's income			
HDI rank	**Country**	**1990**	**2003**
10	USA	0.21%	0.15%
11	Japan	0.31%	0.20%
15	UK	0.27%	0.34%

Activities

1 When do you think it is best to give
  a short-term aid like food?
  b long-term aid?
  Give at least one example in each case.
2 Niger and Zimbabwe are both African countries receiving aid. How are the two examples similar, and how are they different?

3 a What is 'tied' aid?
  b What problems might tied aid cause for countries receiving it?
4 Do you think it's right that MEDCs such as the UK should give 0.7% of their wealth to poorer nations as aid? Do you think they should give more than this, or less? Justify your opinion.

Aid – is it all good news?

In this unit you'll need to think about whether aid is the best way to help LEDCs develop.

The good and the bad

Different types of aid have advantages and disadvantages. Here are some.

1 Government (bilateral)

- ◆ 'Tied' means the LEDC has to buy goods from the donor.
- ◆ Money is often given for specific projects, like big dams, which might not benefit poor people.
- ◆ If the LEDC can't repay the money, they get further into debt, and rely more on the donor.
- ◆ Can provide grants for students to study in MEDCs.

2 International organisations (multilateral)

- ◆ Not meant to be tied but unlikely to be given to countries with unfavourable economic and political systems.
- ◆ Encourages farming and industry – but products are exported to MEDCs.
- ◆ LEDCs depend on aid and get into debt.
- ◆ Helps LEDCs develop new crops, raw materials and industry.

AID

3 Voluntary

- ◆ Not tied.
- ◆ Helps with emergencies.
- ◆ Encourages low-cost, self-help schemes.
- ◆ Benefits poor people.
- ◆ Money available depends on how much people give.

4 Short term/emergency

- ◆ Not tied.
- ◆ Provides help when needed.
- ◆ Is targeted towards people and places who need it most.

5 Long term/sustainable

- ◆ Not tied.
- ◆ Provides people with new skills.
- ◆ Helps develop farming, small industries and schools.
- ◆ LEDCs don't get into debt.

▲ *Ghana got loans from the World Bank, the UK and the USA to build the Akosombo dam in the 1960s. Ghana wanted water for irrigation, and electricity to help the country develop. As part of the deal, an American company called Valco got the right to produce aluminium in Ghana using cheap electricity from the dam.*

Presents £51— £150

counting sheep

A gift of two sheep – a ewe and a ram – quickly multiplies, giving poor families in Senegal a way out of poverty. With her lambs, Mbayang Diop is now able to nourish her children with milk, and use fresh manure to fertilise her crops of millet, peanuts and green beans.

CODE V05 A007 A couple of sheep **£80**

▲ *Many charities offer people in MEDCs, like the UK, imaginative ways to help others.*

Aid – what could be better?

Aid has a part to play in helping LEDCs develop in terms of their economy and reducing poverty. But there are other things which would help.

Aid

◆ MEDCs should give more aid (0.7% of a country's income) and set a definite timetable for it to happen.

◆ MEDCs should make their aid more effective.

Did you know?

In 1990 world leaders pledged to halve the proportion of people living on less than £1 a day. By 2002 the proportion had fallen from 27.9% to 19.4%..

Do they (our world leaders) know how the aid they give can be made more effective?

Other things

◆ Cancel all debt of the world's poorest countries.

◆ Focus less on emergencies and more on chronic problems, for example by providing water storage tanks, and tools so families can plough and irrigate their land and feed themselves.

◆ LEDCs need to develop sound economic policies. These, not aid, lifted millions of people in Asia out of poverty. See South Korea in Unit 11.10 as an example of how countries can develop.

◆ MEDCs should stop exporting subsidised crops which damage poor rural communities around the world.

◆ Reduce tariffs in MEDCs for crops and foodstuffs from LEDCs.

Food aid to Kenya in the 1990s killed local food production and increased dependency on aid.

Activities

1 Summarise what you have learnt about aid. What are the main benefits of each type of aid?

2 Parts of the UK (and other European countries) receive money from the EU because they are relatively poor. Do you think this is aid? Should the UK receive such help, or should it all go to the world's poorest countries?

3 The world's poorest countries owe huge amounts of money to MEDCs in interest payments on loans. Do you think these payments should be cancelled to help these countries? Justify your opinion.

4 'Trade, not aid, is what is needed to help LEDCs develop.' What do you think of this statement?

Ordnance Survey symbols

ROADS AND PATHS

M I or A 6(M)	Motorway
A 35	Dual carriageway
A 31(T) or A 35	Trunk or main road
B 3074	Secondary road
	Narrow road with passing places
	Road under construction
	Road generally more than 4 m wide
	Road generally less than 4 m wide
	Other road, drive or track, fenced and unfenced
	Gradient: steeper than 1 in 5; 1 in 7 to 1 in 5
Ferry	Ferry; Ferry P – passenger only
	Path

PUBLIC RIGHTS OF WAY

(Not applicable to Scotland)

1:25 000	1:50 000	
		Footpath
		Road used as a public footpath
+++++		Bridleway
	+·+·+·+·	Byway open to all traffic

RAILWAYS

	Multiple track
	Single track
	Narrow gauge/Light rapid transit system
	Road over; road under; level crossing
	Cutting; tunnel; embankment
	Station, open to passengers; siding

BOUNDARIES

	National
	District
	County, Unitary Authority, Metropolitan District or London Borough
	National Park

HEIGHTS/ROCK FEATURES

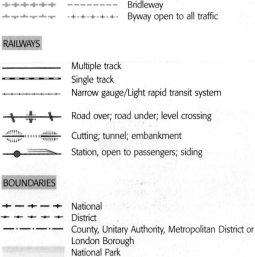

Contour lines

·144 Spot height to the nearest metre above sea level

outcrop cliff scree

ABBREVIATIONS

P	Post office	PC	Public convenience (rural areas)
PH	Public house	TH	Town Hall, Guildhall or equivalent
MS	Milestone	Sch	School
MP	Milepost	Coll	College
CH	Clubhouse	Mus	Museum
CG	Coastguard	Cemy	Cemetery
Fm	Farm		

ANTIQUITIES

VILLA	Roman	✗	Battlefield (with date)
Castle	Non-Roman	*	Tumulus

LAND FEATURES

- Buildings
- Public building
- Bus or coach station
- Place of Worship { with tower / with spire, minaret or dome / without such additions }
- Chimney or tower
- Glass structure
- Heliport
- Triangulation pillar
- Mast
- Wind pump / wind generator
- Windmill
- Graticule intersection
- Cutting, embankment
- Quarry
- Spoil heap, refuse tip or dump
- Coniferous wood
- Non-coniferous wood
- Mixed wood
- Orchard
- Park or ornamental ground
- Forestry Commission access land
- National Trust – always open
- National Trust, limited access, observe local signs
- National Trust for Scotland

WATER FEATURES

Marsh or salting, Towpath, Lock, Slopes, Cliff, High water mark, Low water mark, Aqueduct, Canal, Ford, Flat rock, Lighthouse (in use), Weir, Normal tidal limit, Sand, Dunes, Beacon, Lake, Footbridge, Bridge, Lighthouse (disused), Mud, Shingle, Canal (dry)

TOURIST INFORMATION

- P Parking
- V Visitor centre
- Information centre
- Telephone
- Camp site/Caravan site
- Golf course or links
- Viewpoint
- PC Public convenience
- Picnic site
- Pub/s
- Cathedral/Abbey
- Museum
- Castle/fort
- Building of historic interest
- English Heritage
- Garden
- Nature reserve
- Water activities
- Fishing
- ☆ Other tourist feature

Map of the British Isles

Shetland Islands

Orkney Islands

Cape Wrath

Outer Hebrides

Lewis

NORTHWEST HIGHLANDS

Skye

Great Glen
Loch Ness
River Spey
CAIRNGORMS
River Dee • Aberdeen

1344m ▲ Ben Nevis
GRAMPIAN MOUNTAINS
R. Tay

Mull

SCOTLAND
Dundee

Loch Lomond

Firth of Forth

Islay

Glasgow
River Clyde
Edinburgh

UNITED KINGDOM

SOUTHERN UPLANDS
R. Tweed
CHEVIOT HILLS

NORTHERN IRELAND

R. Bann
ANTRIM MOUNTAINS
Lough Neagh
River Erne

Belfast

Isle of Man

Newcastle upon Tyne
River Tyne
Sunderland

LAKE DISTRICT
River Eden
River Tees
Stockton-on-Tees
Middlesbrough
NORTH YORK MOORS

North Sea

NORTH ATLANTIC OCEAN

REPUBLIC OF IRELAND

Lough Corrib

R. Boyne

River Shannon

R. Liffey
Dublin

WICKLOW MOUNTAINS

Barrow

River Suir

River Blackwater

Cork

St George's Channel

Irish Sea

Anglesey

PENNINES
River Ouse

Blackpool
Preston
Bradford
Leeds
Kingston-upon-Hull
Huddersfield
River Aire
Bolton
Manchester
Liverpool
Stockport
Sheffield
Warrington
River Mersey
River Humber

ENGLAND

WALES

Stoke-on-Trent

R. Dee

Cardigan Bay

CAMBRIAN MOUNTAINS

Telford
Derby
Nottingham
The Wash

Walsall
R. Trent
Leicester
THE FENS
R. Wensum

Wolverhampton
Birmingham
Peterborough
Norwich

Dudley
Coventry

Solihull
Northampton
R. Great Ouse

Ipswich

River Teifi

R. Wye
River Severn
River Avon
Milton Keynes
R. Stour

River Tywi
BRECON BEACONS

River Usk
COTSWOLD HILLS
CHILTERN HILLS
Luton
Basildon

Swansea
Cardiff
Newport
R. Thames
London
Southend-on-Sea

Bristol Channel

Bristol
Reading
SALISBURY PLAIN
NORTH DOWNS

NORTH ATLANTIC OCEAN

EXMOOR
R. Exe

Southampton
SOUTH DOWNS
Bournemouth
Poole
Portsmouth
Brighton

DARTMOOR
Isle of Wight

Torbay

Strait of Dover

Land's End

Plymouth

Isles of Scilly

English Channel

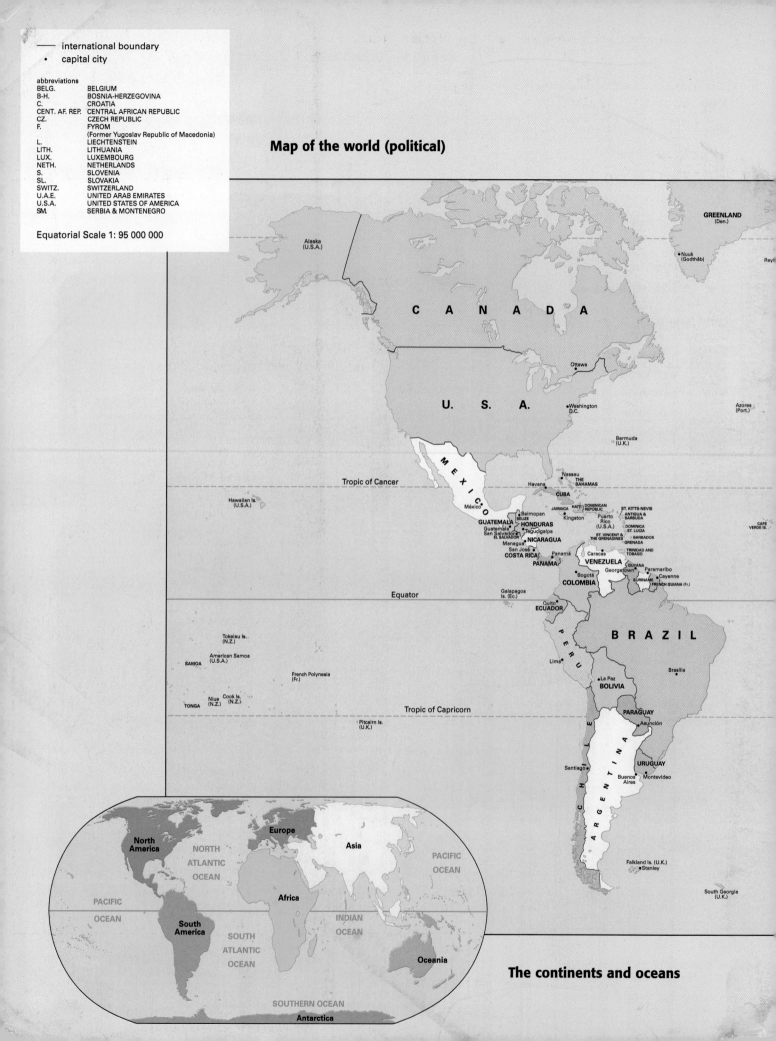

Map of the world (political)

GREENLAND
(Den.)

Nuuk
(Godthåb)

Reyk

Alaska
(U.S.A.)

C A N A D A

Ottawa

U. S. A.

Washington
D.C.

Azores
(Port.)

Bermuda
(U.K.)

Tropic of Cancer

Hawaiian Is.
(U.S.A.)

MÉXICO

México

Nassau
Havana THE
BAHAMAS

CUBA

JAMAICA HAITI DOMINICAN
REPUBLIC

ST. KITTS-NEVIS

CAPE
VERDE Is.

GUATEMALA
Belmopan
BELIZE

Guatemala
San Salvador
EL SALVADOR

HONDURAS
Tegucigalpa

Managua NICARAGUA

San José

COSTA RICA

Kingston
Puerto
Rico
(U.S.A.)

ANTIGUA &
BARBUDA
DOMINICA
ST. LUCIA
ST. VINCENT &
THE GRENADINES
GRENADA
BARBADOS

Panamá

PANAMA

Caracas

TRINIDAD AND
TOBAGO

Bogotá

VENEZUELA

Georgetown Paramaribo

GUYANA

COLOMBIA

SURINAME

Cayenne

FRENCH GUIANA (Fr.)

Galapagos
Is. (Ec.)

Equator

Quito

ECUADOR

B R A Z I L

Tokelau Is.
(N.Z.)

American Samoa
(U.S.A.)

SAMOA

French Polynesia
(Fr.)

P
E
R
U

Lima

La Paz

BOLIVIA

Brasília

TONGA

Niue
(N.Z.)

Cook Is.
(N.Z.)

Tropic of Capricorn

PARAGUAY

Asunción

Pitcairn Is.
(U.K.)

C
H
I
L
E

A
R
G
E
N
T
I
N
A

URUGUAY

Santiago

Buenos
Aires

Montevideo

Falkland Is. (U.K.)
Stanley

South Georgia
(U.K.)

The continents and oceans

North
America

Europe

NORTH
ATLANTIC
OCEAN

Asia

PACIFIC

OCEAN

PACIFIC

OCEAN

Africa

South
America

SOUTH
ATLANTIC

OCEAN

INDIAN
OCEAN

Oceania

SOUTHERN OCEAN

Antarctica

Population of the world's continents		The world's top five languages	
◆ Asia	3.92 billion		(speakers)
◆ Africa	0.90 billion	◆ Chinese (Mandarin)	over 1 billion
◆ Europe	0.72 billion	◆ English	512 million
◆ N America	0.48 billion	◆ Hindi	498 million
◆ S America	0.35 billion	◆ Spanish	391 milion
◆ Oceania	0.03 billion	◆ Arabic	245 milion

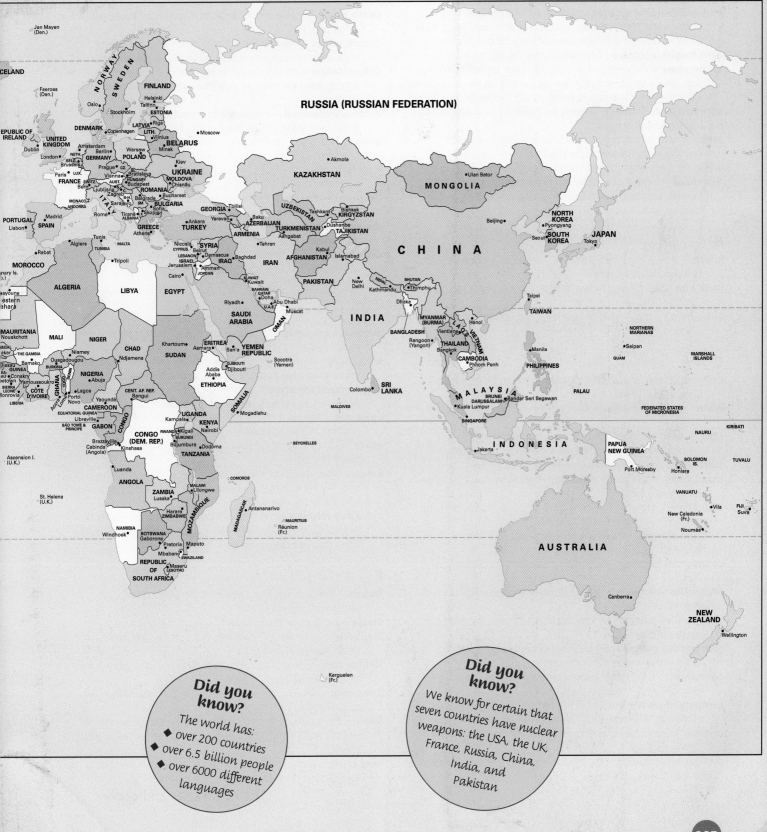

Did you know?

The world has:
◆ over 200 countries
◆ over 6.5 billion people
◆ over 6000 different languages

Did you know?

We know for certain that seven countries have nuclear weapons: the USA, the UK, France, Russia, China, India, and Pakistan

283

Glossary

A

abrasion – the scratching and scraping of a river bed and banks by the stones and sand in the river

afforestation – the replanting of trees

agribusiness – large-scale capital-intensive farming

agri-environment scheme – schemes which combine farming with looking after, and improving, the environment, such as Tir Gofal in Wales and Environmental Stewardship in England

agro-tourist – someone who spends their holiday on a farm

air pressure – the weight of air pressing down on the Earth's surface. Low pressure means warm air is rising, so rain is on the way. (The rising air cools and its water vapour condenses.)

appropriate technology – meets the needs of local people and the environment they live in

arch – a hole right through a headland. It is made by waves eroding through caves in the headland

arête – a sharp ridge between two corries (see corrie)

ash cloud – a cloud of volcanic ash occurring during and after a volcanic eruption; may be carried a long way and can cause damage and death

B

biome – a very large ecosystem. The rainforests are one biome. Hot deserts are another

birth rate – the number of live births in a country in a year, per 1000 people

blow-hole – formed when a cave is eroded upwards by hydraulic action

C

CAP – Common Agricultural Policy set up by the EU and which subsidised farmers

caves – erosion by waves enlarges joints and faults in rocks to form caves

CBD – central business district. It's the area at the centre of a town or city where you find the main shops and offices

cliffs – high rock faces that run along the coast

cloud cover – how much of the sky is hidden by cloud. It is given in eighths (oktas).

cloud type – there are five main types of cloud: stratus, cumulus, nimbus, cumulonimbus and cirrus

collision margin – where two tectonic plates (continental plates) are colliding

commercial farming – outputs from the farm are sold to make a profit

composite volcano – a steep-sided cone-shaped volcano, made from sticky acidic lava

conservative margin – where two tectonic plates are moving past each other

constructive margin – where two tectonic plates are moving apart and new crust is constructed

consumers – living things that eat other living things for food. For example zebra consume grass

continental crust – the part of the Earth's crust that makes the continents; it's between 25 km and 100 km thick

corrie – a circular, armchair-shaped hollow cut into rock by ice during glaciation

counter-urbanisation – the movement of people out of cities to smaller towns and villages

crater – the hollow at the mouth of a volcano. Rain falling into craters may form lakes

crevasse – a vertical or wedge-shaped crack in a glacier

D

death rate – the number of deaths in a country in a year, per 1000 people

decomposers – organisms that break down dead and waste material in an ecosystem. Bacteria and fungi are examples

deforestation – clearing forest for another use. For example cutting down rainforest to make way for a motorway or cattle ranches

deindustrialisation – the decline in manufacturing (secondary) industry, and the growth in tertiary and quaternary industry

delta – a flat area at the mouth of a river, made of sediment deposited by the river

desertification – when soil in a savanna region gets worn out, dusty and useless

destructive margin – where two tectonic plates are moving together and oceanic crust is destroyed by subduction

dietary energy supply – the number of calories per person available each day

distributaries – if sediment blocks a river it has to divide into small channels called distributaries

drumlin – a smooth hill shaped by glaciers

E

economic migrants – people who move voluntarily for jobs and higher wages

ecosystem – a unit made up of living things and their non-living environment. For example a pond, a forest, a desert

employment structure – what % of workers are in the primary, secondary and tertiary sectors of the economy

epicentre – the point on the ground directly above the focus (centre) of an earthquake

esker – a long ridge of material deposited from streams flowing under glaciers

estuary – the mouth of a large river, which is affected by the tides. As the tide rises, sea water flows up into the estuary and mixes with the river water

extensive farming – has smaller inputs of labour, money or technology than intensive farming. Extensive farms are usually larger than intensive farms

F

factors – things which affect where industry, agriculture, settlements etc will locate

favela – name for a shanty town in a South American city

feedback – things are put back into the system – like profits which may be reinvested

fertility rate – the number of children, on average, a woman will have in her lifetime

floodplain – flat land around a river that gets flooded when the river overflows

focus – the centre of an earthquake. It is the exact point where rock moved, setting off the quake. It could be far below the ground

food chain – a chain of names linked by arrows, showing what species feed on. It always starts with a plant

food web – a network of food chains, showing how they link together

footloose – an industry which is not tied to raw materials and so can choose where to locate

fossil fuels – coal, oil and natural gas. They are called fossil fuels because they are the remains of plants and animals that lived millions of years ago

free trade – when goods and services can flow freely from country to country, without any taxes

freeze-thaw weathering – the weathering (breakdown) of rock by the action of water getting into cracks in the rock, freezing and thawing

G

GDP per capita (PPP) – GDP is gross domestic product. It is the total value of the goods and services produced in a country in a year. GDP per capita means the GDP divided by the population. PPP means purchasing power parity. GDP is adjusted because a dollar buys more in some countries than others

glacial trough – a steep-sided U-shaped valley caused by glaciers

global warming – the way temperatures around the world are rising. Scientists think we have made this happen by burning too much fossil fuel

green belt – an area of open land around a city, which is protected from development. This is to stop the city spreading further

Green Revolution – the introduction of high-yielding varieties of cereals such as rice and wheat into LEDCs

green tourism – aims to limit the negative impact of tourism. It is also known as ecotourism or sustainable tourism

greenhouse gases – gases like carbon dioxide and methane that trap heat around the Earth, leading to global warming

groundwater flow – the flow of groundwater through saturated rock or soil

H

hanging valley – a high-level tributary valley with a sharp fall to the main valley; a feature of glacial erosion

high-tech industry – an industry that develops and produces new and advanced products. For example new kinds of mobile phones or medical drugs

hot spot – where volcanoes occur away from plate margins; probably due to strong upward currents in the mantle

humidity – the % of water vapour in the air

I

impermeable – doesn't let water through

infant mortality – the number of babies out of every 1000 born alive, who die before their first birthday

infiltration – the soaking of rainwater into the ground

inputs – things that go into a system. They can be physical, or human and economic.

intensive farming – has large inputs of labour, money or technology to produce high outputs. Farms are usually quite small

interception – the capture of rainwater by leaves. Some evaporates again and the rest trickles to the ground

interlocking spurs – hills that stick out on alternate sides of a V-shaped valley like the teeth of a zip

irrigation – artificial watering of land and crops

K

kame – a mound or heap of material dropped from a glacier

L

lava – melted rock that erupts from a volcano

levees – embankments built up on either side of a river channel

life expectancy – how many years a new baby can expect to live, on average. Life expectancy is higher for females than for males

M

magma – melted rock below the Earth's surface. When it reaches the surface it is called lava

materialism – wanting only belongings or comfort, and having no interest in morals

meander – a bend in a river

misfit stream – a small stream in the bottom of glacial trough

moraine – material carried by a glacier

mouth – the end point of a river, where it enters the sea or a lake

mudflow (lahar) – a river of mud formed when ash and other material from an erupting volcano mixes with water or ice. It can drown towns and villages

N

natural increase – the birth rate minus the death rate for a place. It is always given as a % of the total population

NGO – non-governmental organisation. NGOs work to make life better, especially for the poor. Oxfam, the Red Cross and Greenpeace are all NGOs

O

oceanic crust – the part of the Earth's crust which is under the oceans; it's made of basalt and is between 5 km and 10 km thick

outputs – things that come out of the system (products)

ox-bow lake – a lake formed when a loop in a river is cut off by floods

P

percolation – the movement of water downwards through rock

plates – the Earth's surface is broken into large pieces, like a cracked eggshell. The pieces are called tectonic plates, or just plates

plucking – when ice freezes on to rock, moves, and so plucks the rock away

plug – a rock plug that may be left in the crater of a volcano after an eruption; may be blown off in a future eruption

population density – the average number of people per square kilometre

population growth rate – the number of people added to a population each year due to natural increase and net migration. It is given as a %

porous – lets water soak through

precipitation – water falling from the sky. It could fall as rain, hail, sleet or snow.

primary industry – people extract raw materials from the land or sea. For example farming, fishing and mining

processes – things that happen in the middle of the system to turn inputs into outputs

producers – plants are called producers because they make their own food from carbon dioxide and water

pyramidal peak – the peak formed when three or more corries form round a mountain (see corrie)

pyroclastic flow – a scorching hot avalanche of gas, ash, cinders and rocks that rushes down the slopes of a volcano after an explosive eruption

Q

quaternary industry – people are employed in industries providing information and expert help. For example IT consultants and researchers

quota – a limit on the amount of goods produced or purchased

R

refugee – a person who is forced to flee from danger (for example war or an earthquake) and seek refuge in another country

river channel – the bed and sides of a river form a river channel

river terraces – areas of flatter land above the floodplain

rural-urban fringe – the area where a town or city meets the countryside

S

salinisation – soil becomes increasingly salty (saline) and plants die. Irrigation can cause salinisation

secondary industry – people make, or manufacture, things. For example turning iron ore into steel, making cars and building houses

set-aside land – land which isn't used for growing crops or keeping animals on; farmers are paid for this

shanty town – areas of poor quality housing lacking facilities which develop in unfavourable sites in, and around, cities in LEDCs

shield volcano – a low flat volcano, like an upturned shield, made from runny basic lava

slumping – a mass movement of rock and soil down a slope

solution – the dissolving of minerals from rocks, by water

source – the starting point of a river

sphere of influence – area around a settlement (or shop, or other service) where its effect is felt. London has a very large sphere of influence

SPS – Single Payment System, part of the CAP reform. Farmers now get one single payment a year instead of several different subsidy payments

stack – a pillar of rock left standing in the sea when the top of an arch collapses

striation – scratches in rock caused by abrasion in a glacier

stump – the remains of a stack which the sea has eroded away

subsistence farming – where farmers grow food to feed their families, rather than to sell

surface run-off – rainwater that runs across the surface of the ground and drains into the river

sustainable – can be carried on without doing any harm (to people, or other living things, or the environment)

sustainable development – development that will not lower our quality of life or harm the environment

sustainable management – meeting the needs of people now and in the future, and limiting harm to the environment

system – has inputs, processes and outputs. Industry and agriculture can be described as systems

T

tariff – a tax that a country places on goods being imported or exported

temperature – how hot or cold something is, usually measured in degrees Centigrade

tertiary industry – people are employed in providing a service. For example the health service (doctors, nurses, dentists) and education (teachers)

through-flow – the flow of rainwater sideways through the soil, towards the river

till – jumbled, unsorted material dropped by glaciers

trade balance – the difference between the value of imports and exports of a country

trade deficit – a country spends more on imports than it earns from exports

trade surplus – a country earns more money from exports than it spends on imports

trading bloc – a group of countries that have joined together to improve trade

truncated spurs – where a glacier has eroded and cut off inter locking spurs

U

urban model – a simplified diagram of the way land is used in a city

urban redevelopment – clearance and rebuilding of old inner city areas

urban renewal – improving (without knocking down and clearing) old inner city areas

urban zones – areas of different land use in an urban area

urbanisation – an increase in the percentage of people living in towns and cities

U-shaped valley – see glacial trough

V

visibility – the greatest distance you can see, in km or m. On a foggy day it could be just 1 or 2 metres

V-shaped valley – a valley shaped like the letter V, carved out by a river

W

waterfall – where a river or stream flows over a steep drop

wave-cut platform – the flat rocky area left behind when waves erode a cliff away

wind direction – the direction the wind blows from

wind strength (speed) – how fast the wind blows

World Trade Organisation – a body set up to help trade between countries

Index